O L I V E

PRODUCTION

M A N U A L

Technical Editors:

LOUISE FERGUSON,

G. STEVEN SIBBETT,

AND

GEORGE C. MARTIN

1994

University of California
Division of Agriculture and Natural Resources
Publication 3353

ORDERING

For information about ordering this publication, write to
  Publications
  Division of Agriculture and Natural Resources
  University of California
  6701 San Pablo Avenue
  Oakland, California 94608-1239

  Telephone (510) 642-2431
  Fax (510) 643-5470

Publication 3353
ISBN 1-879906-15-5

Library of Congress Catalog Card No. 94-60033.

Please use this standard form when citing this book: Louise Ferguson, G. Steven Sibbett, and George C. Martin. 1994. *Olive Production Manual.* University of California, Division of Agriculture and Natural Resources, Oakland, CA. Publication 3353. 160 pp.

GENERAL WARNING ON THE USE OF CHEMICALS

Pesticides are poisonous. Always read and carefully follow all precautions and safety recommendations given on the container label. Store all chemicals in their original labeled containers in a locked cabinet or shed, away from foods or feeds, and out of the reach of children, unauthorized persons, pets, and livestock.

Confine chemicals to the property being treated. Avoid drift onto neighboring properties, especially gardens containing fruits and/or vegetables ready to be picked.

Mix and apply only the amount of pesticide you will need to complete the application. Spray all the material according to label directions. Do not dispose of unused material by pouring down the drain or the toilet. Do not pour on ground: soil or underground water supplies may be contaminated. Follow label directions for disposing of container. **Never burn pesticide containers.**

Phytotoxicity: Certain chemicals may cause plant injury if used at the wrong stage of plant development or when temperatures are too high. Injury may also result from excessive amounts or the wrong formulation or from mixing incompatible materials. Inert ingredients, such as wetters, spreaders, emulsifiers, diluents, and solvents, can cause plant injury. Since formulations are often changed by manufacturers, it is possible that plant injury may occur, even though no injury was noted in previous seasons.

To simplify information, trade names of products have been used. No endorsement of named products is intended, nor is criticism implied of similar products that are not mentioned.

3m-pr-1/94-WJC/PAE/VFG/ALS

CONTENTS

DEDICATION

This *Olive Production Manual* represents the work of many contributors, not only the authors of each chapter. We have all accumulated valuable information from previous olive manuals—those written at the beginning of the twentieth century as well as the vast body of knowledge developed in more recent years. Despite the research efforts of olive scientists in California and the rest of the world, some problems prevalent in the early twentieth century remain with us at its close. Nature yields information grudgingly, and pests continue to mutate and resist our treatments. Throughout the travail, olive growers have remained stoic and eager to learn how to accomplish the task at hand in a better way. This *Olive Production Manual* is dedicated to the California olive growers.

HISTORY AND SCOPE OF THE OLIVE INDUSTRY

JOSEPH H. CONNELL

ORIGIN AND HISTORY

The olive tree, *Olea europaea*, valued for both its beauty and its fruit, has been a part of Mediterranean civilization since before recorded history. As early as 3000 B.C., Semitic peoples in Syria cultivated the olive and traded in its oil. Numerous biblical references to the olive, its cultivation, and use of its oil date it from 2000 B.C. Semitic influence spread olive cultivation northward into what is now Turkey and south into Egypt.

Three to four thousand years ago the Egyptians traded in olive oil and cured olives. Their dead were adorned with olive branches and preserved in part with oil, and cured olives were left in the tombs of the Pharaohs for food in the afterlife. From Egypt, olive culture spread west in the Arab world, through north Africa to southern Spain.

The inhabitants of ancient Crete were probably responsible for the spread of olive culture to the early Greeks and Romans. Around 900 B.C., Homer in the *Odyssey* referred frequently to the olive. In the fifth century B.C., Herodotus described Athens as a vast center of Greek olive culture. A profitable export of that time was olive oil as well as the technology associated with olive culture and curing.

By the beginning of the fifth century B.C., the Romans were becoming familiar with the uses of olive products and with olive cultivation. They are credited with inventing the screw press to extract olive oil. Cato described several quality grades and uses for the oil in Roman society. The Roman methods for producing oil remained unchanged for the next two millennia, until the advent of the modern centrifuge. At the fall of the Roman empire, olives were cultivated throughout the Arab and Roman world. Olive products were a principal item of commerce in the Middle East, throughout north Africa and the Mediterranean, and as far west as Spain and Morocco.

Figure 1.1. Mission San Diego de Alcalá.

From the late Renaissance through the colonial period of the European powers, olives were dispersed by the explorers and colonists. In 1560, olive cuttings were carried to Peru by Spanish explorers. In the early 1700s, Jesuits established missions in Mexico and Baja California; olives were among the few fruits that were grown in those early mission settlements. Franciscan padres journeying north from Mexico founded their first California mission at San Diego in 1769 (fig. 1.1). Olives were soon being grown there, but not until a century later did a commercial industry become well established in California.

DISTRIBUTION AND PRODUCTION

In the Mediterranean basin, olive trees were thoroughly distributed by both the Arabs and the Romans. Today, most of the world's olives are still grown in the Mediterranean region (table 1.1). The olive tree is best suited to areas with a Mediterranean climate: a long, hot growing season and a relatively cool winter with minimum temperatures above a lethal limit.

Table 1.1. Total number of trees, oil production, and table olive production in 1986 in the leading olive-producing countries of the world.

Country	Number of trees (× 1,000)	Oil production Provisional 1986–87 (1,000 tons)	Oil production Percentage of world	Table olive production Provisional 1986–87 (1,000 tons)	Table olive production Percentage of world
Spain	218,000	493.5	29.7	224.0	26.1
Italy	189,000	400.0	24.1	50.0	5.8
Greece	123,000	300.0	18.0	80.0	9.3
Turkey	81,000	120.0	7.2	115.0	13.4
Tunisia	59,000	120.0	7.2	10.0	1.2
Portugal	53,000	40.8	2.5	21.1	2.5
Morocco	29,000	35.0	2.1	70.0	8.1
Syria	27,000	85.0	5.1	53.7	6.2
Argentina	8,000	7.0	0.4	33.0	3.8
USA (California)	2,600	1.0	0.1	96.2	11.2
Egypt	2,000	—	—	21.0	2.4
All others	97,590	60.5	3.6	85.9	10.0
World total	889,190	1,662.8	100.0	859.9	100.0

Commercial olive-producing areas of the world are found between 30° and 45° north and south latitudes. The trees do not usually survive below about 10°F (–12°C), and most cultivars are injured at 15°F (–9°C). In tropical regions nearer the equator, olives grow vegetatively, but most cultivars do not set fruit due to insufficient winter chilling, which prevents flower formation.

Carried from its Mediterranean homeland by explorers and colonists, olive culture failed in England and the eastern United States due to inhospitable climates. Olive production has been commercially successful on a relatively small scale in parts of South America, in South Africa, and in Australia.

The most extensive olive cultivation is practiced in Spain, which produces nearly 30 percent of the world's olive oil and about 26 percent of the world's table olives. Italy, Greece, and Turkey are the other major olive producers. Together these four countries account for 79 percent of the olive oil and 54.6 percent of the table olives produced in the world (table 1.1). The United States produces only 0.1 percent of the world's olive oil, since U.S. oil production is primarily a salvage operation. The relatively small U.S. industry does, however, produce 11.2 percent of the world's table olives.

CULTIVARS AND THEIR USE

In the Mediterranean basin, where olives have been cultivated for thousands of years, hundreds of cultivars have been selected over the centuries for their adaptation to various microclimates and soil types. Within each country, certain cultivars predominate in different producing districts.

Some cultivars are best suited for oil production, others for table use, and still others are used either way depending on the relative prices of oil and table olives.

Some cultivars are common only locally, whereas others are found in several countries. Throughout the Mediterranean region there is considerable cultivar confusion: the same name may be given to similar but clearly different selections, and different names may be used for identical cultivars.

In Spain, major cultivars used for oil production include Picual, Cornicabra, Hojiblanca, and Lechín de Sevilla; Manzanilla, Manzanilla Cacereña, Hojiblanca, and Gordal Sevillana are the major cultivars processed for use as table olives. Most Spanish table olives are processed green-ripe. The manufacture of pitted stuffed olives is also a major component of the Spanish industry. In recent years, Spanish olives, processed using the California black-ripe method, have made significant inroads into the U.S. domestic olive market (fig. 1.2).

Italy has many cultivars used for oil production and several that are commonly processed for table use. Notable among the oil cultivars are the Leccino and the Frantoio. Tondaiblea and Giaraffa are used to produce black table olives and Cerignola, Ascolana tenera, and Nocellara etnea are varieties known best as green table olives. Italian olives may be salt brine cured, salt brine cured and packed in vinegar, or dry salt cured, rubbed with oil, and packed in herbs.

In Greece, table olives are a prominent export crop. Kalamata is a black olive that is brine cured and packed in vinegar. Conseruolea is another black cultivar of importance, and Chalkidikis is used both as a table variety and

2

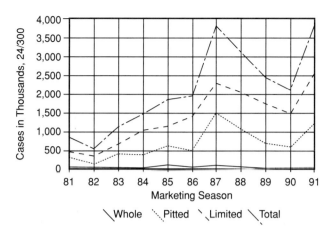

Figure 1.2. Imported canned ripe olives and bulk olives processed into canned ripe olives, 1981–82 to 1991–92.

as an oil olive. Agrinion is Greece's most famous green olive cultivar.

Turkey is unique among the four major olive-producing countries in that its table olive production is nearly as large in tonnage as its production of olive oil (table 1.1). The cultivars Domat, Szmir, and Trilya are grown both for oil and for table olive use.

Throughout the Mediterranean region, olive cultivars are grown with a specific climate, use, and method of processing in mind. Over the centuries, the best use for each particular cultivar has been highly developed. Cultivars adapted to humid coastal areas, dry continental climates, frost-free maritime zones, and frosty uplands have all been selected. Cultivars exist that thrive under a wide variety of soil and nutritional conditions. Olives ideal for oil production, salt brine pickling, black processing, green processing, and dry salt curing are produced throughout the region.

In contrast to the rest of the world, the California olive industry relies on one product: the black-ripe olive. Other olive products are produced in relatively small amounts. The California industry uses the five cultivars Mission, Manzanillo, Sevillano, Ascolano, and Barouni interchangeably.

CALIFORNIA HISTORY

The olive was brought to California in the late 1700s by Franciscan padres who journeyed north from San Blas, Mexico. Led by Father Junipero Serra and sent by José de Galvez, the Franciscans established Mission San Diego de Alcalá in 1769 (fig. 1.1). Within two decades, olives were being grown at the mission. It is likely that the first mills and screw presses for the production of olive oil were built by artisans who arrived at the mission around 1800. Father Lasuen wrote in 1803 that Mission San Diego de Alcalá had harvested olives and produced some very good oil. This is the earliest record of oil production in California. Distributed from San Diego, olive trees were soon in production at all missions along the coast south of San Francisco.

Early explorers, such as George Vancouver in 1792 and Edwin Bryant and John Fremont in 1846, wrote of seeing olive trees in California. Bryant noticed olive trees growing at Mission San Luis Obispo, and Fremont wrote that olives and other fruits grew luxuriantly together in spring-fed valley gardens among the hills south of San Diego.

In 1834, secularization of the missions led to the decline of most of the mission orchards and gardens. Olives in the mission orchards survived neglect, drought, and browsing cattle for several decades until early American pioneers between 1855 and 1875 began to propagate new trees using cuttings from the old mission orchards.

Considerable variation existed in early mission olives, as the trees were both seedlings and rooted cuttings. Olive pits found in adobe bricks from early California mission buildings are of variable shape and size. The Mission cultivar that eventually predominated from the early planting at San Diego probably originated through vegetative propagation of superior trees from the original mixed seedling source.

Statistics from the California State Agricultural Society indicate that by 1855, 503 olive trees were growing in the state. A renewed interest in olive oil production led to significant expansion of the industry between 1870 and 1900. In 1872, Frank and Warren Kimball secured olive cuttings from among the 347 trees remaining at Mission San Diego de Alcalá and planted an orchard at their ranch in National City in San Diego County. Ellwood Cooper of Santa Barbara planted six olive orchards in different locations, the first near Goleta in 1870. Edward E. Goodrich had an 80-acre orchard at his El Quito ranch near Los Gatos in Santa Clara County. All these early pioneers were involved in the production of olive oil. Aside from the early efforts in the missions, the first commercially produced olive oil in California probably came from the Camulos oil mill, established in 1871 in Ventura County.

John Wolfskill of Winters, George C. Roeding of Fresno, F. M. Hunt of Redlands, and John S. Calkins of Pomona were other early orchardists who experimented with olive trees. The old olive trees at Mission San Jose served as a source for many subsequent plantings in northern California. In the mid-1890s, Warren Woodson, a land developer, established the Corning olive district by planting as many domestic olive trees as he could get. His planting was supplemented with imported Spanish trees when the domestic supply fell short. Trees procured from Spain turned out to be the Sevillano cultivar, which was disappointing as an oil producer but later became valuable for its large, pickled fruit. About the same time, growers in Lindsay in Tulare County

Figure 1.3. Eugene Woldemar Hilgard came to the University of California in 1874. He did early studies on processing olives by variety and by size. SOURCE: The Bancroft Library.

Figure 1.4. Frederic Bioletti, UC professor, improved olive-processing methods and perfected a method of canning olives in tins. SOURCE: The Bancroft Library.

Figure 1.5. Freda Ehmann of Oroville commercialized the black-ripe processing method that became the industry standard. SOURCE: Butte County Historical Society.

discovered that olives were well suited to their soils. Initially, Mission olives were used as windbreaks and as ornamentals, but after the black-ripe pickled olive became popular, planting increased. Lindsay became the leading olive-producing district in the state by the early 1900s.

Between 1850 and 1900, numerous olive cultivars from Mediterranean countries were introduced to California, primarily for the purpose of improving oil production. The cultivars other than Mission that are important in the contemporary olive industry were all introduced into California during the boom period between 1875 and 1905.

By 1885, California growers had learned to produce olive oil equal to the best imported oil. With this success in oil production, the number of trees planted in the state went from 5,603 in 1876 to 539,568 by 1901. Though the heavy increase in production that followed led to lower prices, growers found that they could not compete with the less expensive European olive oil. Shortly thereafter, the industry shifted its emphasis to the production of pickled olives, the mainstay of the California industry ever since.

PICKLED OLIVES

Before 1900, the early olive producers had experimented with processed olives as a sideline to their oil operations. Ellwood Cooper of Santa Barbara used a water cure process to remove the bitterness from the fruit and then packed the olives in a light brine. Frank Kimball of National City and A. D. Thacker of Pomona used a lye process to remove the bitterness, leached the lye out with water, and then packed the fruit in brine. Olives were also salt-cured and sometimes served in olive oil. Different producers using various processes pickled olives in four stages of ripeness: some were processed when green, some when they had a reddish cast, some after turning black, and some that had shriveled on the tree.

The various processing methods led to marketing problems, since some products were clearly inferior. Eugene Hilgard's research at the University of California at Berkeley indicated that different varieties of olives should be processed separately (fig. 1.3). Work done at UC by Frederic Bioletti (fig. 1.4) and G. E. Colby in 1899 proved that when properly processed, large-fruited olives were palatable and nutritious. They demonstrated that ripe olives could be preserved indefinitely in a weak brine when sufficiently heated and hermetically sealed in glass. Within a decade, Bioletti perfected a method of canning olives in tins, and that gave growers better control of product supply. His high-temperature, high-pressure method of retorting gained consumers' confidence, and the modern olive industry had its start.

One of the first to make use of the new methods was Freda Ehmann (fig. 1.5), founder in 1898 of the Ehmann Olive Company in Oroville. She contacted Professor Hilgard at UC Berkeley in 1897, requesting a recipe for processing ripe olives. She used his method for lye curing and shortly thereafter began to market her product in barrels, kegs, and glass jars. By 1905 Ehmann Olive Company had begun canning ripe olives. This mild ripe olive became the olive of choice in the United States.

The new, superior method of canning and the encouraging economic outlook created a statewide planting boom between 1900 and 1920. The major olive-producing districts in Oroville and Lindsay developed mostly at that time. In 1916, Lindsay olive growers formed a cooperative processing plant to take advantage of the new canning methods developed by Bioletti.

Meanwhile, in the Corning district it was discovered that processing Sevillano olives the same way as Mission blistered the fruit. Fred G. Beresford of Corning and W. V. Cruess, professor of food technology at UC Davis, developed a new method of processing Sevillanos that prevented damage. As a result, growers in Corning began grafting their groves over to the Sevillano cultivar in 1913. Today, the Corning area primarily grows the Sevillano variety, although this may change as growers graft over to still more desirable varieties.

Disaster struck in 1919, when 35 people died of botulism after eating improperly canned black olives; there was a sudden subsequent drop in demand for canned olives. It took 10 years to convince consumers that with safe canning methods and rigid inspection, canned olives were indeed safe.

Canning methods developed by the University of California and carried to the marketplace by pioneer canners like Freda Ehmann set the stage for widespread acceptance of the California "black-ripe" olive. By 1910, the foundation was laid for the California olive industry. There were 26,000 acres in production by 1925, and the industry was stable at that level for the next five decades. In the mid- 1970s, an expansion of olive acreage occurred in the southwestern San Joaquin Valley due to the increased availability of water from the newly completed California Water Project. This new acreage was decimated just as it came into production in the mid-1980s. Tree losses due to verticillium wilt and olive knot made plantings in this area uneconomical.

CURRENT PRODUCTION

All commercial olive acreage in the United States is in California. With approximately 0.3 percent of the world's olive trees, California produces roughly 11 percent of the world's table olives and 0.1 percent of its olive oil.

More than 99.5 percent of commercial olive acreage in California is located in the interior valleys of central California, although olive trees grow throughout the state from San Diego County in the south to Shasta County in the north (fig. 1.6 and table 1.2). Economic advantages such as suitable soils, water availability, and low land prices resulted in the current distribution and concentration of olive acreage in the Central Valley. Conditions in southern California and the coastal area were less suitable for olive production, since those areas had no competitive advantage in yields. Acreage steadily declined there over the past seven decades in response to reduced profitability (fig. 1.7).

Within the Central Valley there are two major producing areas. In the northern Sacramento Valley, the counties of

Figure 1.6. Olive acreage distribution and production areas in California, 1992 (each dot equals about 100 acres).

Bearing	30,076
Nonbearing	4,136
Total	34,212

Leading olive-producing areas	
District	Percent of acreage
Sacramento Valley	35.1
San Joaquin Valley	64.6
Southern California and all others	0.3

Table 1.2. Olive acreage in California by district and county, 1992.

District	County	Bearing acreage	Nonbearing acreage	Total
Sacramento Valley	Butte	2,755	41	2,796
	Colusa	58	38	96
	Glenn	1,934	1,033	2,967
	Sacramento	5	0	5
	Shasta	623	0	623
	Sutter	9	0	9
	Tehama	4,911	520	5,431
	Yolo	57	0	57
	Yuba	9	0	9
	Total	10,361	1,632	11,993
San Joaquin Valley	Calaveras	200	0	200
	Fresno	1,335	40	1,375
	Kern	2,187	41	2,228
	Kings	526	0	526
	Madera	1,696	80	1,776
	Merced	74	0	74
	San Joaquin	78	0	78
	Stanislaus	5	0	5
	Tulare	13,515	2,343	15,858
	Total	21,047	2,504	22,120
Southern California	Orange	1	0	1
	Riverside	37	0	37
	San Diego	36	0	36
	Total	74	0	74
All Others*		25	0	25

* Placer, Santa Clara, and Sonoma counties.

Butte, Glenn, and Tehama have 33 percent of the state acreage, and in the southern San Joaquin Valley, the counties of Fresno, Kern, Madera, and Tulare have 62 percent of the acreage. Together, these seven counties have nearly 95 percent of the state acreage.

The Orland and Corning areas in Glenn and Tehama counties are noted for Sevillano production while the Oroville district in Butte County produces primarily Mission olives. Manzanillo is the major cultivar of the Lindsay area of Tulare County and on the west side of Kern County.

Olive acreage in the Sacramento Valley has remained relatively stable at around 10,000 acres for the past 60 years. Acreage in the San Joaquin Valley remained at a similar level between 1925 and 1965. In the late 1960s and early 1970s an accelerating increase in San Joaquin Valley acreage began as better-quality water became available from the state water project. Thousands of acres of olives were planted on lands in western Kings and Kern counties previously planted to cotton. The soilborne fungal pathogen of cotton, verticillium wilt, was common in many of these westside soils. Losses due to verticillium wilt and olive knot on tree trunks spread by mechanical harvesting caused a decrease in San Joaquin Valley olive acreage (fig. 1.7).

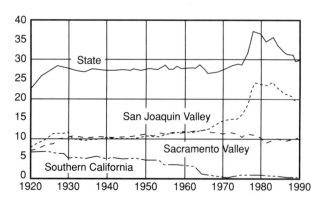

Figure 1.7. Bearing acreage (in thousands) of olive trees, statewide and by districts, from 1920 to 1990.

6

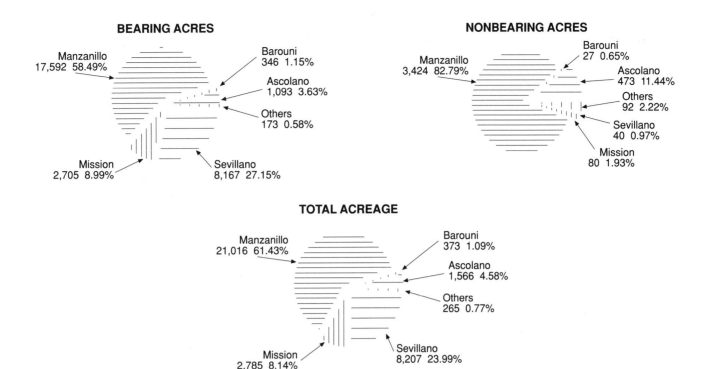

BEARING ACRES

Manzanillo
17,592 58.49%

Barouni
346 1.15%

Ascolano
1,093 3.63%

Others
173 0.58%

Mission
2,705 8.99%

Sevillano
8,167 27.15%

NONBEARING ACRES

Manzanillo
3,424 82.79%

Barouni
27 0.65%

Ascolano
473 11.44%

Others
92 2.22%

Sevillano
40 0.97%

Mission
80 1.93%

TOTAL ACREAGE

Manzanillo
21,016 61.43%

Barouni
373 1.09%

Ascolano
1,566 4.58%

Others
265 0.77%

Mission
2,785 8.14%

Sevillano
8,207 23.99%

Figure 1.8. California olive varieties' acreage and planting trends; acreage standing in 1992.

CULTIVARS

Between 1850 and 1950, more than 75 cultivars of olive were imported, primarily from countries surrounding the Mediterranean Sea. Some were oil varieties, but in the later years most were table olive varieties thought to have potential in California. Although an extensive search was made for improved material, over the past 100 years four major varieties have come to account for 98 percent of the olive acreage in the state. Recent planting trends suggest that the predominance of the Manzanillo cultivar will continue in the future (fig. 1.8).

Although the total olive acreage has not changed a great deal in the past 50 years, the shift in varietal composition of the industry has been significant (fig. 1.9). The Mission cultivar was the most important olive in the state in 1936, accounting for 52 percent of the acreage. By 1992, Mission trees constituted just 9 percent of the bearing acreage. Manzanillo has steadily become more important over the past five decades and today accounts for more than 58 percent of the bearing acreage. Sevillano increased in importance until the mid-1970s, when its popularity waned; yet it still accounted for more than 27 percent of bearing acreage in 1992. Ascolano has always been less important than the other three major cultivars since it bruises easily and is difficult to process without damage. In recent years there has been a small increase in Ascolano acreage, to

about 3.6 percent of the bearing acreage. The Barouni cultivar, with 1 percent of California bearing acreage, has a small market as a fresh shipping fruit for home processing. It has not changed significantly in importance over the past 50 years. The shifts in varietal composition were accomplished by topworking existing acreage and by replacing orchards of undesirable varieties with more desirable cultivars. Average quality, measured by canning percentage, limited-use fruit, undersize fruit, and cull fruit varies by variety (fig. 1.10). Quality and resultant returns to the grower are also implicated in variety shifts over time.

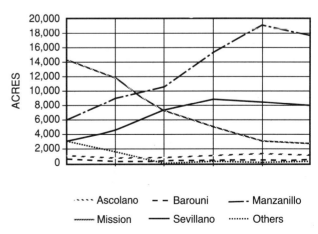

····· Ascolano   – – Barouni   – · Manzanillo
------- Mission   —— Sevillano   ······· Others

Figure 1.9. Bearing acreage of California olives by variety, 1936 to 1992.

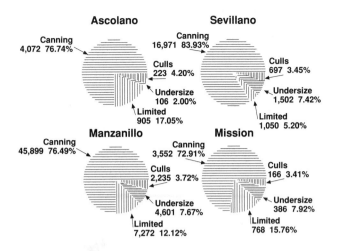

Figure 1.10. Quality of California olives by variety; average tons delivered to handlers during the 1980s.

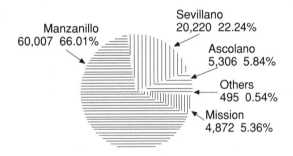

Average Total Tons = 90,901

Manzanillo 60,007 66.01%

Sevillano 20,220 22.24%

Ascolano 5,306 5.84%

Others 495 0.54%

Mission 4,872 5.36%

Figure 1.11. Average yield (in tons) of California olives by variety in the 1980s.

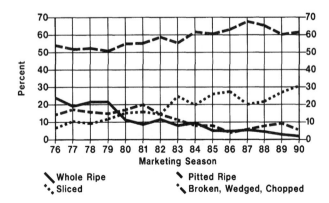

Figure 1.12. Change in pack of canned ripe olives in California, 1976–77 to 1990–91.

During the 1980s, an average of 90,901 tons of fruit was delivered to olive handlers annually. In this period the annual crop ranged from a low of 42,926 tons in 1981–82 to a high of 145,977 tons in 1982–83. On the average, two-thirds of yearly production was from the Manzanillo cultivar, 22.2 percent from Sevillano, 5.8 percent from Ascolano, and 5.3 percent from Mission (fig. 1.11). Among the four major cultivars, Manzanillo and Ascolano accounted for a larger percentage of production than their acreage would warrant. Both Sevillano and Mission produced fewer olives relative to their acreage.

FRUIT USES

The California olive industry is based almost entirely on the production of canned ripe olives. Generally, about 90 percent of the crop is canned. Canning packs include ripe (whole or pitted); green-ripe (whole or pitted); and sliced, chopped, wedged, and broken (all pitted). The largest-volume canned product is pitted ripe olives, followed by sliced olives (fig. 1.12). Pitted ripe olives increased by 15 percent and sliced olives by a huge 457 percent between 1976 and 1990. Over this time, packs of whole ripe, green-ripe, broken pitted, wedged, and chopped were all reduced. The whole-ripe pack dropped to only 8 percent of its former size. Broken, pitted, wedged, and chopped olives dropped to one-third of their former levels, compared with 15 years earlier (fig. 1.12). The green-ripe olive pack declined to insignificance during this same period.

Olives that are too small for canning, culls, and those damaged by frost are diverted to oil production. Due to low grower returns, the production of olive oil in California has been almost entirely a salvage operation. Spain and Italy ship olive oil to the United States more cheaply than California can produce it. Land and labor costs in the United States are generally too high for our industry to produce olives solely for oil production unless a high-priced specialty product can be marketed and sold.

A limited amount of specialty olive products such as Spanish green processed, Greek or Sicilian style, and salt-brined olives are also processed in California, but their production is not a significant factor in the California industry. A very small portion of the Barouni olive crop is sold fresh and shipped to eastern markets for home processing.

Five basic processes are used to produce olives for table use. Each effectively leaches the bitter principle from the olive to produce an edible product. The standard method in California is lye-curing, which produces the most popular black-ripe olive. This method is used by all California olive canners. The other four methods are used to produce a small volume of specialty olives in California but are of major importance in other parts of the world. Oil-cured olives are soaked for one to a few months in olive oil. Water-cured olives have the bitterness removed by simple leaching. They are soaked in water, rinsed, and soaked again for a period of months. Olives that are brine-cured are soaked in a salt-brine solution for one or more months. Dry-cured olives are packed in salt for one or more months, then rubbed with olive oil. Olives cured by these last four methods are more strongly flavored than the mild black-ripe olive that is the American standard.

Of the four major cultivars grown in California, the Mission is the best for oil production, since 21.8 percent of its fresh weight in winter is oil. Manzanillo has 20.3 percent oil and is also used for olive oil production. Sevillano (14.4 percent oil) and Ascolano (18.8 percent oil) are too low in oil content to be useful for oil extraction.

Two general processes are used in olive oil production. The first, cold pressing, produces the highest-quality oil. Cold pressing involves crushing the fruit, placing the mash in sacks layer upon layer, and then applying pressure with a screw or hydraulic press to drive off the oil and water. The product goes to a settling tank where much sediment is left behind and the oil floats off the top. Centrifuged to remove the last water, the oil is then filtered and ready to bottle. This "virgin olive oil," as defined by the U.S. Food and Drug Administration, comes from the fruit in the first pressing of the olives and is immediately suitable for human consumption. The second process is an industrial chemical refining process using solvent extraction to recover the olive oil. In the refining process, cull olives are ground into meal and the meal is dried. Dry meal is exposed to solvent extraction, and the solvent and oil go through a refining tower. The solvent is recovered, and the oil is further refined and deodorized into a clear amber tasteless liquid. Refined oil is often blended with a small amount of virgin oil to restore some flavor. Oil produced with this method may be labeled as "pure olive oil." Oil yield using the refined process is greater than when using cold pressing, but is of lesser quality. Since oil production in California has been a salvage operation and is marginal economically, most of the olive oil produced in the state has been refined oil.

In recent years, the upscale American consumer has begun to value virgin oil for its flavor and nutritional qualities. It is vegetable oil—without cholesterol—and is monounsaturated. The market for virgin oil is likely to continue to grow among health-conscious Americans. Renewed interest in virgin oil has recently led canners and oil producers to devote more effort toward producing a top-quality table oil.

As its value is recognized, the olive and its products will likely take a more significant place in the American diet. The olive, important in commerce from the dawn of western civilization, will undoubtedly continue to occupy a unique position for both producers and consumers far into the future.

....

REFERENCES
....

California Agricultural Statistics Service. 1966, 1976, 1984–1992. *California Fruit and Nut Acreage* reports.

California Olive Committee. 1980–81 to 1991–92. *California Olive Industry Statistics.*

Doutsias, G. T. 1988. The production of table olives as an alternative to the production of olive oil. *Olivae* 5(20): 9–11.

Economic and Table Olive Committees. 1988. 57th session of the International Olive Oil Council. *Olivae* 5(20): 5–7.

Foytik, J. 1960. California olive industry: Trends and outlook. *Calif. Agric. Ext. Serv. Circ.* 492.

Johnston, W. E., and G. W. Dean. 1969. California crop trends: Yields, acreages, and production areas. *Calif. Agric. Ext. Serv. Circ.* 551.

Nuckton, C. F., and W. E. Johnston. 1985. California tree fruits, grapes, and nuts: Location of acreage and trends in acreage, yields, and production, 1946–1983. *Giannini Foundation Information Series* 85-1.

....

THE OLIVE INDUSTRY

CALIFORNIA'S OLIVE INDUSTRY: TRENDS AND PROSPECTS

DESMOND A. JOLLY

This chapter presents a brief overview of the structure and performance of California's olive industry over the decade 1980–1990, focusing on the primary production segment of the industry. The processing segment is treated to the extent that it affects the economic performance of the production sector through its effects on raw product price and on the terms and conditions of grower-processor transactions. From trends in acreage, production, and prices over this period, inferences can be drawn with respect to industry performance. The final section examines changes in demand and makes tentative projections of market demand for the rest of the 1990s. Actual market outcomes will depend on many different factors—macroeconomic ones such as levels of employment, consumer incomes, and foreign exchange rates; demographic ones, such as the growth and distribution of population; and microeconomic ones, such as changes in labor and capital markets.

PRODUCTION

California's olive industry encompasses approximately 1,400 growers, most of them located in two growing areas in the northern and southern parts of the Central Valley. The California Agricultural Statistics Service estimated 1990 olive acreage at 37,580 acres, consisting of 33,430 bearing and 4,150 nonbearing acres. This compares with 33,723 acres in 1985, of which 1,434 were nonbearing. Acreage increased by nearly 4,000 acres over those five years, all of which is nonbearing.

An orchard survey conducted in 1984 by the California Olive Committee found that about 58 percent of California's olive trees were more than 20 years old, suggesting a relatively mature industry. Another 39 percent represented trees between 11 and 20 years old. Nonbearing trees (10 years old or less) represented a mere 3.5 percent of acreage.

Acreage distribution

The great majority of California olive plantings in 1984 were the Manzanillo variety, which accounted for 64 percent of olive acreage. Sevillanos made up 23 percent, and other miscellaneous varieties about 13 percent.

Most olive growers are small producers. Of the 1,415 growers identified in the 1984 survey, 43 growers (3 percent) accounted for 54 percent of the industry's raw tonnage. Each of these top growers averaged more than 200 tons. The 9 percent of the growers that produced between 51 and 200 tons accounted for another 22 percent of total raw tonnage. The 31 percent producing between 11 and 50 tons and the remaining 57 percent of growers, with less than 11 tons per crop, combined to account for 24 percent of the industry's total output. In fact, the 43 largest growers outproduced all of the other 1,372 growers.

TRENDS IN CONSUMER DEMAND

Consumer demand is clearly increasing, albeit not at a very rapid rate. Per capita annual consumption increased from 0.55 pound in 1980–81 to 0.71 pound in 1989–90 (table 2.1). Of this increased demand, 0.05 pound was met by domestic and 0.11 pound by imported olives. Between increasing per capita consumption and the increase in the population, total olive consumption has grown from an average of 112.4 million pounds per year in the 1980–83 period to an average of 174.7 million pounds in the 1987–90 period. Thus, the market has increased by over 62 million pounds, more than 55 percent, during the decade.

As olives are a tree crop with a long lag between planting and production, the domestic industry has been less able to capture the increasing market than it would be if production response could be more immediate. California

Table 2.1. Market for canned ripe olives (1980–81 to 1989–90).

Season	Total domestic production (× 1,000 cases)	Total domestic production (× 1,000 pounds)	U.S. population (millions)	Domestic consumption (pounds per capita)	Imports (× 1,000 pounds)	Domestic and imports (pounds per capita)
1980–81	10,654.0	123,852.8	226.5	0.55	—	0.55
1981–82	7,397.4	85,994.8	233.3	0.37	9,794.0	0.41
1982–83	9,567.1	111,217.5	235.5	0.47	6,267.0	0.49
1983–84	10,823.1	125,818.5	236.6	0.53	13,223.4	0.58
1984–85	11,541.3	134,167.6	237.5	0.56	16,936.4	0.63
1985–86	11,868.7	137,973.6	239.7	0.57	21,542.2	0.66
1986–87	12,736.0	148,056.0	242.1	0.61	22,340.1	0.70
1987–88	10,866.5	126,323.1	242.2	0.52	44,597.3	0.71
1988–89	11,867.3	137,957.4	246.9	0.56	36,553.7	0.71
1989–90	12,927.9	150,286.8	250.4	0.60	28,310.6	0.71

SOURCES: California Olive Committee, *California Olive Industry Statistics*, 1989–90; U.S. Department of Agriculture, U.S. Census Bureau.

production of canned olives averaged 85,605 tons between 1980 and 1983, 86,966 tons between 1984 and 1987, and 80,158 tons between 1987 and 1990. The increased consumption came largely from imported olives. In fact, imports grew by 189 percent over the decade, going from 9,794,000 pounds in 1981–82 to 28,310,600 pounds in 1989–90 (table 2.1). Seemingly, the aggressive marketing campaigns of the marketing order and the private brands generated a market that exceeded the capacity of the domestic industry. In 1987–88, 26 percent of supply came from imports. Since then, changes in currency exchange rates and the size of Mediterranean harvests have mitigated the sharp rate of increase in imports (see fig. 2.1). By 1990, imports represented 16 percent of U.S. supply.

Changes in consumption patterns—in particular, patterns

of eating away from home—favor increased olive consumption. Other things equal, one would reasonably anticipate an increase in per capita consumption to at least 0.75 pound per year by 2000. The market then should demand approximately 103,728 tons. This compares with a production of some 59,000 tons in 1987–88 and 76,000 r~ in 1988–89 (table 2.2). Such a demand would be ʼ tons above the 1987–89 average. Although 4,150 a presently nonbearing acreage should be in full beari the year 2000, the industry may be able to profitabl port at least an equivalent amount of new acreage, pai larly considering that much of the present acreage cor of old trees or is planted to varieties for which the mark less robust. In fact, varietal conversion and the need more acreage could provide a stimulus for much activ..y during the ensuing decade.

Table 2.2. California olive production and prices per ton (1978–79 to 1989–90).

Year	Total (tons)	Canning size Tons	Canning size Avg. price* ($)	Limited size Tons	Limited size Avg. price ($)	Overall avg. price (1977 = 100)	Average in constant (1977 = 100
1978–79	115,019	99,028	227	15,991	70	205	—
1979–80	55,304	52,296	412	3,008	226	402	228
1980–81	92,771	76,836	404	15,935	65	345	218
1981–82	40,223	37,793	725	2,430	450	708	445
1982–83	123,820	97,877	549	25,943	399	517	321
1983–84	51,328	47,722	496	3,606	300	482	308
1984–85	82,113	76,411	482	5,702	200	462	308
1985–86	83,360	74,944	511	8,416	250	485	319
1986–87	95,424	83,519	556	11,905	272	521	325
1987–88	58,765	53,281	578	5,484	320	554	346
1988–89	76,376	68,000	580	8,376	321	552	330
1989–90	105,332	92,115	607	13,217	318	570	331

* Average Price = independent price, not including standard bonus, extra bonus, or handling allowance.

SOURCE: California Olive Committee, *California Olive Industry Statistics*, 1989–90.

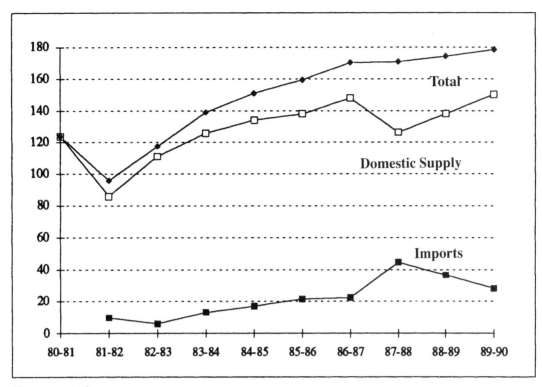

Figure 2.1. U.S. market for canned ripe olives, in thousands of pounds. SOURCE: California Olive Committee, *California Olive Industry Statistics*, 1989–90.

GROWER PRICES

We assume that supply responds to changes in economic performance. When prices are rising, producers generally increase acreage and production. When prices decrease over time, producers tend to decrease production by taking marginal acreage out of production or by spending less on the care and nurturing of the crop. Thus, trends and changes in acreage are indicators of economic performance.

By looking at changes and trends in grower prices, we may also draw inferences as to the likely effect on supply response. Table 2.2 shows that whereas olive prices were $402 per ton for canning and limited-size olives in the 1979–80 season, the price for the 1989–90 crop was $570—an increase of $168, or 42 percent. The Prices Paid Index for farmers—the index that tracks cost of production items such as interest, taxes, wage rates, and other production items—increased by 14 percent between 1981 and 1990. After 1980, real prices (table 2.2, far right column) for raw olives underwent a discrete increase of about $100 per ton. The average price in 1977 dollars was $312 per ton for the 1982–85 period compared with $336 for the 1987–90 period. Hence, between 1980 and 1990 the compensation for raw olives increased significantly. If 1982 is used as the benchmark year, prices increased by 7 per-

cent from 1982 to 1990, about 1 percent per year in real 1977 dollars. Thus, we could infer a positive price signal to olive producers. Rate of return varies with the age and productivity of orchards.

SUMMARY AND CONCLUSION

This analysis of the performance of California's olive industry demonstrates some salient trends. Demand for canned olives has increased significantly over the past decade. However, because of a relatively inelastic supply response, much of the increase in supply has come from imports. Demand for olives should continue to increase throughout the ensuing decade because of population growth and further increases in per capita consumption. Nonbearing acreage has increased over the past five years, indicating positive grower response to the increases in demand and real prices. Particularly because of the cyclical nature of olive production, acreage should increase further over the rest of the decade. By the end of the decade, the olive market should be at an average of approximately 104,000 tons. The industry still has some marketing problems deriving from a varietal mismatch between supply and demand as well as an excess supply of small sizes. But overall market prospects are favorable.

13

3

···

THE OLIVE INDUSTRY
···

CALIFORNIA TABLE OLIVES: MARKETING, IMPORTS, AND THE FEDERAL MARKETING ORDER

DAVID J. DANIELS

PROCESSED OLIVE MARKETING

The dominant products of California's olive industry are canned black-ripe and green-ripe olives. These styles account for 90 to 95 percent of the California fresh olives grown in the state. Other products are olive oil, Sicilian, Greek, green, tree-ripened, and other styles of processed table olives.

For many years olive sales fluctuated with the crop size. Figure 3.1 shows the last decade's total market for canned ripe olives in the United States, and the proportion filled by domestic and import sources. Market expansion has been tied to increased production of fresh olives and actually started with the first 100,000+ -ton crop in 1978. The industry responded by selling more than 10 million cases for the first time, and from that point on the major limiting factor on sales growth has been short crops.

Along with growth in the total market, a shift in the outlets and product mix has also affected the ripe olive industry. In 1978, the food service market, restaurants, and other non-commercial mass feeders accounted for 35 percent of ripe olive sales, and retail sales through stores accounted for 65 percent. By 1988, the respective percentages had changed to 49 and 51 percent. Figure 3.2 shows the change over time in sales for each market segment and the growth of food service sales from 1976 to 1985. This change has affected the canners' profit, since the margin on sales of large can sizes for food service is not as high as on sales of retail-size containers.

The product mix has changed since 1978, as shown in figure 3.3, and the decline in sales of whole fruit and growth in sales of pitted and sliced olives affected the industry. First, more olives had to be pitted and quicker pitting machines had to be developed and installed. Second, the growth in sales of sliced olives, spurred by increased sales to pizza restaurants, prompted canners to install more slicing equipment, also increasing costs. Finally, as sales of whole olives

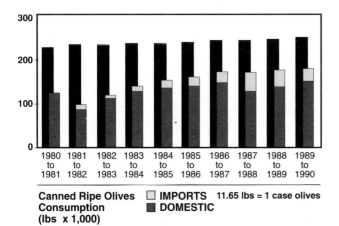

Canned Ripe Olives ☐ **IMPORTS** 11.65 lbs = 1 case olives
Consumption ■ **DOMESTIC**
(lbs x 1,000)

Figure 3.1. Consumption per capita of canned ripe olives from 1980 to 1990. SOURCES: California Olive Committee, *Acreage and Grower Survey*, 1984, and *California Olive Industry Statistics*, 1989–90.

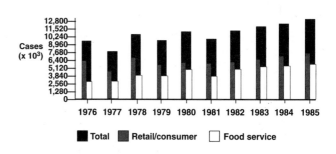

■ Total ■ Retail/consumer ☐ Food service

Figure 3.2. Change in olive sales by market segment, 1976 to 1985. SOURCES: See figure 3.1.

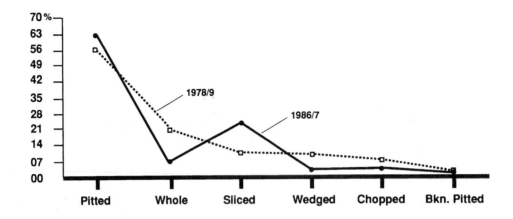

Figure 3.3. Comparison of percent change in sales of pitted, whole, sliced, wedged, chopped, and broken pitted olives from 1978–89 to 1986–87. SOURCES: See figure 3.1.

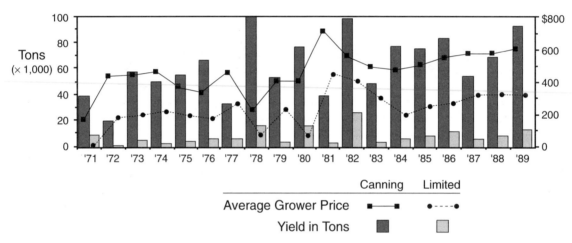

Figure 3.4. Comparison of canning- versus limited-size olive grower prices, 1971 through 1989. SOURCES: See figure 3.1.

declined, retail stores discontinued slower-moving items. The discontinued items were not replaced with additional sizes of pitted olives, and as a result the olive industry lost valuable retail shelf space.

Another factor increasing the canners' cost has been the small crops of "limited-size" olives. Limited-size olives are those with pit-to-flesh ratios too large to be acceptable as whole or pitted olives; their use is therefore limited to sliced, chopped, or wedged styles. Growers have historically received lower prices for limited-size olives than they have for canning-size olives (fig. 3.4). The demand for sliced olives has prompted canners to slice canning-size olives to meet demand.

These factors—increased sliced sales and insufficient production—came to a head in 1981 when the total California olive crop was only 43,000 tons. When California canners could not meet the demand for sliced olives, food service customers began to purchase imported product.

IMPORTS

Imported canned ripe olives were supplying around 20 percent of the U.S. market at the end of 1990 (fig. 3.1). Before 1982, imports of canned ripe olives were almost nonexistent. The market for Spanish-style green olives, olive oil, and specialty olives is dominated by imports. Some California-grown olives are used for these products, but with the exception of olive oil, the market for these items has not been growing. The recent rise in concern about types of dietary fat, coupled with interest in "new" food preparation methods, has caused olive oil sales to increase. Olive oil imports rose 15.4 percent per year from 1981 through 1991.

Imports of canned ripe olives became a factor after the small 1981 harvest, when large food service customers began to order canned product from Spain. As figure 3.1 shows, imports have become a significant factor in the market. Most of these imported olives have been sliced, pitted, and wedged styles.

Most of the imports have been of the Hojiblanca variety, a variety grown primarily for oil. This olive has a strong flavor and a tough skin, two points against its acceptance as a direct replacement for the California product. Varieties with a milder flavor that are more direct competitors of the California product have also been imported.

Olive imports can affect domestic growers in two ways. First, the domestic growers lose market share to imported product. If these losses continue, growers and canners will no longer be able to sell all of the product produced in California. So far this loss has been concentrated in one product area, and California growers have not been directly affected.

Second, the lower price of the imported sliced olives to the food service trade hurts domestic product sales. The difference between California and imported sliced olives is about $6 to $10 per case. California canners have had to reduce their selling prices to be competitive, and that has reduced their profit margins. This could cause grower prices to decline, and reduce the growers' returns.

MARKETING AND IMPORT SUMMARY

The marketing of canned ripe olives will continue to evolve as tastes and eating habits change. Olives are considered a nonessential food item, and retail sales are affected by impulse buying and feature prices. In the food service area, price and availability will continue to be major factors as imported product competes with California product in the domestic market.

THE OLIVE MARKETING ORDER

California olive growers and ripe olive canners have had a Federal Marketing Order in place since 1965. The Marketing Order, approved by grower vote, establishes a California Olive Committee, consisting of eight growers elected from various olive-producing districts and eight canner representatives designated by their firms.

The committee can recommend regulations to the U.S. Department of Agriculture for processed ripe olive grades and sizes and can provide for third-party inspection and size-grading of fresh olives delivered to canners. It collects money from the canners for crop research and market development activities. It also collects and publishes olive industry statistics. All actions taken by the committee must be approved by the USDA before they can be implemented, but when approved the committee's rules and regulations carry the authority of federal law. The committee supports University of California crop research projects, both basic and production-oriented, dealing with all aspects of olive production and processing.

The California Olive Committee also has a marketing function, the goal of which is to increase consumption of olives. Current specific goals include developing and promulgating new uses for olives, and maintaining the California olive's distinction as superior to imported product. To accomplish these goals the committee has been a consistent advertiser in magazines for consumers and the food service industry. Magazines provide the editorial environment and the medium for showing ripe olives as attractive additions to recipes, and they give readers the opportunity to write in for further recipe information. The committee sends recipes and nutritional information to newspaper and magazine editors as a way of encouraging them to feature ripe olives in their articles and recipes.

....
REFERENCES
....

California Agricultural Statistics Service, *California Fruit and Nut Acreage,* 1989.

California Olive Committee, *Acreage and Grower Survey,* 1984.

California Olive Committee, *California Olive Industry Statistics,* 1989–90.

4

BOTANY OF THE OLIVE

GEORGE C. MARTIN

Olive is a member of the family *Oleaceae*, which contains the genera *Fraxinus* (ash), *Forsythia* (golden bell), *Forestiera* (*F. neomexicana*, the California "wild olive"), *Ligustrum* (privet), *Olea* (olive), and *Syringa* (lilac). Commercial olives belong to the species *Olea europaea* L., one of about 20 species of *Olea* found in tropical and subtropical regions of the world. Only *Olea europaea* L. produces edible fruit.

GENERAL DESCRIPTION

Olive is a long-lived evergreen tree; some specimens have been reported to live for 1,000 years. The wood resists decay, and when the top of the tree is killed by mechanical damage or environmental extremes, new growth arises from the root system. Whether propagated by seed or cuttings, the root system generally is shallow, spreading to 3 or 4 feet even in deep soils. The aboveground portion of the olive tree is recognizable by the dense assembly of limbs, the short internodes, and the compact nature of the foliage (fig. 4.1). Light does not readily penetrate into an olive tree unless the tree is well managed and pruned to open light channels toward the trunk. If unpruned, olives develop multiple branches with cascading limbs. The branches are able to carry large populations of fruit on terminal twigs, which are pendulous and flexible, swaying with the slightest breeze.

LEAF

Olive leaves are thick, leathery, and oppositely arranged. Each leaf grows over a 2-year period. Leaves have stomata on their lower surfaces only. Stomata are nestled in peltate trichomes that restrict water loss and make the olive relatively resistant to drought (fig. 4.2). Some multicellular hairs are present on leaf surfaces. Olive leaves usually abscise in the spring when they are 2 or 3 years old; however, as with other evergreens, leaves older than 3 years are often present. Yellow leaves in the spring signal the abscis-

Figure 4.1. Mature olive tree.

Figure 4.2. Surface structure of olive leaf showing peltate trichomes. Notice how the trichomes overlap.
SOURCE: Courtesy of K. Pinney and V. S. Polito.

sion process, but yellow leaves may also reveal other physiological and pathological problems discussed elsewhere in this book.

Figure 4.3. Olive inflorescence and open flowers on 1-year-old twig.

Figure 4.4. Olive inflorescence prior to opening of flowers. Actual size is approximately 1 1/4 inch (3 cm) long.

Figure 4.5. Perfect flower, showing stamen and pistil.

INFLORESCENCE

Flower bud inflorescences are borne in the axil of each leaf. Usually the bud is formed on the current season's growth and begins visible growth the next season. Buds may remain dormant for more than a year and then begin growth, forming viable inflorescences with flowers a season later than expected. When each leaf axil maintains a developing inflorescence, there are hundreds of flowers per twig (fig. 4.3). Each inflorescence contains between 15 and 30 flowers, depending on developmental processes for that year and the cultivar (fig. 4.4).

FLOWER

The flowers borne on the inflorescence are small, yellow-white, and inconspicuous. Each contains a short, four-segmented calyx and a short-tubed corolla containing four lobes. The two stamens are opposite on either side of the two-loculed ovary that bears a short style and capitate stigma. Two types of flowers are present each season: perfect flowers, containing stamen and pistil (fig. 4.5), and staminate flowers, containing aborted pistils and functional stamens. The proportion of perfect and staminate flowers varies with inflorescence, cultivar, and year. Large commercial crops occur when 1 or 2 perfect flowers are present among the 15 to 30 flowers per inflorescence. As a rule, more staminate flowers than pistillate flowers are present.

The perfect flower is evidenced by its large pistil, which nearly fills the space within the floral tube (fig. 4.5). The pistil is green when immature and deep green when open at full bloom. Staminate flower pistils are tiny, barely rising above the floral tube base. The style is small and brown, greenish white, or white, and the stigma is large and plumose as it is in a functioning pistil (fig. 4.5).

The reasons for flower and young fruit abscission are not well known. However, pistil abortion is often involved. Stress from lack of water and nutrients during floral development can lead to pistil abortion and large proportions of staminate flowers. Also, excessive populations of flowers or leaf loss up to a month before full bloom contribute to pistil abortion.

Ultramicroscopic and histochemical evidence shows that flower buds begin forming by November. By about 8 weeks before full bloom, flower formation is visible under low-power microscopic examination. During the next 8 weeks, flower development is rapid. Full bloom in California occurs during May; blooming generally occurs 1 to 2 weeks earlier in the southern than in the northern parts of the state. The viable pistil has two carpels, each containing two ovules, but only one is fertilized and developed; thus, in the fruit only one carpel containing one seed is present.

FRUIT

The olive fruit is a drupe, botanically similar to almond, apricot, cherry, nectarine, peach, and plum. The olive fruit consists of carpel, and the wall of the ovary has both fleshy and dry portions. The skin (exocarp) is free of hairs and contains stomata (fig. 4.6). The flesh (mesocarp) is the tissue eaten, and the pit (endocarp) encloses the seed. Fruit shape and size and pit size and surface morphology vary greatly among cultivars.

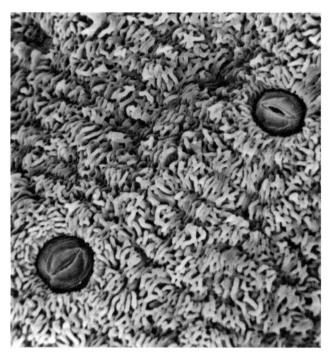

Figure 4.6. Young olive fruit (pistil) surface showing stomata and wax. SOURCE: Courtesy K. Pinney and V. S. Polito.

SEED

The seed undergoes most of its development starting in July and ending in about September (fig. 4.7). The fruit is horticulturally mature in September or October (ready for the California black-ripe or green-ripe process), and physiologically mature in January or February. The seed is horticulturally mature by October, and if harvested and stratified at that time it will achieve maximum germination. When the fruit is physiologically mature by January, seed germination is greatly reduced.

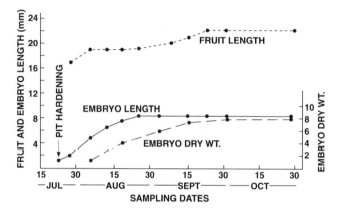

Figure 4.7. Seasonal growth curves for olive fruit and embryo.

The mature seed is covered with a thin coat that covers the starch-filled endosperm. The latter surrounds the tapering, flat leaflike cotyledons, short radicle (root), and plumule (stem). Seed size and absolute shape vary greatly with cultivar.

5

ORCHARD PLANNING

OLIVE CULTIVARS AND PROPAGATION

ELLEN G. SUTTER

Of the many known cultivars of *Olea europaea*, only five are used commercially in California for processing as table varieties: Manzanillo, Sevillano, Mission, Ascolano, and Barouni. The fruitless cultivar, Swan Hill, is used as an ornamental tree. Factors determining selection of cultivars include suitability for processing, size of fruit, climatic limitations, and disease resistance. Tables 5.1 and 5.2 summarize the characteristics and harvest periods of these cultivars.

CULTIVARS

Manzanillo

Manzanillo, introduced into California from Spain about 1875, is the most popular cultivar used for canning in California and the most widely planted.

Table 5.2. Order of harvest of major olive cultivars.

Cultivar	Sept	Oct	Nov	Dec
Ascolano	••••••••••••••			
Manzanillo	•••••••			
Sevillano		••••••••••••••		
Barouni		••••••••••••		
Mission			••••••••••••••••••	

Physical characteristics. Manzanillo has a characteristically low-spreading growth habit, reaching about 15 to 30 feet (5 to 10 m) in height at maturity. Fruit are borne singly, are oval, and are uniform in size and shape. Average fruit weight is 4.8 grams; the majority of fruit range in

Table 5.1. Characteristics of major olive cultivars grown in California for fruit.

Cultivar	Mean fresh weight per fruit (grams)	Flesh-to-pit ratio	Oil content (percent of fruit)	Main uses
Ascolano	9.0	8.2:1	18.8	Black-ripe Green-ripe
Barouni	7.4	6.8:1	16.5	Fresh Black-ripe
Manzanillo	4.8	8.2:1	20.3	Black-ripe Green-ripe Spanish green Oil
Mission	4.1	6.5:1	21.8	Black-ripe Green-ripe Oil
Sevillano	13.5	7.3:1	14.4	Black-ripe Green-ripe Spanish green

weight from 4.0 to 5.5 grams. Flesh-to-pit ratio after canning is 8.2:1. Manzanillo trees are commonly propagated by rooted stem cuttings.

Climatic adaptation. Manzanillo is grown mostly in Tulare, Kings, and Fresno counties in the southern San Joaquin Valley, where it produces high yields. Manzanillo has had limited usage in Tehama and Butte counties in northern California, because it is not tolerant of cold winter temperatures.

Bearing, harvest, and uses. Although the fruit matures in October or early November, Manzanillo fruit is harvested in late September to avoid injury during early frosts. Fruit are processed mostly as black-ripe and green-ripe olives. Some fruit are used to produce fermented Spanish-style green olives. Oil content in fruit in winter averages approximately 20.3 percent of fresh weight, making the fruit suitable for oil extraction.

Diseases and pests. Manzanillo is very susceptible to olive knot and verticillium wilt. Its susceptibility to black scale is similar to that of other cultivars.

Sevillano

Sevillano, the second most popular variety of olive, was introduced into the United States from Spain in 1885.

Physical characteristics. Sevillano trees have a spreading growth habit. Growth can be quite variable; trees reach a height of 25 to 35 feet (8 to 11 m) at maturity. Sevillano trees can be trained to stay low, making them relatively easy to harvest by hand. Sevillano fruit is the largest of the cultivars grown in California, with an average weight of 13.5 grams; flesh-to-pit ratio averages 7.3:1. The fruit grow singly on peduncles and vary in shape from plump and ovate to elongated oval. Sevillano is difficult to root from cuttings; consequently, the cultivar is produced commercially by grafting. The predominant method of propagation is to graft shoots onto 1-year-old Manzanillo rooted cuttings. The variations in size seen in mature Sevillano trees may be due to effects of seedling rootstocks.

Climatic adaptation. Sevillano is planted mostly in the Corning area of Tehama County in northern California, but small plantings have been established in Butte and Tulare counties. It is somewhat resistant to cold damage. Sevillano is also used as a pollinizer for Manzanillo.

Bearing, harvest, and uses. Bearing is variable in Sevillano. In addition to normal alternate bearing for which the periodicity is annual, it reportedly has several "off" years followed by one year with a heavy crop. The fruit mature relatively late and are harvested in October. The main disadvantage of Sevillano is that the fruit are difficult to process; they bruise easily, and split pits can be a problem. Sevillano fruit must be harvested at an earlier stage than other cultivars for acceptable processing results. Sevillano is used mostly as a canned ripe olive or as fermented Spanish-style olives. Its low oil content (averaging 14 percent in winter) precludes its use for oil extraction.

Diseases and pests. Sevillano is resistant to peacock spot fungus (*Spilocea oleaginea*), but it is susceptible to olive knot (*Pseudomonas savastanoi*). It is also susceptible to several physiological disorders, including soft nose (which causes the fruit to darken at the apex and to shrivel), split-pit (which causes the pit to split into two parts), and shotberry (which aborts seeds, and thus arrests fruit growth).

Ascolano

Ascolano originated in Italy and was introduced into California in about 1885.

Physical characteristics. The Ascolano tree has a naturally rounded shape and grows to 20 to 30 feet (6 to 10 m) at maturity. Fruit grow singly or in clusters. Ascolano is characterized by large fruit with a soft texture. The fruit are very tender and difficult to pick without bruising. Shape of the fruit varies from round to oval, and most range in size from 9.8 to 11.1 grams. Ascolano's value is that it has a very high flesh-to-pit ratio (8.2:1).

Climatic adaptation. Ascolano makes up approximately 3 percent of California's total acreage. Most plantings are in the San Joaquin Valley, particularly in Kings and Tulare counties. Ascolano is resistant to cold injury and grows well in all olive-producing areas of California.

Bearing, harvest, and uses. Ascolano bears regularly when trees are young, but develops alternate bearing at maturity. The fruit mature early and are picked from mid-September to early October, earliest of all commercial cultivars. The main disadvantage of Ascolano is that its fruit bruise easily during harvest. Ascolano fruit are used as canned ripe olives. The Spanish green pickling process shrivels the fruit. The average oil content of Ascolano olives is 18.8 percent.

Diseases and pests. Ascolano is fairly resistant to both peacock spot and olive knot. Ascolano is considered somewhat more susceptible to olive knot than Mission, but is more resistant than Manzanillo, Sevillano, and Barouni. Ascolano shows some resistance to verticillium wilt.

Mission

Mission was originally introduced into the United States from Mexico in 1769.

Physical characteristics. Mission trees grow tall and upright, often reaching 40 to 50 feet (12 to 15 m) as mature trees when they are not cut back. They must be kept topped to make hand harvesting practical. The fruit are relatively small, averaging only 4.1 grams. Mission has the lowest flesh-to-pit ratio (6.5:1) of any commercial cultivar. Fruit are borne singly or in clusters and are broad-oval to oval-elongated in shape. Mission is propagated commercially by rooted cuttings.

Climatic adaptation. Mission is the most cold resistant of all commercial cultivars in California. Mission is a preferred cultivar in Butte and Tehama counties because of its cold resistance. Trees have been known to survive 8°F (–13°C). Many Mission trees in the southern San Joaquin Valley have been topworked to cultivars that do not require cold hardiness and have more favorable fruit characteristics.

Bearing, harvest, and uses. Mission bearing patterns are somewhat erratic. Both alternate bearing and consistent annual crops have been reported, depending on the orchard and the area where trees are grown.

Mission is the latest-maturing variety in California; harvest often starts in late October and continues through November. Harvest dates depend on use of the fruit. Mission olives can be picked when green for Spanish-green processing; when the fruit develop some red coloration, they can be used for ripe olive processing. Because the fruit mature late in the season, early fall frost can damage them, making them useless for pickling. Mission olives are primarily used for pickling, but can be used for oil extraction because of their high oil content (21.8 percent). When used to produce oil, they are harvested from mid-December to late February.

Diseases and pests. Mission is very susceptible to peacock spot and also develops olive knot. Its susceptibility to scale insects is similar to that of other cultivars.

Barouni

Barouni was introduced into California from Tunisia in 1905. It was planted in the early 1920s in California, but there have been no recent plantings.

Physical characteristics. Barouni trees are relatively small, reaching 15 to 25 feet (5 to 8 m) at maturity, with spreading tops. Their natural growth habit makes the fruit easy to harvest by hand. The fruit are large and borne singly on peduncles. Fruit shape ranges from oval to oval-elongated. Barouni has a low flesh-to-pit ratio, which averages approximately 6.8:1.

Climatic adaptation. Barouni is grown mostly in Butte County; Tulare County has some small acreage. The trees show resistance to cold damage.

Bearing, harvest, and uses. A major advantage of Barouni is that it exhibits regular, dependable bearing. Fruit are harvested from mid-October to early November. Barouni olives are usually sold as fresh for home processing, since they process poorly as a commercial canned product. Fruit processed commercially are used for black-ripe table olives. Barouni olives have a low oil content (16.5 percent) and are not used for oil extraction.

Diseases and pests. Barouni is susceptible to olive knot and somewhat resistant to peacock spot. Barouni is thought to be more resistant to peacock spot than Mission, but less resistant than Sevillano, Manzanillo, and Ascolano.

Oblonga

When Oblonga is used as a rootstock for Manzanillo, it produces smaller trees than own-rooted Manzanillo trees produced from cuttings. Oblonga can carry verticillium wilt without showing symptoms of the disease. The fungus continues to proliferate in the rootstock, and when it reaches the scion, the scion dies. Oblonga is widely used as a rootstock for Swan Hill in Arizona.

Allegra

Allegra has potential as a verticillium-resistant rootstock. It is reportedly also resistant to nematodes. Allegra does not dwarf Manzanillo as does Oblonga.

Swan Hill

Swan Hill was introduced into the United States from Australia by H. T. Hartmann in 1961 and was patented in the United States by the University of California. It has some verticillium wilt resistance, which would be useful if it could be propagated as a rootstock. Swan Hill has not been commercially successful as a rootstock—it is extremely difficult to root from cuttings. It produces predominantly staminate flowers and thus sets very few fruit, making it desirable as an ornamental tree. It has been used as an ornamental in Arizona. Although research reports indicate that 80 to 90 percent of subapical cuttings taken in July or August could be rooted, these results are difficult to repeat on a commercial scale. Some nursery workers have reported less than 10 percent rooting. When propagated commercially as an ornamental, Swan Hill is often grafted onto an Oblonga rootstock.

PROPAGATION OF OLIVE TREES

Olive trees do not come true from seed; moreover, seedlings retain juvenile characteristics for long periods, and fall short of full production for as long as 10 years. Although breeding and rootstock production rely on seed propagation, olive trees are vegetatively (asexually) propagated for commercial production. This approach results in greater uniformity in critical factors, such as time of harvest, size of fruit, shape of trees, and oil content of the fruit, than could be achieved with seed propagation. Olive trees may be propagated by a variety of methods, including rooting of stem cuttings, grafting, and budding.

Seed

The pit is the structure handled for seed propagation; it is composed of the seed together with the stony endocarp, the hard covering surrounding the seed itself. In botanical terms, the endocarp, being derived from the ovary, is not part of the seed, whereas seeds are derived from the ovule. Olive seeds germinate slowly, taking 1 to 6 months or longer. Germination is also unreliable, ranging from 5 to 90 percent, depending on the cultivar. These variations are due to incompletely satisfied internal dormancy requirements, which may involve inhibitors in the embryo or seed coat. Slow and unreliable germination is also attributed to mechanical dormancy, the inability of the embryo to penetrate the endocarp.

For seed production, the fruit should be harvested when ripe, but before they turn black. This period extends from late September to mid-November, depending on the cultivar. The pit is removed from the flesh of the fruit with a seed-cleaning machine.

Pits can be planted directly, but germination is slow and uneven. Pregermination treatments are designed to overcome both mechanical and internal dormancy. Mechanical or chemical scarification is used to treat mechanical dormancy. In scarification, the endocarp can be cracked mechanically or clipped at the radicle end, with care taken not to damage the embryo. Clipping just the cotyledonary end of the endocarp does not improve germination. Pits may also be soaked in concentrated sulfuric acid to soften the endocarp. Soaking time depends on the thickness of the endocarp; typical soaking times for Manzanillo are between 24 and 30 hours. The acid bath is followed by 1 to 2 hours of rinsing in water.

The pits can be planted directly after the endocarp treatments. Pits should be planted at a depth approximately two to three times their diameter. Seeds planted outdoors in December do not germinate until the following spring. Pits can also be planted in pots or in a seedbed in a greenhouse maintained at a 70° to 75°F (21° to 24°C) daytime temperature. Germination takes up to 3 months. It is critical that the seeds not dry out after germination begins.

Germination is quicker and more uniform when treatments to overcome internal dormancy are carried out in addition to scarification. The most successful of these treatments on a commercial scale is stratification, also known as moist chilling. Pits are scarified as described above and then soaked in water at room temperature for 24 hours. The pits are mixed with moist sand or vermiculite and then placed

in the dark in a controlled environment. The temperature is kept at 55°F (15°C) for 30 days. Stratification is thought to reduce abscisic acid (which inhibits germination) within the embryo or seed coat. After stratification, pits can be planted outdoors if the weather is suitable; severe weather can cause losses. Pits can be planted in a greenhouse maintained at a 70° to 80°F (21° to 27°C) daytime temperature. Bottom heat is necessary. Germination should occur within 1 month. Transplanting seedlings from the greenhouse to the nursery should include steps to harden the seedlings, such as partial shade provided by a lathhouse. Adequate irrigation and fertilization are recommended to ensure continued rapid growth.

Cuttings

Rooting shoot cuttings is the major method of propagating olive trees in California and in other major olive-producing areas, such as Spain and Italy. Cultivars vary widely in their ability to produce roots on cuttings. Rooting percentages range from 20 to 30 percent in Sevillano to 95 to 98 percent in Manzanillo, Nevadillo, or Picual. Success in rooting cuttings depends on the type of wood used and the season in which cuttings are made. Cuttings can be made from hardwood or leafy stems, suckers, ovuli, or truncheons.

Hardwood cuttings

Hardwood cuttings are made from 3- to 4-year-old wood, ranging from 1 to 3 inches in diameter. Wood for cuttings is gathered in late January or early February. All leaves are removed and the wood is cut into sections 8 to 12 inches (20 to 30 cm) long. It is preferable that the bottom cut be made below a node. The base of the cutting is soaked in a water solution of 10 to 20 ppm indolebutyric acid (IBA) for 24 hours. Cuttings should be planted with correct polarity (that is, with the basal end of the cutting in soil) in a flat with a mixture of equal parts perlite and vermiculite and kept moist in a greenhouse at 70° to 75°F (21° to 24°C) until roots start to form. Rooting may take as long as 3 months. Rooted cuttings can be transplanted to pots or planted directly in the nursery. They should be buried one-half to three-fourths of their length. Cuttings should be protected from excessive sunlight and water stress for 2 to 3 weeks after transplanting and should be hardened gradually.

Another method for handling hardwood cuttings is to treat them with IBA as described earlier. Then place them, with correct polarity, in a box, and cover them completely with moist sawdust. After storage for approximately 30 days at 60° to 70°F (13° to 21°C), they can then be planted in pots or flats in the greenhouse or taken directly to the field or nursery with the same precautions previously described.

Hardwood cuttings may have less reliable rooting than smaller leafy stem cuttings. Use of hardwood cuttings involves removing fruiting wood, which can significantly affect fruit production if many cuttings are made from one tree.

Leafy stem cuttings

Propagation by leafy cuttings was made possible by the use of intermittent mist, a technology introduced by Hudson Hartmann in the 1950s. This method reduces transpiration and leaf temperature and increases relative humidity, enabling cuttings to remain turgid throughout root induction. Leafy cuttings are prepared using 1- to 2-year-old wood from vigorous shoots. Cuttings should be approximately ⅛ inch (3 mm) in diameter. Larger diameter wood ranging up to ⅜ inch (9 mm) can also be used. One schedule indicates that July or August is the best time to collect wood for leafy cuttings. The succulent, terminal portion of the shoot is discarded. The stem is trimmed to 4 to 5 inches (10 to 12 cm) long, with a slant cut on the top and straight cut on the bottom to mark the correct polarity. The bottom cut is made just below a node. If the bottom cut is too far below the node, the cutting will not root. Leaves are removed from all but the top inch (2.5 cm) of the cuttings and the base is dipped for 5 seconds into a 50 percent alcohol solution of 4,000 ppm IBA. Prepared root-inducing products, such as Hormex and Hormodin, powders that contain IBA and talc, may also be used. The cutting's base is dipped briefly into water and then into the powder.

The basal end of the cutting is inserted 2 inches (5 cm) into the rooting medium. The medium used for root induction must be porous and drain well, yet retain some moisture. Perlite and vermiculite in equal parts are generally used, although peat moss may be used instead of vermiculite. The cuttings are then placed in a greenhouse at 70° to 75°F (21° to 24°C) daytime temperature under intermittent mist. Bottom heat at 70°F is required to maintain the temperature in the medium because evaporation of water can significantly cool the medium. Alternatively, the cuttings can be placed in a closed frame in which the relative humidity is kept high. Bottom heat is not necessary as the closed frame results in adequate temperatures of air and rooting medium. Cuttings take 8 to 12 weeks to form roots.

Rooted cuttings are kept in a greenhouse all winter. They would not survive if moved outdoors in September or October as they would not be hardened sufficiently to survive winter. They are moved to individual pots under lath in early spring. Growth is often slow for a period after roots form. The new trees are trained in containers to a single stem about 2 feet (60 cm) long with three main scaffolds arising from the top of the single stem.

The trees are ready to be sold in July after the winter in which the cuttings were rooted. They are usually not planted in summer but kept in the nursery until the following March because early spring is a far better time than July to plant trees. Thus, although one can obtain a complete plant in 12 months, it actually takes about 18 to 20 months from the time cuttings are taken to the time trees are planted.

Another schedule for producing trees from rooted cuttings has been implemented recently. Cuttings are taken in February using shoots grown the previous year (1-year-old wood), approximately ¼ inch (6 mm) in diameter. The thin, terminal section is discarded and the leafy stem cuttings are treated with IBA as described. The cuttings are placed under fog in a greenhouse. Bottom heat is maintained at 56°F (13°C), which is somewhat warmer than the outside temperature at that time of year. If the temperature of either the air or rooting mix is too high, the buds break and the cuttings do not root. After the cuttings root, in 2½ months, they are potted in gallon cans and kept in a greenhouse at 86°F (30°C) in high relative humidity. These conditions promote growth of shoots and roots without cessation of growth as occurs in cuttings taken in July. The advantage of this method is that trees can be planted in March, 1 year after cuttings are taken.

Suckers

Suckers are shoots that originate on roots or basal parts of trunks of older trees. When suckers are separated from the tree with part of the root attached, they can produce a tree ready to be planted in the orchard in 1 year. Suckers are cut back to about 18 inches (45 cm) and planted in the nursery, together with the root section, which should be about 3 inches (7.5 cm) in diameter. Alternatively, suckers can be removed from the tree without any root portion and be treated as a leafy stem cutting as described previously. As suckers retain some juvenile characteristics, they are often easier to root than stem cuttings taken from higher in the tree. One disadvantage of this method is that juvenile characteristics often make the tree develop and come into production more slowly than trees grown by cuttings and grafting or budding. One must also be certain that suckers grow from the scion, not from the rootstock, when they are taken from grafted trees.

Ovuli

Ovuli are protuberances composed of meristematic tissue that form at the base of older olive trees. Ovuli can be induced to form shoots and roots by removing them from the mother tree and covering them with soil to exclude light. Propagation from ovuli is practiced mostly in North Africa. The relative scarcity of ovuli and the damage done to the mother tree when removing them limit their use for propagation.

BUDDING AND GRAFTING

Uses and compatibility

Seedlings or rooted cuttings may be used as rootstocks to propagate cultivars difficult to root as cuttings. Rootstocks may also be used when special characteristics, such as verticillium wilt resistance and dwarfing, are desired. There appears to be no incompatibility among most cultivars of *Olea europaea*.

Incompatibility has been reported when *Olea europaea* has been grafted onto other species of *Olea*, such as *O. ferruginea* and *O. chrysophylla*, or onto other members of the *Oleaceae*, such as *Syringa*, *Fraxinus*, and *Forestiera*. Grafting within cultivars of *Olea europaea* can affect vigor. In studies by Hartmann, own-rooted Mission and Manzanillo trees were more vigorous than trees produced by grafting these cultivars onto rootstocks, regardless of which of 12 rootstocks was used. Own-rooted Sevillano, however, was less vigorous than trees produced by grafting Sevillano scions onto vigorously growing rootstocks, such as Mission and Manzanillo. The cultivars Oblonga and Allegra appear to dwarf Manzanillo somewhat but have no effects on Sevillano, Ascolano, or Mission. Use of seedling rootstocks is thought to impart variability to the tree.

General technique

Either seedlings or rooted cuttings can be budded and grafted. Seedlings are produced as described and are budded or grafted when 1 year old, at which time they are approximately ¼ to ⅜ inch (6 to 9 mm) in diameter. Rooted cuttings are budded or grafted 1 year after the cutting is taken. Rooted cuttings should also be ¼ to ⅜ inch in diameter. Thus, cuttings taken in July or August are rooted the first year and then budded at the beginning of the second year. The trees must be grown during the second year before they are ready for planting. Because it is advisable to plant in spring rather than in summer, budded or grafted trees are held in the nursery until the following spring (beginning of the third year) before planting. It takes an additional year to produce a tree that is grafted or budded onto a rooted cutting compared with a tree produced on its own roots from a cutting. Rooted cuttings of Manzanillo are often used as rootstock to produce difficult-to-root cultivars, such as Sevillano, whose seeds are difficult to germinate and whose seedling rootstocks are thought to impart variability to the complete tree.

Budding

For budding propagation, the T-bud (also known as the shield bud) is most often used. The rootstock is budded in March or April when the bark is slipping. The bark of the stock must be slipping for T-budding. The stock is cut back to the new bud 2 to 3 weeks after budding to stimulate growth of the bud. Details of T-budding are available in Hartmann, Kester, and Davies (1990).

Grafting

Grafting is done on 1-year-old seedlings or on 1-year-old plants produced from cuttings. Nursery workers prefer grafting to budding because of the relative ease of preparation and the added insurance of success as several buds are present on grafted scionwood. Grafts do not require the bark of the stock to be slipping and thus can be made during winter as well as in spring and early fall. The greatest success appears to be in February or March with the growth of shoots in spring. Either V-grafts (saddle grafts) or side grafts are used. V-grafts have become more popular because they are relatively easy and quick to perform and have a high rate of success.

Grafting is also used in topworking, to change the cultivars of an established tree or an entire orchard. Bark grafting is commonly used and is best done between early March and late April as bark grafting requires that the bark be slipping. Three well-spaced, primary scaffolds from 4 to 6 inches (10 to 15 cm) in diameter are selected and are cut back close to the trunk of the tree. Several nurse branches are left on the tree until the graft has made sufficient growth. This may take up to 2 years.

Scionwood should be 1-year-old wood, ¼ to ½ inch (6 to 12 cm) in diameter. It should be cut into sections containing two nodes above the point of grafting. Two to three scions are inserted on each limb. All exposed surfaces should be covered with grafting wax or a similar compound immediately after grafting. Painting the graft union, scions, and trunks of the trees with white latex paint or a commercially available whitewash compound will reduce the temperature of the wood and prevent sunburn. Aftercare includes removing suckers from below the graft union, being prudent with fertilization and irrigation, and gradually removing the nurse branches after 1 or 2 years. Only one of each set of grafts on any limb is retained.

REFERENCES

Crisosto, C., and E. G. Sutter. 1985. Improving 'Manzanillo' olive seed germination. *Hort. Sci.* 20:100–102.

Crisosto, C., and E. G. Sutter. 1985. Role of the endocarp in 'Manzanillo' olive seed germination. *J. Amer. Soc. Hort. Sci.* 110:50–52.

Hartmann, H. T. 1967. 'Swan Hill' . . . a new ornamental fruitless olive for California. *Calif. Agric.* 21:4–5.

Hartmann, H. T., D. E. Kester, and F. T. Davies. 1990. Plant propagation: Principles and practices, 5th ed. Englewood Cliffs, N.J.: Prentice Hall.

Hartmann, H. T., and F. Loreti. 1965. Seasonal variation in rooting leafy olive cuttings under mist. *Proc. Amer. Soc. Hort. Sci.* 87:194–98.

Hartmann, H. T., K. W. Opitz, and J. A. Beutel. 1980. Olive production in California. *Univ. Calif. Div. Agric. Sci. Leaf.* 2474.

Hartmann, H. T., and P. Papaioannou. 1951. Olive varieties in California. *Calif. Agric. Exp. Stn. Bull.* 720.

Hartmann, H. T., and J. E. Whisler. 1970. Some rootstock and interstock influences in the (*Olea europaea* L.) cv. Sevillano. *J. Amer. Soc. Hort. Sci.* 100:670–74.

Lagarda, A., G. C. Martin, and D. E. Kester. 1983. Influence of environment, seed tissue, and seed maturity on 'Manzanillo' olive seed germination. *Hort. Sci.* 18:868–69.

Lee, C. I., H. C. Kohl, and J. L. Paul. 1983. Propagation of 'Swan Hill' fruitless olive by leafy cuttings. *Plant Propagator* 29:11–13.

Loreti, F., and H. T. Hartmann. 1964. Propagation of olive trees by rooting leafy cuttings under mist. *Proc. Amer. Soc. Hort. Sci.* 85:257–64.

Nussbaum, J. J., and A. T. Leiser. 1972. Rooting cuttings of 'Swan Hill' fruitless olive. *Calif. Agric.* 26:10–12.

SITE SELECTION AND PREPARATION, TREE SPACING AND DESIGN, PLANTING, AND INITIAL TRAINING

G. S. SIBBETT AND JOSEPH OSGOOD

A mature olive orchard must produce moderate crops of large fruit annually in order to be profitable. Equally important, the new olive orchard must reach "economic bearing," that point at which crop proceeds exceed harvesting costs, as soon as possible after planting, and yields must increase quickly during its formative years. Proper planning that includes site selection, preparation, orchard design and tree spacing, planting, and initial training is critical to attaining these objectives.

SELECTING THE SITE

The site of the orchard strongly affects its capacity to produce. Growers must give considerable attention to the local climate, the physical and chemical qualities of the soil, and the amount and quality of the water that will be available to the trees.

Climatic considerations

The best olive production and quality occur in areas having mild winters and long, warm, dry summers to mature the fruit. Olives are subtropical trees, sensitive to hard freezing temperatures. The small wood and branches are injured, often killed, by temperatures below 22°F (−5°C). Minor freeze injury to fruit wood causes openings easily invaded by the olive knot bacterium, which kills the injured area. Large limbs and whole trees can be killed if temperatures fall below 15°F (−10°C). The vegetative growth of Manzanillo is more sensitive to freezing than Mission, Sevillano, and Ascolano. Olive fruit are injured by freezing temperatures during the growing and maturation period. Districts having a high probability of frost before harvest should be avoided. Winter temperatures fluctuating

between 35°F and 65°F (1.5°C and 18°C) are ideal, supplying the needed winter chilling for subsequent flower development.

Areas where summer rainfall is common should also be avoided. Epidemics of fungal and bacterial diseases can injure trees in such areas and reduce their productivity.

Soil

Although olive trees adapt to a wide variety of soils, production is best where the trees can develop roots without chemical or physical restriction. The soil's physical and chemical condition is critical to olive production.

Physical soil condition. The physical condition of a soil describes its texture, depth, and stratification. Olives prefer nonstratified, moderately fine textured soils, including sandy loam, loam, silt loam, clay loam, and silty clay loam. Such soils provide aeration for root growth, are quite permeable, and have a high water holding capacity. Sandier soils do not have good nutrient or water holding capacity, and heavier clays often do not have adequate aeration for root growth. These soils are difficult to manage for maximum production.

Olive trees are shallow rooted and do not require very deep soils to produce well. Soils having an unstratified profile of 4 feet (1.2 m) are suitable for olive. Stratified soils, either cemented hardpan or varying soil textures within the described profile, impede water movement and may develop saturated layers that damage olive roots.

Soil chemistry. Olives tolerate soils of varying chemical quality. Trees produce well on moderately acid (pH greater than 5) or moderately basic (pH less than 8.5) soils as well as those having relatively high levels of boron or chloride. Basic (alkaline) or sodic soils should be avoided, since their poor structure prevents water penetration and drainage, creating saturated soil conditions that kill olive roots.

Water

Olive trees require about 3 acre-feet of water per acre to be productive. Although olives are drought tolerant, California orchards require supplemental irrigation during the growing season to satisfy the trees' water requirements. Adequate water must be available throughout the season for tree growth and maximum production.

Olive trees tolerate water relatively high in boron, up to 3 ppm. However, irrigation water high in nitrogen promotes excessive vegetative growth that hinders fruit production. Excess sodium in supplemental water accumulates in the soil, causing water penetration problems. Water analysis can be a valuable tool in selecting the site and in managing the orchard.

PREPARING THE SITE

Proper site preparation is essential to the ultimate profitability of the olive orchard. Preparation includes ensuring uniform water application to the trees by leveling the land or selecting appropriate irrigation systems, deep tillage to destroy cemented or compacted layers that impede water movement in the soil profile, fumigation to destroy plant parasitic nematodes, and installation of the irrigation system. Site preparation is completed before the orchard is planted. The best time to prepare the site is before rains begin in fall of the year before spring planting.

Leveling

Maximum production occurs when all of the trees are uniformly supplied with water. How much to level or grade the land to promote this uniform water supply depends on the original terrain and the cost of moving earth versus the cost of an irrigation system designed for rolling or sloping land.

If the orchard is to be flood or furrow irrigated, leveling the land for uniform water application to all trees is recommended. For all but quite sandy soils, the orchard floor should be leveled flat. It is better to shorten irrigation runs than to level to grade as a way to facilitate moving water long distances; the latter practice results in overly wet "ends" with less water available to the middle portion of the row. If flood or furrow irrigation is to be used on sandy soils where it is difficult to move water, leveling to a slight grade (½ to ⅟₁₀ foot per 100 feet of irrigation run) is recommended.

Some sites have rolling or sloping terrain, where levelling would cause either excessive costs or environmental dam-

age. In such sites, sprinkler or low-volume irrigation would be more cost effective.

Deep tillage

Once the land has been leveled, the next step is deep tillage. This process breaks compacted, cemented, or textural layers that impede water movement within the soil profile; olive trees are killed by poor drainage where saturated soil conditions exist in the root zone. Soils with 4 feet (1.2 m) of uninterrupted profile do not usually require deep tillage.

"Ripping," pulling a 3- to 5-foot (0.9 to 1.5 m) shank through the soil profile by a track-layer tractor, breaks up cemented "hardpan" layers. Once these layers are shattered, they will not recement during the life of the orchard.

Slip plows are used to invert the soil profile where the blade is placed. This practice is more costly, since it usually requires more power than ripping, but it is more effective if the layers are compacted or textural and not cemented. A backhoe can be used to excavate individual tree sites, but the local "flowerpot" effect may eventually impede water drainage. Ripping or slip plowing is usually done in the proposed tree row.

Fumigation

After leveling and deep tillage, fumigation destroys parasitic nematodes and eliminates weeds. Any nematode or weed problem should be assessed carefully before planting to determine whether fumigation is necessary.

Fumigation is an expensive practice and must be done correctly to be effective. It is essential that the soil be prepared and be at the proper temperature and moisture conditions for treatment. Manufacturers of fumigants and commercial applicators supply directions for proper soil preparation.

Selecting and installing the irrigation system

The irrigation system should be selected and installed before the olive grove is planted. All irrigation systems can deliver the proper amount of water to the trees under the circumstances for which they are designed to operate.

System selection is based upon its initial cost, its maintenance, the terrain to be irrigated, and the cost and availability of water. Low-volume systems—drip systems, mister/fogger systems, mini-sprinkler systems, and fan jet systems—are expensive but efficient and well adapted to sloping land. They apply small, precise amounts of water (usually 1 to 15 gallons per hour) to localized areas around the trees and are useful and economical when the terrain cannot be economically leveled to the degree necessary for less expensive systems. Low-volume irrigation is also useful when water is costly and must be used most efficiently, and when automation is desired. Sprinkler systems are expensive, but useful on sloping terrain. Sprinklers apply more water per hour than low-volume systems and are suitable where runoff does not occur. Sprinklers can be permanently set in the orchard or on movable hoses or pipelines. Movable systems have less initial expense, but their use is labor intensive. Furthermore, movable systems operate every day, so some part of the orchard is wet on any given day, hindering access for other cultural work. Pipeline systems and open-ditch systems are usually the cheapest and are quite effective if water is cheap and abundant and the orchard floor is flat to ensure uniform distribution.

The irrigation system should be installed before planting. The best time to install the system is after preplant fumigation. Once the trees are planted it becomes much more difficult to install an irrigation system.

TREE SPACING

Optimal olive orchard designs involve planting trees to utilize space efficiently. Maximum production from the young and mature orchard is a result of effective orchard design. The following considerations are important in designing a new olive orchard.

Sunlight

The olive tree bears fruit on 1-year-old wood found on its outer periphery in the presence of adequate sunlight (fig. 6.1). Olive shoots do not flower and do not produce fruit in full shade. If the trees are planted too closely, shading eventually reduces orchard production. A mature orchard is considered at optimum bearing potential when trees are spaced at the greatest density that still lets them intercept enough sunlight for annual productive shoot growth throughout the tree's periphery.

New olive orchards must produce economic crops as soon as possible. How soon an orchard reaches economic bearing depends on tree density. Before trees reach full size and utilize all allotted space and sunlight, per-acre production is directly related to the number of producing trees. Olive orchards are therefore commonly planted with "filler" trees at high densities to use the sunlight most efficiently and reach maximum production before the trees reach full size. Such high-density planting assumes that filler trees are removed as they grow crowded and their shading interferes with production. Although tree-to-tree competition for water and nutrients increases with tree density, competition alone does not restrict tree size enough to prevent the necessity of tree removal.

Tree size and soil type

The ultimate size of an olive tree is the primary determinant of final tree spacing in a mature orchard. Cultivar and soil type largely determine the tree's ultimate size. Sevillano, Mission, and Ascolano cultivars are vigorous and grow to a

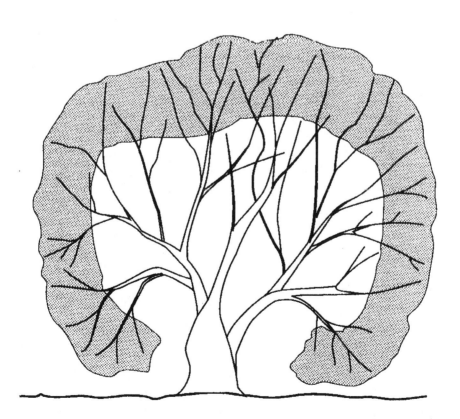

Figure 6.1. Location of most productive bearing area in an olive tree.

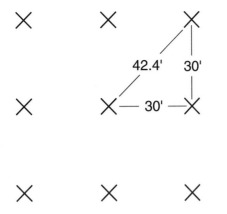

Figure 6.2. Square design in olive orchard (48 trees/acre).

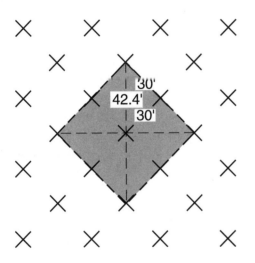

Figure 6.3. Offset square design in olive orchard (48 trees/acre).

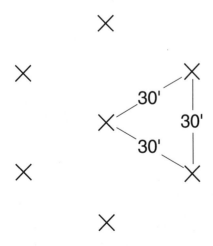

Figure 6.4. Hexagonal/equilateral triangle design in olive orchard (56 trees/acre).

large size. Manzanillo is a moderately sized, spreading tree and requires much less space than other cultivars. All cultivars develop their maximum size on fertile, well-drained soils. Trees on marginal soils do not grow as large. Larger-growing olive cultivars on good soils require approximately 40 feet (12 m) between trunks. Manzanillo requires only a 30-foot (9 m) spacing.

DESIGNING THE OLIVE GROVE

There are several appropriate orchard designs for olives. In all cases, the design must (1) provide maximum sunlight exposure of the planned number of trees both initially and when they reach full size, and (2) allow for efficient orchard equipment operation.

Designs for permanently set trees

Square. The square pattern is the most popular design and is used by most olive orchardists. Trees are equally spaced within and between rows so that a line drawn from one tree to its closest neighbor in the next row forms a right angle to the rows (fig. 6.2). The square is popular because it is easy to lay out and orchard operations can be carried out in both directions. It is not normally used when filler trees are planned, since distances between trees and within rows eventually become too small for efficient orchard care.

Offset square. This system is similar to the square design, except that trees in adjacent rows are offset (fig. 6.3). At a given tree spacing, the square and offset square designs have an equal number of trees per acre and an equal area per tree.

This design is less popular than the square. It is more difficult to lay out, and unless farmed on the "diagonal," the rows are closer.

Hexagonal/equilateral triangle. The hexagonal/equilateral triangle design is similar to the offset square except that distances between trees in any direction are equal, so that lines drawn between three trees produce an equilateral triangle (fig. 6.4). The system is adaptable only to plans without filler trees. The disadvantage of this design is the difficulty in layout. However, it allows 17.5 percent more trees per acre than the square or offset square at any given spacing, and therefore is the most efficient in use of both sunlight and land.

Designs using "filler" trees

The first decision to be made before selecting a design is whether or not filler trees are to be used to increase tree density and early production. The choice depends on the grower's goals. Filler trees increase (and usually double) tree density during the first 6 to 10 years. Such a high-density orchard begins production sooner and reaches higher levels than an orchard with standard spacing during the same period. However, the greater number of trees per acre translates into higher development and managerial costs. Also, any cultural practice done on a "per-tree" basis (such as training, pruning, or fertilizing) results in higher per-acre production costs. Finally, removing filler trees once the orchard gets crowded is expensive.

Filler trees are usually placed between permanent trees set 30 to 40 feet apart in a square design. Two designs are well suited for filler trees: hedgerow and offset square/diamond.

Hedgerow. The hedgerow design places trees closer within rows than between rows (fig. 6.5). Usually, permanent olive trees are spaced 30 to 40 feet (9 to 12 m) apart down the row in a square design and filler trees are placed between. This allows easy access by equipment, but does not allow efficient use of sunlight as the trees crowd quickly within the rows. Row direction is not a significant factor in hedgerow olive plantings that use filler trees. Tree removal takes place before shading reduces production.

Hedgerows are not appropriate for permanently set olives. The in-row spacing is too close for mature trees, so shading occurs in the row, reducing optimal production. Removing trees from such a planting often results in inefficiently spaced trees.

Quincunx. In the quincunx design, the permanent trees are set in a square pattern with a filler tree in the center of each square (fig. 6.6). Like the hedgerow, this system uses twice as many trees per acre; however, since the filler tree is between rows rather than in the row, it uses sunlight more efficiently. Filler trees can be left in the orchard longer before their shade interferes with permanent tree production.

The main disadvantage of the quincunx design is that initially there are twice as many tree rows as will be in the permanent planting, so establishment and operating costs are proportionally higher. The rows of filler trees may need separate irrigation lines, adding to orchard development costs. Access with equipment is more difficult, and more middles must be driven to perform cultural practices. Unplanted "drive rows" should be left every 6 to 10 rows to allow access for harvest equipment.

Pollinizer placement

Pollinizer varieties are used in large blocks or isolated locations to enhance pollination for optimal production of olives (see chapter 9). Research has shown that the most effective dissemination of the wind-blown pollen occurs within a 100-foot (30 m) radius of the pollinizer. Pollinizer rows should be spaced every 200 feet (60 m) in the new orchard. Olive varieties differ in ultimate tree size, and row or tree spacing may need to be adjusted accordingly for the pollinizer rows.

Figure 6.5. Hedgerow design in common use for young olive groves. Requires eventual tree thinning to avoid crowding (97 trees/acre).

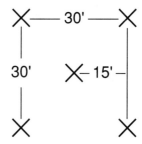

Figure 6.6. Quincunx design, showing filler tree in the center of each square (97 trees/acre).

PLANTING AND TRAINING OLIVE TREES

Planting

Olive nursery trees are commonly sold as "canned" or "balled" stock; trees are rooted for 2 to 3 months in beds then transplanted to 1-gallon cans or burlap/plastic tubes and grown for 12 to 18 months in the nursery. They are usually trained to a single trunk 36 to 48 inches (90 to 120 cm) long (fig. 6.7). These trees are planted with the soil intact around the root system.

Canned or balled trees can be planted throughout the year, since the soil is intact around the roots. The best time to plant in the interior valley olive districts, however, is in March or April at the start of the growing season, when the threat of frost is past. Plantings made in the hot midsummer are more difficult to establish, and growth is mediocre the first year. Nursery trees planted in September and October can be severely damaged by a freeze, so it is recommended that nursery stock be held over and protected until the next March or April. Districts with more moderate climates have more flexibility in planting date.

Olive trees are occasionally available as bare-root trees. Bare-root trees are produced by rooting directly in the nursery row, growing the trees for at least 2 years (often longer), then digging them up during late winter for direct orchard planting. Ideally, bare-root trees are trained to one trunk, but more often they come with several low shoots near ground level. All but one should be removed at planting time.

Bare-root trees are dug in mid- to late winter for orchard planting in January, February, or March, before the onset of new growth. In heavy soils, planting should be delayed to avoid root damage from saturated soil. Bare-root trees must have their roots kept moist at all times. If planting is delayed, bare-root trees must be "heeled" in moist soil to prevent root desiccation.

Some growers plant large portions of olive branches, called truncheons. These pieces are 3 to 4 inches (7 to 10 cm) in diameter, approximately 12 inches (30 cm) long, and are planted horizontally several inches deep in late winter. Numerous shoots develop from truncheons, making them difficult to train in a conventional manner. Erratic survival and multiple shoot growth are disadvantages of this type of planting stock.

Digging holes and planting the trees. The hole for new olive trees should be large enough to accommodate the root system and, if trees are canned or balled, the accompanying soil. Take care not to glaze the sides of the tree hole during digging, which will limit lateral root growth and water movement. Once the tree hole is dug, chop at the sides with a shovel to destroy any glazing before planting. The tree's roots should not be crammed into the hole, and the tree should not be planted deeper than in the can or nursery.

When planting the new olive tree, prune off any broken roots and long roots that do not easily fit into the tree hole. Once the tree is placed at the desired depth, refill with soil, tamping firmly until the hole is filled. At this point, the tree should be very difficult to pull up by hand.

Immediately after planting, the soil around the tree should be wetted thoroughly. Adequate moisture should be maintained around the tree during the growing sea-

Figure 6.7. Canned nursery olive tree.

son, but take care not to overwater: olive trees are sensitive to saturated soils. Once the tree is established, proper weed control and light nitrogen applications will ensure good growth throughout the season.

Sunburn protection. Trunks of newly planted trees sunburn readily if left exposed. Protective paper or foil wrappers 18 inches (45 cm) high provide adequate protection and prevent contact by weed killers. As the trunk grows, the wrappers must be removed to prevent the ties from girdling the trunk. Painted-on whitening agents such as interior

36

water-based white latex paint prevent sunburn, but do not protect trees from contact weed killers.

Training

There are two training objectives during the first 3 years of olive orchard development. The first is to develop a strong, well-spaced framework of uncongested scaffold branches to support heavy crops and facilitate shaker attachment for mechanical harvest. The second is to bring the new olive trees into bearing as soon as possible. Therefore, pruning, while it should be sufficient to direct the tree's growth, should also be kept to a minimum to promote early production. Initial training and pruning during these 3 years are largely responsible for reaching these objectives simultaneously.

At planting. Once the tree is planted, only shoots below a 30-inch (75 cm) height should be removed, and the leader should be pinched at 36 to 40 inches (90 to 100 cm) to stimulate lateral growth. If lateral shoots above 30 inches have begun growth on the tree in the nursery, no pinching of the terminal is necessary.

First summer. Early in the growing season, select three to five lateral-growing, upright shoots to be the scaffold branches. Space the scaffolds around the trunk, leaving sufficient distance between them to allow eventual shaker access. One- to two-inch (2.5- to 5- cm) vertical separation between scaffolds is necessary to provide strength in attachment to the trunk. Remove any other vigorous shoots on the trunk while they are quite small to direct growth into the selected scaffolds. Avoid larger cuts late in the growing season, since they would delay production.

Training and pruning olive trees should be avoided during dormancy. Such pruning usually requires heavier cutting, which would adversely affect production, and also renders the new tree more susceptible to freezing injury when the protective branches are removed.

Second and third growing seasons. The only training and pruning suggested for the second and third growing seasons serves to continue directing tree growth into the framework branches. Usually all that is required is the early removal of suckers, watersprouts, and excessively low-hanging shoots. Excessive cutting, which delays the onset of bearing, should be avoided. Once bearing begins, ideally in the third growing season, a secondary scaffold system of two to three branches per primary scaffold can be selected and developed. Heavy cutting should be avoided until moderate bearing begins.

7

THE OLIVE TREE AND FRUIT

CARBOHYDRATE AND NITROGEN ASSIMILATION

WILLIAM H. KRUEGER

Sixteen elements are considered essential for plant growth and development. Two, carbon and oxygen, come from the air; the others are provided by the soil. In order of magnitude required by the plant they are carbon, hydrogen, oxygen, nitrogen, phosphorus, potassium, sulfur, calcium, magnesium, iron, manganese, copper, boron, zinc, molybdenum, and chloride. The first nine are referred to as macronutrients because they are required in large quantities; the remaining seven are known as micronutrients because they are required in minute quantities.

Carbon in combination with hydrogen, oxygen, nitrogen, phosphorus, and sulfur enable living organisms to store and transfer energy via chemical binding and transformation. Only green plants and some bacteria have the ability to convert inorganic substances to organic (carbon-containing) compounds by photosynthesis. In this process (fig. 7.1), energy from the sun is trapped in green pigments (chlorophyll) and is used to convert carbon dioxide and water into simple carbohydrates, giving off oxygen in the process. Carbohydrates are carbon containing compounds that contain hydrogen and oxygen at a ratio of 2:1.

In the reverse process—respiration—these carbohydrates are broken down to carbon dioxide and water, and energy is released. Respiration is basic to all plant and animal life and, unlike photosynthesis, can occur without light or chlorophyll.

PHOTOSYNTHESIS

In photosynthesis, six molecules of carbon dioxide combine with six molecules of water to form one molecule of glucose and six molecules of oxygen. Glucose is transformed into other simple sugars such as fructose, sucrose, and a sugar alcohol known as mannitol. Mannitol is thought to be the main translocated sugar in olives and is also an important storage product. Glucose serves as a building block for other carbohydrates such as starch, cellulose, hemicellulose, pectins, and gums.

Carbon dioxide (CO_2), which makes up about 0.03 percent of the earth's atmosphere, diffuses into the olive leaf through stomata, specialized pores located on the leaf undersurface. Water is distributed by the plant's vascular system. In addition to allowing for the entry of CO_2 into the leaf, the stomata allow the loss of water vapor into the atmosphere through transpiration. The opening of the stomata is actively regulated to allow just enough CO_2 into the leaf for photosynthesis to continue. If water is in short supply, the stomata close to reduce water loss and photosynthesis is reduced.

Carbon dioxide is absorbed by chlorophyll-containing cells and photosynthesized during daylight hours into water-soluble carbohydrates.

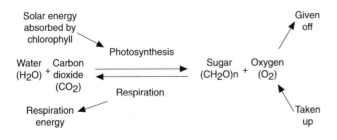

Figure 7.1. The use of solar radiant energy to convert carbon dioxide and water into energy-rich sugars and oxygen is called photosynthesis. In the reverse reaction, respiration, sugar is broken down by living cells into carbon dioxide and water, releasing chemical energy.

39

Factors influencing photosynthesis

Light intensity. An olive leaf exposed to full sun can only use a portion of the light for photosynthesis. It becomes light saturated, reaching its maximum photosynthetic rate, at approximately 30 percent full sun (fig. 7.2). Only leaves on the outer edge of the canopy are ever exposed to full sun, and these only for a portion of the day as the sun crosses the sky. Therefore, for most of the day photosynthesis in most of the leaves is not light saturated. Light becomes even more limiting inside the tree canopy. Because light management's goal is to see that the maximum number of leaves are photosynthesizing at peak efficiency, it is an important part of maximizing yields.

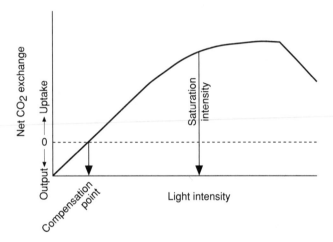

Figure 7.2. A model light intensity versus carbon dioxide (CO_2) exchange curve, depicting the compensation point and saturation intensity.

Temperature. Photosynthesis is optimal in olive at temperatures between 59° and 86°F (15° to 30°C). During California summers, low-temperature inhibition of photosynthesis is rare, but photosynthesis may often be reduced by excessive heat.

Carbon dioxide concentration. Carbon dioxide concentration in the earth's atmosphere rarely varies enough to affect photosynthesis. However, carbon dioxide must enter the leaf to be utilized, and anything that reduces diffusion into the leaf reduces photosynthesis.

Nutrient supply. Every molecule of chlorophyll contains four nitrogen atoms and one magnesium atom. Phosphorus plays a vital role in energy transfer and metabolism. Iron, manganese, molybdenum, and zinc regulate enzyme activity. Deficiencies in one or more of these elements result in chlorosis and limit photosynthesis. Additionally, any deficiency in nutrients such as nitrogen that reduces leaf growth also reduces photosynthesis.

Water supply. Water stress limits photosynthesis by directly affecting the photochemical processes involved or by causing stomata to close, which limits carbon dioxide availability.

Leaf number and exposure. Any tissue containing chlorophyll is capable of photosynthesis. Leaves are the primary units of photosynthesis in olives. Therefore, optimal exposure of the greatest number of leaves to sunlight results in the highest yield of dry matter.

The total leaf area of a tree divided by the land area the tree occupies is called the Leaf Area Index (LAI) and is one criterion for land productivity. Optimum LAI occurs when all leaves can contribute to the carbon gain in the plant.

Because light intensity and leaf area are critical to maximum photosynthesis, plant spacing, row orientation, and pruning and training are important considerations in starting a new orchard. By increasing plant density and minimizing pruning, early yields can be enjoyed. As trees become crowded LAI increases, but the efficiency of photosynthesis declines and pruning costs may become excessive.

In a typical olive leaf with good sun exposure on a summer day, the stomatal opening increases as light intensity increases, reaching its maximum by mid-morning. Afternoon temperatures may be excessive, and stomata may narrow or close in response, to prevent water loss.

Translocation and storage of photosynthates

Many of the photosynthates produced in olive leaves are stored in the leaf as mannitol, and some are translocated out for use or storage in other plant parts.

Mature leaves, which remain on the tree for 2 years, are the main source of photosynthates. Growing shoot and root tips and developing fruit utilize these photosynthates and are referred to as sinks. Half-expanded leaves are highly efficient photosynthetically, but need to retain much of their photosynthates for growth; thus, they are both source and sink. The concept of source-sink relationships is used to describe the internal competition for photosynthate within the plant.

During years of heavy crop, much demand for photosynthate from developing fruit results in reduced vegetative growth. Previously deposited storage products are mobilized into developing fruit.

Photosynthates move from leaves through the phloem and join other vascular bundles in the midrib and continue out the petiole to twigs and limbs. In limbs, phloem tissue is found on the inner side of bark and consists primarily of specialized pipelike structures called sieve tubes, which transport organic substances to new developing root and shoot tips and to newly forming cells (the cambium) that add girth to trunk and roots.

The xylem is made up largely of vascular bundles and mainly serves to conduct sap—water and nutrients absorbed from the soil solution—to the leaves. In stems, trunk, and roots, the xylem tissue is the wood. Each year as the tree grows, the new xylem adds another ring to the trunk. Mineral elements dissolved in the sap usually remain in the leaf cells, while the water evaporates from leaf surfaces or passes through the stomata.

RESPIRATION

In respiration, the reverse of photosynthesis, the photosynthates are broken down, using oxygen, to yield chemical energy and carbon dioxide (fig. 7.1). This energy is used for carrying on metabolism in other parts of the plant.

Respiration can be divided into two types: maintenance and growth. Maintenance respiration goes on continually and is necessary to keep tissue healthy and functioning efficiently as metabolically active compounds, such as enzymes, are continually being broken down and rebuilt. Maintenance respiration takes place at a lower rate during winter than in summer. Growth respiration occurs when new tissues are developing, as photosynthates are converted into products required by the plant to build new tissue.

Factors influencing respiration

Temperature. Respiration is catalyzed by enzymes that are temperature sensitive. Near-freezing temperatures change the fluidity of the protein and the water, and the reaction rate slows. At temperatures greater than 104°F (40°C), the enzymes can be denatured so the reaction slows.

Oxygen. Oxygen is generally not limiting in aboveground parts; however, in heavy or waterlogged soils it can be limiting in the roots. This can reduce respiration and limit root growth and nutrient uptake.

Soluble carbohydrates. In a healthy olive tree, mannitol and sugars are produced in the leaf and exported to all parts of the tree. They are converted to glucose at their destination and used in respiration or stored as reserve food in the form of starch. Factors that inhibit photosynthesis thus limit carbohydrate supplied to the cells and reduce respiration.

Internal factors. Changes in the physiological state of the plant tissues affect respiration rates. Plant tissues are less active during winter, so respiration rates are lower. Hormones are thought to regulate the physiological state of plant tissue and therefore indirectly affect respiration rates.

CARBOHYDRATE ECONOMY OF THE TREE

The carbon economy of an olive tree as discussed to this point can be summarized in a diagram like that of figure

7.3. Carbon in the form of CO_2 is taken up during photosynthesis and converted to carbohydrates, which are transported to various parts of the plant. These serve as energy sources for maintenance and growth respiration or as building blocks in new plant parts. Carbon is lost in three ways: in crop harvest, pruning and leaf loss, and losses to pests and diseases.

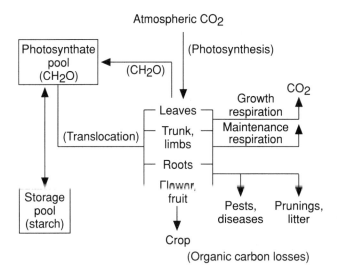

Figure 7.3. Diagram of an olive tree's carbon economy.

NITROGEN CYCLE IN ORCHARDS

Nitrogen is the element most often deficient in the soil solution and the one on which most fertilizer programs are based. The earth's atmosphere is 78 percent nitrogen. Atmospheric nitrogen is not readily available for use by plants and must first be converted to various organic and inorganic forms common in soils. This conversion process is known as nitrogen fixation. While some fixation occurs in the atmosphere due to photochemical reactions and lightning discharges, the bulk of it occurs in the soil, accomplished by a variety of soil-dwelling microorganisms. They convert atmospheric nitrogen to proteinaceous material and ammonium ion (NH_4^+). This fixed nitrogen finds its way into the organic fraction of the soil and is retained in semistable form. The mineralization, breakdown, and release of nitrogen in soil organic matter and its reabsorption by plants and return to the soil in residues make up the continuous process known as the nitrogen cycle (fig. 7.4). In an olive orchard, where nitrogen is removed in the crop and prunings, it is necessary to return nitrogen through fertilizer to maintain high yields.

Soils generally contain no more than 1 percent nitrogen, of which only 2 to 10 percent is water soluble. Stored nitrogen in organic matter becomes available through mineralization (fig. 7.5). The first step in mineralization is the formation of amino (NH_2) compounds through enzymatic hydrolysis of proteins. These amino compounds are either utilized by microorganisms or rapidly transformed to ammonia (NH_4^+) by ammonification. The ammonia ion can be absorbed by plants or microorganisms or it may be held as an exchangeable ion by soil particles.

The ammonia ion is usually rapidly converted, first to nitrite (NO_2^-) by a group of bacteria known as *Nitrosomas*. Nitrite is then converted to nitrate (NO_3^-) by the *Nitrobacter* group of bacteria. Normally, the conversion to nitrate is more rapid than the conversion to nitrite, and nitrite does not build up in the soil. Nitrate is the most common form of nitrogen that is absorbed and utilized by olive.

Nitrates and ammonia are removed from the soil solution and used by the olive in photosynthesis to produce amino acids and, in turn, proteins. When the leaves fall or the plants die or are eaten by nematodes, insects, or animals, all the nitrogen is eventually returned to the soil.

Nitrogen may be lost from the soil through crop removal, pruning, denitrification, volatilization, and runoff. In denitrification, nitrate is reduced to volatile oxides of nitrogen and elemental nitrogen by microorganisms. This loss is greatest under low oxygen and abundant nitrate conditions.

NITROGEN UPTAKE AND ASSIMILATION

The nitrate taken up from the soil is reduced to the ammonia ion in root cells, which reacts immediately with organic acids and respiration by-products to form various nitrogenous compounds. The simplest of these are amino acids, the building blocks for protein.

Some of the amino acids are converted to proteins by the growing roots, and some are transported to aerial plant parts, mostly through the xylem. A portion of the nitrogenous component is absorbed by cells in the cambium of the trunk and scaffold limbs, to be assimilated by the newly dividing cells that add to the girth of the tree. As these cells mature, their contents are redissolved and carried upward to newer tissues. Cells in mature vessels lose their endwalls and thus become very efficient at transporting water and solutes. This accounts for the presence of nitrogenous compounds in sap.

Dissolved substances not absorbed in transit are carried to growing shoot tips where they are assimilated into various structures. The kinds and amounts of different nitrogen compounds assimilated by tissues depend on their physiological age and such factors as plant age and light exposure. Cultural practices may affect assimilation patterns inasmuch as they affect stress in the plant and light distribution within the canopy.

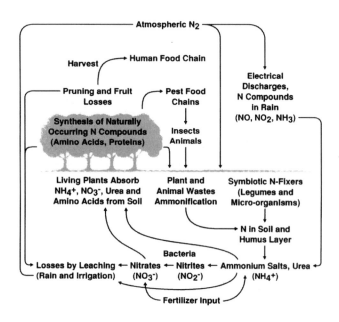

Figure 7.4. The nitrogen cycle.

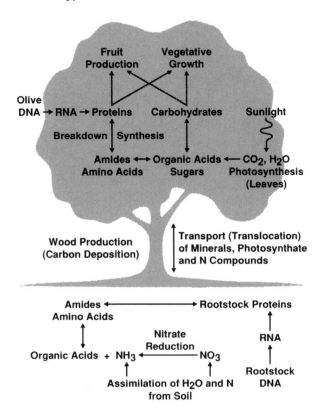

Figure 7.5. Nitrate reduction and related processes for the formation of organic nitrogenous compounds during vegetative and reproductive development of the olive tree.

42

8

ROOT PHYSIOLOGY AND ROOTSTOCK CHARACTERISTICS

JOSEPH H. CONNELL AND PETER B. CATLIN

Tree root systems are difficult to study, as the examination itself usually profoundly alters them. Thus, the extent and quality of information about roots in their natural environment is subject to considerable uncertainty. The extent, bulk, and perennial nature of the olive root system adds further complexity, with carryover effects from season to season. Fortunately, research has revealed a general similarity in behavior among woody perennial plants, so that reasonable interpretations and projections are possible.

Until a problem affecting roots becomes severe enough to limit shoot growth or production, the underground part of the tree is often taken for granted. The tree's aboveground and underground parts depend intimately upon each other; thus, an appreciation of what is, or should be, occurring in the roots is fundamental to understanding the tree.

ROOT SYSTEMS AND COMPONENTS

Roots and root systems consist of a number of components. A framework consisting of relatively few large roots extends both laterally and vertically (fig. 8.1). From this root framework there are branching and rebranching laterals of decreasing diameter. This branched network terminates with the tips of recently formed fine roots. Root systems are shorter vertically and more spreading than the aboveground growth, a profile especially common in species such as olive that are cutting propagated. Because olives are commonly planted on shallow soils, olive roots are frequently restricted to the top 3 to 4 feet (0.9 to 1.2 m); even in deeper soils they tend to remain shallow rooted. As with other orchard species, olives generally have approximately 70 percent of their roots in the top 2 feet (0.6 m) of soil.

Figure 8.1. Form of root system expected for a mature olive tree.

Branching or lateral root formation does not fit a regular pattern, and roots are not uniformly distributed in the soil. Root systems remain in balance with the shoots, but this balance changes with age and can be altered by cultural management. Tree root systems are considerably lighter than aboveground portions on a weight basis.

Root systems consist of at least two different types of roots, those that are short-lived and those that develop secondary enlargement. The form and tissues of recently formed roots, including the root tip, are shown in figure 8.2. New roots may become highly branched with laterals arising from cell division and differentiation originating in the pericycle. Elongating and recently matured new roots may persist for varying lengths of time, but these are usually short-lived, frequently lasting only several weeks.

In some new roots, a vascular cambium forms and secondary development or enlargement occurs. Cell division in the cambium produces new xylem (wood) toward the inside and new phloem (bark) toward the outside (fig. 8.3a).

As this occurs, tissues external to the pericycle collapse, are sloughed off, and decay. Other changes are the formation of periderm and suberization. Periderm (fig. 8.3b) is analogous to the corky outer bark of stems. Suberin, a complex mixture of fatty substances, resins, and tannins, is deposited in association with cell walls of the outer periderm. Death of outer periderm cells and suberin account for the dark external color of older roots. As the diameter of large framework roots increases, there is a greater proportion of xylem in relation to exterior tissues, which are gradually sloughed off (fig. 8.3b).

Variations in the fine roots described occur in woody perennial plants. In one type, the cortex and associated tissues are lost, surfaces become suberized and turn brown, but little if any secondary thickening occurs. In other instances roots become brown, but the cortex remains. Both types persist as fine brown roots, 2 mm or less in diameter, for up to several seasons. These small roots probably account for more than 80 percent of the total length of the root system. Outer cells appear to be suberized.

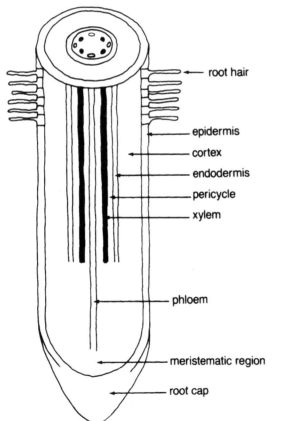

Figure 8.2. Diagram of a recently formed, growing root, including the tip and internal tissues.

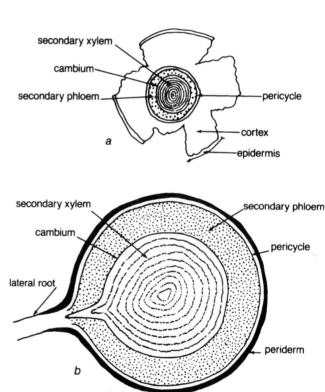

Figure 8.3. Cross-section diagrams of roots with secondary development: (a) early stage; (b) advanced stage.

ROOT FUNCTIONS

Roots provide five primary functions: anchorage, absorption of water, absorption of nutrients, synthesis, and storage of chemicals. How well they carry out these functions has much to do with the growth and production of the above-ground part of the tree (scion). Root function can depend upon the type of rootstock, the scion variety, the soil environment, and especially cultural management practices.

Anchorage

Good anchorage results when root systems are deep and spreading. Such systems are more likely to occur when the scion is vigorous and when the rootstock is from seedlings rather than from cuttings. Deep, spreading root systems are difficult to realize in shallow soils or in soils with restrictions to root growth such as sand layers, clay pans, high or fluctuating water tables, or very fine texture. Anchorage characteristics can differ with rootstock, cultivar, and method of propagation. Poor anchorage of young olive trees propagated as rooted cuttings is rare compared with problems with other cutting-propagated tree species.

Absorption of water and nutrients

Trees with deep and spreading root systems are best suited for performing the two most commonly recognized functions: absorption of water and absorption of mineral nutrients. Such root systems have the best potential for exploiting the soil profile. Absorption of water and absorption of nutrients are different physiological processes. Uptake of water depends on physical forces in the soil and within the plant. Selective and active absorption of nutrients requires expenditure of respiratory energy and the existence of cells and tissues characteristic of the root tip region.

Absorption of water and nutrients was once thought to occur mainly, or even exclusively, in the root tip region. The efficiency and rate of absorption appear greatest near the root tip, but there is increasing evidence that other parts of roots participate in uptake. Uptake of water and nutrients has been demonstrated by both secondarily thickened and fine, "browned" roots. It is uncertain whether suberization in these roots causes selective absorption of nutrients or increased resistance to water movement. The very small-diameter brown roots appear capable of contributing significantly to total absorption because of their extensive length and surface.

Synthesis of chemicals

The fourth root function, one frequently overlooked, is conversion or synthesis. Each year a considerable amount of nitrogen is lost from the tree in the crop, leaves, and prunings; this nitrogen must be replenished each year. Nitrogen absorbed from the soil as nitrate is reduced by root enzymes to the ammonium form. Carbohydrate from the leaves is converted to organic acids that, combined with ammonium, form amino acids and amides—the basic units of protein and the forms in which nitrogen is transported to the shoot.

Two types of hormones, gibberellins and cytokinins, are formed in the apical portions of roots and move to the scion, mainly via the xylem. They are involved in controlling vegetative and reproductive growth. Reduced hormone supply due to root problems is one cause (among many) of small leaves and lack of vigor. Experimental restriction of roots, preventing new root formation, has been shown to reduce shoot growth.

Another hormone, ethylene, can arise in roots and at low levels stimulates root growth and branching. With root damage or various stresses, high levels of ethylene may form, inhibiting root growth, and, if transported to shoots, causing senescence and abscission of leaves. Still another growth substance, abscisic acid, is synthesized in the root cap and when transported to leaves can affect stomatal behavior.

Storage of chemicals

The fifth function of roots is storage of carbon and nitrogen. Carbon is stored as starch and soluble carbohydrate, which provide metabolic intermediates, respirable substrate for energy production, and the basic structural units for root growth. Nitrogen is stored mainly as amino acids and protein. Part of the nitrogen absorbed, especially in late summer and autumn, is retained for later use. Accumulation of suitable reserves at this time is particularly important for development of olive flower buds and resumption of growth the following spring.

Storage, as well as other root functions, depends on the supply of photosynthetic products from leaves. Any condition or cultural practice that adversely affects photosynthesis is potentially harmful to root performance. Downward translocation of sucrose and mannitol from leaves in the phloem cannot be unduly restricted or all root processes will be affected. Under optimum conditions about half of the photosynthate produced by leaves is transported to below-ground tissues. Roughly half of this is consumed, principally in growth and respiration, and the remainder is stored for use when supplies from shoots are low.

ROOT GROWTH AND ACTIVITY

Root growth is essential for optimal root performance. Olive trees can remain alive with limited root growth, but tree size and production can be severely limited. Smaller trees on very fine-textured, wet soils are examples of this.

Increases in diameter of large roots and laterals provide the framework, anchorage, and storage capacity. Enlargement of major laterals is regular and rapid in young trees. In mature trees secondary thickening of individual roots (fig. 8.3) may stop for several years but then resume.

Formation, extension, and branching of small-diameter laterals is of major importance as these include the root tip (fig. 8.2). Recently formed fine roots are white and are often referred to as new roots, white roots, or feeder roots. As noted, absorption and synthesis are major activities with fine roots. With many plants, root hairs—lateral extensions of epidermal cells—exist just behind the root apex. Root hairs greatly increase the absorbing surface.

New white roots can vary from a few millimeters to more than 60 centimeters long and are usually 2 millimeters or less in diameter. Most live from 1 to several weeks and later are replaced by new white roots, provided soil or plant conditions are not limiting. Before dying naturally, new white roots become suberized and brown, this change progressing from base to tip. In contrast, browning that progresses from the tip toward basal portions indicates damage from soil environmental or pathogenic causes.

Not all new roots die. A few undergo secondary thickening and become part of the perennial root framework. Others, persisting as fine brown roots, have been described previously. Although these fine brown roots provide considerable length and surface and some absorptive capacity, it is uncertain whether they fulfill storage or extensive synthetic functions.

Effects of shoot pruning on root growth

Pruning, if severe enough to stimulate vigorous shoot growth, tends to suppress root growth in spring. This is likely because of retention of photosynthate in aboveground parts of the tree. Except where pruning is drastic, as with "dehorning," greater root growth later in the season would be expected.

Root activity

In other publications, the term "root activity" often means uptake of water and nutrients. That use is limited; in this publication, root activity includes synthesis and storage of chemicals as well as root growth. This is because these functions are interrelated; deficiencies in one or more affect others and, ultimately, the scion's performance. Probably the most important component is root growth, because this provides the potential for realizing other functions.

SOIL ENVIRONMENTAL EFFECTS ON ROOTS

Nematodes, bacteria, and fungal pathogens are important components of the root-soil environment. These are discussed in detail in other chapters. Water relations and irrigation are also treated in detail elsewhere. Because of

the importance of soil moisture—too little or too much—this subject is treated here from the standpoint of its effects on roots. It is also a variable that can be controlled in arid irrigated areas like California.

Readily available moisture is necessary for optimal root activity. Roots do not grow through dry soil, and their exploration for available resources is limited under these conditions. Uptake of water and nutrients becomes more difficult with reduced available moisture. Movement of nutrients to roots is slower with low soil moisture—for this reason, potassium deficiency can sometimes be corrected by improving irrigation practices. Insufficient moisture or a partially dry soil profile can suppress root activity and reduce vegetative and reproductive growth in spring. Synthetic functions of roots (and, thus, supplies to the shoots) are reduced with restricted root growth. Root growth is markedly inhibited by increasing soil strength (mechanical resistance to penetration) as soil water content decreases.

Under certain conditions, too much water in the soil can be more damaging than too little. Olives are very sensitive to water excess and subsequent lack of oxygen. Air is displaced from the pore spaces of the soil when they fill with water; thus, the supply of oxygen to roots is removed. This can occur with flooding, seepage, perched or fluctuating water tables, or even irrigation. Excessive soil moisture is also a strong influence in soil-pathogen effects (root and crown rots), but discussion here is restricted to direct effects on oxygen requirements of roots.

Terminals of new roots can be killed within 1 to 4 days in a saturated soil. Such short periods of waterlogging may inhibit shoot growth. As saturation is prolonged, damage to roots becomes greater and can lead to chlorosis and leaf abscission. In olives, entire root systems can be killed in extreme cases. The effects of waterlogging proceed faster as soil temperatures increase. Survival in water-saturated soils during winter results from a combination of low soil temperature, low respiration rate, and a paucity of active roots.

There is greater danger of damage to roots from excessive moisture with fine-textured or compacted soils because reentry of oxygen is slower after saturation. Deficient aeration is partly responsible for shallower root systems and smaller trees in fine-textured soils even without excessive water. A fluctuating water table can have more serious effects than a static one because of periodic encroachment on active roots.

Olive is sensitive to excessive soil moisture. Little experimental work has been done, but responses of olive would be expected to be comparable to those of plum and some apple rootstocks. As with other plants, differences could exist among both different seedling types and own-rooted cultivars. There is no specific information about California-type rootstocks.

Effects of salt

Excessive salt, always potentially a problem in irrigated agriculture, is of increasing concern in some parts of California. High levels of sodium or chloride, and sometimes sulfate, in the soil or irrigation water can cause these ions to accumulate within the tree and ultimately cause toxic reactions (specific ion toxicity) in leaves. Leaf symptoms begin with chlorosis at their edges, then necrosis, and later leaf abscission. Symptoms become more prevalent late in the season. Fruit drop can also occur. Concentrations in leaves are considered injurious at greater than 0.5 percent chloride or 0.2 percent sodium on a dry weight basis.

Specific ion toxicity is only one way in which salinity can adversely affect olives and other tree crops. Effects of total salts on water relations (osmotic effects) can also be significant. In a soil solution more water than salt is absorbed; thus, salt concentration in the soil increases, and greater forces are required to extract additional water. As a result, water stress is more likely to occur.

Grower concern mainly centers on leaf toxicity symptoms; if these are absent, the potential for adverse effects is often ignored. However, reduced shoot and root growth and lower fat content in fruit due to salinity have been reported without the appearance of leaf symptoms.

Olive is considered moderately tolerant of salinity. It can withstand levels of salt that would cause extensive damage or death of deciduous tree fruit and nut crops. Certain cultivars of olive are more tolerant of salinity than others; responses may also differ depending on the rootstock. Unfortunately, the relative responses among cultivars and rootstocks grown in California are not known.

In North Africa, various olive cultivars have been found to differ in their degree of tolerance to high salinity; in some, root growth and stem elongation are reduced, but in other cultivars these parameters are not affected. Compared with other species, olive translocates less salt to its leaves and retains more in its roots. This difference is a possible explanation for olive's salt tolerance. The uptake and transport of salt to the shoots is a rootstock-related phenomenon.

Effects of mycorrhizae

Mycorrhizae are beneficial fungi that commingle with roots. In woody perennial plants, mycorrhizae can have a positive effect on growth. Some mycorrhizal fungi penetrate the root; others are mainly on the root surface. This association can provide increased surface as well as specific absorptive capacities, especially for phosphorus or zinc.

Plant species differ considerably in their dependence on mycorrhizal fungi, and specific information on olive is not available. Positive responses usually have been associated with conditions of low fertility; in fact, regimes of regular high fertilization suppress mycorrhizae. Mycorrhizal fungi occur naturally in most soils, but these may be of questionable importance given the intensive cultural practices being employed in fertile soils in California. Mycorrhizal inoculations have sometimes shown beneficial effects in nursery or replant situations after fumigation.

ROOTSTOCKS

Historically, olives have been grown from cuttings as own-rooted plants. Sometimes seedlings are grown and are then budded or grafted to the desired variety. Ease of propagation has been the primary consideration in selecting a rootstock. The potential difference in tree performance is given little thought when deciding whether to plant an orchard with cutting-propagated trees or to plant by grafting on seedling or clonal rootstocks.

Today, easily rooted cultivars like Manzanillo and Mission are often grown on their own roots. Those difficult to root, like Sevillano, are almost always grafted. In years past, grafting on seedling rootstocks was practiced largely to aid propagation. Seedlings of all varieties vary in size and vigor as each plant is genetically unique, differing slightly from every other plant. Much of the irregular tree performance observed in California olive orchards could result from the variable influence of seedling rootstocks. In the propagating of seedling rootstocks, small-fruited olive varieties such as Mission or Redding Picholine were often selected as stock because their seeds generally germinate faster and in higher percentages than do those of large-fruited varieties. Today, rooting cuttings is preferred in olive propagation. It may take 2 years longer to produce a tree by growing seedlings than with rooted cuttings.

ROOTSTOCK INFLUENCES

There is no ideal rootstock for olive. With olive, the influence of a rootstock on the vigor and performance of one variety cannot necessarily be expected to be the same for another scion variety. Rootstock selections and effects must be considered for each rootstock-scion combination.

Rootstock effects on a variety of parameters were measured by H. T. Hartmann in several long-term rootstock trials conducted in Lindsay, Winters, and Corning, California. A wide range of rootstock material was examined, with three prominent varieties—Mission, Manzanillo, and Sevillano—used in various rootstock-scion combinations.

Tree size and yield

One of the principal rootstock influences on the scion variety observed in these trials was vigor. When grown from cuttings on their own roots, Mission and Manzanillo were more vigorous and yielded more fruit than when they were grafted on any other rootstock. The significant yield differences measured generally reflected differences in tree size. Sevillano on its own roots was only intermediate in size, but showed greater vigor when grown on Mission or Redding Picholine seedling rootstocks or on Oblonga clonal stock.

Fruit characteristics

Rootstocks that produce satisfactory scion growth generally showed slight differences in their effects on fruit characteristics. Manzanillo and Sevillano fruit were slightly larger from trees on their own roots than from trees on other rootstocks. Mission fruit has shown little size variation among scions on the various rootstocks. The same variety relationships are observed regarding flesh-to-pit ratios.

Fruit shape is affected to some extent by rootstock. Own-rooted Manzanillo and Sevillano trees produced fruit that was no different in shape from that on other stocks. Mission, however, produced fruit with a slightly greater length-to-width ratio on its own roots compared with fruit from trees on other stocks.

Shotberry production typically varies by cultivar. Sevillano has the greatest tendency to form shotberries, followed by Manzanillo and Mission. Production of shotberries had no relationship to the rootstock used.

Production of split-pit fruit has been observed to be strongly influenced by rootstock in the case of Sevillano. Own-rooted Sevillano had as much as 30 percent split-pit fruit; Sevillano on Mission seedling rootstock exhibited about 6 percent split-pits. The influence of rootstock on split-pit in other varieties has not been documented.

Maturity

Evaluation of Mission, Manzanillo, and Sevillano scions grafted onto rootstocks producing acceptable scion growth showed no consistent relationships between rootstock and rate of fruit maturity. Soft nose, an undesirable softening and darkening of the mesocarp at the distal end of the fruit, has been observed when Sevillano was grafted onto Mission seedling rootstock. That combination resulted in 13 percent soft nose; Sevillano on its own roots averaged about 3 percent soft nose.

Mineral nutrition

Mineral nutrient levels in olive leaf tissue show no consistent relationships relative to rootstock. Across the range of rootstocks tested by Hartmann, all leaf nutrient levels were within the range usually found in olive leaves in well-maintained orchards.

Dwarfing effects

Size-controlling rootstocks have a place in olive production, much as they do with other fruit crops. A useful reduction in tree size, while maintaining or enhancing fruitfulness and lowering harvesting costs, is a desirable objective. Some production problems can accompany dwarfing or size control, however. With fruit production on 1-year-old shoots, some balance needs to exist between provision of sufficient shoot growth for adequate fruiting versus restriction of shoot growth to obtain dwarfing effects. Extreme dwarfing effects are often unsatisfactory. As with other characteristics discussed, dwarfing and invigoration vary with the rootstock-scion combination. Several combinations that impart dwarfing to the scion have been observed:

- Ascolano seedling rootstocks have had a rather uniformly dwarfing influence on Mission, Manzanillo, and Sevillano scions, although Manzanillo is the most dwarfed by Ascolano roots.

- Oblonga rootstock has had a pronounced dwarfing effect on Manzanillo and somewhat less dwarfing on Mission, but it has invigorated Sevillano.

- Sevillano grown on its own roots makes a smaller tree but one that is acceptable if planted at higher density.

- Redding Picholine rootstock severely dwarfs Manzanillo, making growth unacceptable. It dwarfs Mission somewhat, but greatly invigorates Sevillano.

- Genetically dwarfed interstocks tested by Hartmann produced satisfactory graft unions and were compatible with both Mission and Sevillano. They have not been used commercially.

The potential advantages offered by dwarfing rootstocks have not been exploited in olive, although appropriate rootstock material for certain cultivars seems to be available.

HISTORICAL ROOTSTOCK SELECTIONS

As indicated earlier, ease of propagation has been the primary consideration in choice of rootstock. Certain stocks were selected for their invigorating characteristics or disease resistance. Some plantings of varieties have existed as own-rooted trees but later became rootstocks when the orchard was topworked to a different cultivar. These situations have all occurred in the past and are outlined in the following discussion of common and specialty olive rootstocks.

Mission

Early Mission orchards were grown as own-rooted trees propagated by cuttings or planted as seedling orchards and grafted. The 200-year history of Mission in California has led to several strains of the variety. Depending on the source, Mission seedling rootstocks can be quite variable, and this may account for variation in commercial orchards on Mission seedling rootstock. Fruit are generally borne singly, are slightly oblique in shape, and mature in mid- to late October (fig. 8.4).

Sevillano has been commonly grafted to Mission seedling stock in the past. As the California olive industry developed, many older clonal Mission orchards were topworked to the Manzanillo or Sevillano varieties. At one time, about 20 percent of the Corning district and Tulare County olive districts were Mission. Most of these orchards have since been topworked, resulting in Manzanillo or Sevillano orchards on Mission rootstock.

Redding Picholine

This variety was imported from France in 1872 by B. B. Redding and was originally thought to be a large pickling variety. It turned out to be a small-fruited seedling and not the true French Picholine (fig. 8.5). Although a vigorous tree, it was unacceptable for pickling and produced oil of poor quality. For many years it was used as a rootstock for other varieties such as Sevillano and Mission. Redding Picholine roots very readily from cuttings and its small oval seeds germinate easily when the tip end is clipped, resulting in a high rooting percentage. The small oval fruit are borne in clusters and mature to a velvet black color in late September to early October.

Nevadillo

This variety was imported from Spain about 1885 by F. Pohndorff. It became an established variety in California and was generally used for oil extraction. Fruit are oval, slightly oblique, and pointed. It somewhat resembles the Mission but is generally longer in proportion to its diameter. The pit is small, curved, and generally pointed at both ends. Fruit often form in clusters and mature to a velvet black color in October (fig. 8.6).

As the oil market declined in the early 1900s, this variety was often topworked to more desirable pickling varieties. Considerable acreage existed in the Corning district and hence current Sevillano orchards in that area may be found growing on this rootstock. For the same reason, Mission in the Oroville area and Manzanillo in Tulare County can be found on this stock.

Oblonga

The history of this variety is uncertain, but a volunteer seedling in the Earl Malott orchard near Corning, California, in 1940 was the progenitor of Oblonga tested in experiments at UC Davis. The tree was noted for its rapid

Figure 8.4. Mission olives.

Figure 8.5. Redding Picholine olives.

growth and large size. Sevillano scions grafted onto this rootstock developed into large, heavy-producing trees. On the other hand, Oblonga has a dwarfing effect on Manzanillo. Mission and Ascolano on Oblonga have not shown dwarfing.

H. T. Hartmann's field trial in Tulare County showed that the Oblonga stock prevented the movement of the verticillium wilt fungus (*Verticillium dahliae* Kleb.) from the soil into the susceptible Sevillano scion top. While other rootstocks with Sevillano scions succumbed to verticillium wilt, none of the 10 Sevillano-Oblonga trees showed verticillium symptoms for 16 years in a heavily infested

Figure 8.6. Nevadillo olives.

orchard. In repeated tests, Oblonga has shown resistance but not immunity to verticillium wilt. Other cultivars grafted onto Oblonga have died as verticillium wilt is transported to the scion.

Oblonga must be clonally propagated to maintain these characteristics. Small leafy Oblonga cuttings can be readily propagated under intermittent mist when cutting bases are dipped in rooting hormones.

Allegra

Allegra is another cultivar that, when grown on its own roots, has shown some resistance to verticillium wilt. Wilt-susceptible scions grafted on Allegra and exposed to infested soil contract verticillium wilt and die. This suggests that although the cultivar is resistant, when used as a rootstock, the pathogen is transmitted through the stock and graft to the susceptible scion, as is the case with cultivars grown on Oblonga roots.

Effects of Allegra on top growth of commercial cultivars have not been thoroughly tested. There is some evidence that it has a dwarfing influence on Manzanillo.

Other rootstocks

Several other types of seedling rootstocks have been tested over the years. These have mostly been other species of olive, and no advantages have been revealed.

Grafting *Olea europaea* on seedlings of *Olea ferruginea, Olea verrucosa,* and *Olea chrysophylla* has not provided good results. Trees may show overgrowth at the graft union, have delayed fruit maturity, produce excessive numbers of shotberry fruit, or may develop large numbers of yellow leaves and ultimately die of incompatibility.

Sevillano on *Olea chrysophylla* seems to produce normal, healthy trees with adequate crops, but Mission and Manzanillo on this stock display obvious incompatibility.

In rootstock trials, seedlings of California wild olive, *Forestiera neomexicana,* proved to be unsuccessful as rootstocks for Mission, Sevillano, and Manzanillo. Severe dwarfing, fruit quality problems, and incompatibility occurred.

Olive cultivars have been grafted on ash (*Fraxinus*) and on lilac (*Syringae*), but although the plants lived for several years, they displayed little new growth and eventually died.

9

FLOWERING, POLLINATION, FRUITING, ALTERNATE BEARING, AND ABSCISSION

GEORGE C. MARTIN, LOUISE FERGUSON, AND VITO S. POLITO

The physiological process leading to spring flowering starts in the preceding summer. The vegetative bud present in the axil of each leaf begins developmental changes that result in a vegetative shoot or an inflorescence containing flowers. In summer, environmental factors interact with the trees' physiology to start the induction process. Induction concerns the chemical changes in vegetative buds that cause conversion to inflorescence buds.

Once induction is under way, floral initiation occurs by November, after which flower parts form. Eventually, these can be seen with a microscope. Unlike deciduous fruits with a short induction-to-initiation cycle, induction in olive may occur as early as July or about 6 weeks after full bloom whereas initiation is not easily seen until 8 months later in February. Complex microscopic and histochemical techniques reveal evidence of floral initiation by November, but the process of developing all the flower parts starts in March.

FLOWERING

Floral induction and initiation

Well-managed, pest-free, thrifty trees with moderate crops are most likely to flower and fruit each year. During the growing season, orchard managers are both culturing the current crop and influencing the formation of next year's crop. As vegetative shoot growth and fruit growth occur, the vegetative bud in the axil of each leaf competes for raw materials to start floral induction and subsequently initiation.

The floral developmental process depends on good nutrition, and many elements potentially limit floral development. Usually nitrogen is the major element required for olive, and proper nitrogen management is an annual necessity. Excess nitrogen can increase flower set in some situa-

tions and indirectly decrease it in others. For example, pruning large limbs and then applying too much nitrogen leads to excessive vegetative growth, which decreases cropping. Pruning to open trees for better light distribution benefits floral development. Moisture availability is crucial. In droughts, the internal water supply favors leaves over developing fruit or floral buds. Stress caused by pest infestations similarly takes essential materials away from developing fruit and floral buds.

In winter, temperature greatly influences the continuing development of flowers among California olive cultivars; they are unfruitful unless exposed to a minimum of cold. In experiments at UC Davis, half of a group of young, bearing Mission trees growing in large containers were kept in a warm greenhouse all winter; the other half remained outdoors. The greenhouse trees failed to bloom or fruit; the outdoor trees bloomed and fruited normally. When a single branch on a greenhouse tree was exposed to winter cold through an opening in the greenhouse wall, it bloomed and fruited normally. Likewise, a single branch on an outdoor tree extended into a warm greenhouse failed to bloom although the rest of the tree bloomed heavily.

Some olive cultivars, such as those grown in Crete, southern Greece, Egypt, Israel, and Tunisia, bloom and fruit heavily with very little winter chilling; those originating in Italy, Spain, and California require substantial chilling for good fruiting.

In experiments with the cultivars grown in California, optimum flowering occurred when the temperature fluctuated daily between 60° to 65°F (15.5 to 19°C) maximum and 35° to 40°F (2° to 4°C) minimum. Trees held at a constant temperature of 55°F (13°C) also bloomed profusely but had poor pistillate flower formation. If temperatures did not rise above 45°F (7.5°C) or fall below 60°F (15.5°C), trees did not bloom. At 55°F (13°C) both chilling and warmth are sufficient for flowering but not for complete flower development. In contrast to flower buds, vegetative buds of olive seem to have little if any dormancy, growing whenever the temperatures are much above about 70°F (21°C). In addition to winter chilling, inflorescence formation requires leaves on the fruiting shoots. Therefore, it is important to prevent defoliation. The occasional occurrence of hot, dry winds during the blooming period has been associated with reduced fruit set. Winds or heat increase the amount of natural abscission.

Prolonged abnormally cold weather during April and May, when the olive flower buds should be developing rapidly, can have a detrimental effect on subsequent flowering, pollination, and fruit set. Such weather occurred in California in the spring of 1967, delaying bloom by several weeks and leading to flower abnormalities and a crop of only 14,000 tons, the lightest in modern California history. In California, fruit on the tree by July 1, as a rule, continue on to maturity.

Floral differentiation

Differentiation takes place between late February and bloom in May when the formation of each flower part occurs in the inflorescence. Flower parts form from the outside in: the sepals form first and the pistil last (fig. 9.1; also see chapter 4). The 8- to 10-week period of differentiation before bloom in May is the critical period for perfect flower development. Stress during those weeks can ruin an otherwise good flower population. As mentioned, stressed flowers compete poorly with leaves for available water. Lack of water during flower differentiation results in partially developed flowers with malfunctioning or absent pistils (see the staminate flowers in fig. 9.1). This occurs more frequently than expected and is only evident when flowers are closely examined. In some seasons, orchards have been observed in which practically every flower was staminate. As mentioned elsewhere, it is best to start the growing season with a moist soil profile. Once vegetative growth and fruit growth start, and warm weather occurs, the irrigation capacity of most growers is not sufficient to replenish a depleted soil profile.

Several experiments have shown that girdling the tree (removing a quarter-inch strip of bark around the limb or trunk) in mid-February can increase the proportion of perfect flowers and subsequent fruit set. Apparently girdling retains carbohydrates above the girdle. Girdling is not recommended in California because olive knot can enter each girdle site, but it can successfully influence cropping in countries like Israel where olive knot is not present. Long-term use of this practice may, however, be detrimental to root growth.

In orchards infected with olive knot it is likely that the bacteria will become established in girdling cuts unless cuts are immediately covered with hot grafting wax, then a Bordeaux-mixture paste, and finally an asphalt-emulsion grafting compound. Bordeaux paste applied directly to the girdling cut causes considerable injury to the tissues and is not advised. Girdling tools should be disinfected between trees to prevent spread of the bacteria in girdling wounds.

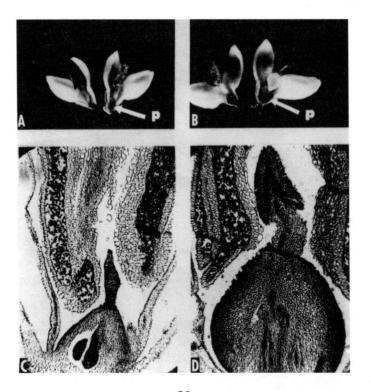

Figure 9.1. Staminate (A, C) and perfect (B, D) flowers. C shows an aborted pistil in a staminate flower; D shows a normally developed pistil in a perfect flower (P = pistil).

Full bloom

At full bloom flowers are delicately poised for pollination, the critical event discussed next. Some 500,000 flowers are present in a mature tree; a commercial crop of 3 tons per acre or more can be achieved when 1 or 2 percent of these flowers remain as developing fruit. By 14 days after full bloom, most of the flowers destined to abscise have done so. By that time, about 494,000 flowers have abscised from a tree that started with 500,000 flowers.

Some years a tree may not have sufficient perfect flowers to produce a satisfactory crop, despite heavy bloom, because the flowers produced are primarily staminate (male or pollen bearing). The relative proportion of perfect to staminate flowers varies greatly among inflorescences, branches, trees, cultivars, and seasons, but is generally small (table 9.1). There are no commercial production practices that enhance the percentage of perfect flowers, except for girdling in late winter, which is not recommended in California for reasons discussed previously.

Olives are monoecious; the same tree bears perfect and imperfect flowers. The flowers are borne axially along the shoot in inflorescences named panicles (fig. 9.2). The panicles of Barouni, Manzanillo, Mission, and Sevillano carry an average of 12 to 18 flowers; Ascolanos average 20 flowers. Perfect flowers, those with both pistillate (female) and staminate (male) parts, normally consist of a small calyx, four petals, two stamens and filaments supporting large pollen-bearing anthers, and a plump green pistil with a short thick style and a large stigma (fig. 9.1a, b). Figure 4.5 in chapter 4 shows a perfect flower with the parts indicated. Perfect flowers are borne apically in an inflorescence, and within the typical triple-flower inflorescence the middle flower is generally perfect. Imperfect flowers are staminate (pollen-bearing or male), with the pistil either lacking or rudimentary (fig. 9.1a, b). Flowers with abortive anthers also occur and are common in Sevillano. Table 9.2 shows the average sizes of the different flower parts of five olive cultivars.

Table 9.1. Fruit set, based upon number of inflorescences, flowers, or perfect flowers, resulting from natural pollination of interplanted olive cultivars at Winters, California, 1951, 1952.

Cultivar	Year	Number of inflores-cences	Number of flowers	Number of flowers per inflores-cence	Number of perfect flowers	Percent perfect flowers	Mean number of fruit set per 100		
							Inflores-cences	Flowers	Perfect flowers
Ascolano	1951	507	9,937	19.6	932	9.38	22.98	1.23	12.14
Ascolano	1952	573	12,320	21.5	541	4.39	9.95	0.46	10.54
Barouni	1951	769	13,842	18.0	2,925	21.13	9.10	0.50	2.43
Barouni	1952	598	7,654	12.9	770	10.06	7.19	0.56	5.58
Manzanillo	1951	337	4,819	14.3	2,219	46.05	22.55	1.58	3.42
Manzanillo	1952	646	10.077	15.6	1.731	17.18	29.10	1.86	10.86
Mission	1951	900	13.500	15.0	2,371	17.56	12.22	0.81	4.64
Mission	1952	1,508	18,850	12.5	7,393	39.22	34.15	2.73	6.97
Sevillano	1951	546	9,446	17.3	2,153	22.79	9.34	0.54	2.37
Sevillano	1952	728	11,502	15.8	1,661	14.44	11.68	0.74	5.12

Table 9.2. Average size of olive flower parts at Winters, California,1963.*

Cultivar	Diameter of flower (petal tip to tip)	Length of pistil	Length of ovary	Diameter of ovary	Length of stigma	Width of stigma	Thick-ness of stigma	Length of style	Length of anther	Width of anther	Thick-ness of anther	Length of fila-ment
Ascolano	8.17	3.80	1.72	1.47	1.30	0.77	0.77	0.78	3.03	1.18	1.15	1.12
Barouni	7.66	2.90	1.57	1.62	0.95	0.76	0.52	0.38	3.25	2.25	1.50	1.00
Manzanillo	7.20	3.04	1.47	1.36	1.20	0.82	0.58	0.37	2.65	2.50	1.10	0.60
Mission	7.52	2.99	1.27	1.06	1.24	0.67	0.48	0.48	2.84	2.13	1.32	0.73
Sevillano	8.37	3.65	2.41	2.42	1.10	1.03	0.75	0.14	2.68	2.24	1.46	1.52

* Sizes are given in millimeters.

Figure 9.2. Manzanillo olive shoot showing inflorescences.

Olive pollination occurs by self-pollination or by cross pollination. The former requires no agent, though bees or wind may serve as agents. Cross pollination between trees requires wind.

With self-pollination, the pollen simply falls from anther to pistil in the same flower. The anthers of most perfect flowers are close enough to the stigma so that, at dehiscence, pollen falls upon the stigma easily. Wind or bees could also effect self-pollination simply by disturbing blossoms. In some flowers the filaments are flattened, spreading the anthers away from the stigma. Among California cultivars Ascolano is the most likely to have flowers with spreading anthers. In these flowers, dehiscence does not ensure automatic pollination, and wind or bees must be the agents of self-pollination.

Wind is the primary agent of olive cross pollination; further, bees are not universally present in sufficient numbers or sufficiently attracted to olive flowers to be a factor in pollination. If present during pollination, bees can improve set, but they have never been shown to be necessary for cross pollination.

Once pollen lands on the stigma, the pollen grain germinates. The inner wall expands through one pore into a tube, and the grain's cytoplasmic contents move into it. This pollen tube, enclosed by an extension of the inner pollen wall, conveys the male germ cells (sperm) to the female germ cell (egg). Over the span of about 1 week, the tube penetrates between the cells on the stigma's surface and grows through the pistillate flower tissues until it reaches the egg cell in the embryo sac. When a pollen tube arrives, it releases its two sperm cells; one fuses with the egg. The product of this fusion is a single-celled zygote. Within 10 days the zygote divides into two cells, an event that starts the complex development leading to formation of an embryo—seed and carpel—that forms the olive fruit.

Successful pollination requires the pollen grain to germinate and its pollen tube to grow fast enough to reach a still viable embryo sac. Fruit set can be decreased by cool temperatures that result in slow pollen tube growth. In such cases the tube either fails to reach the embryo sac or grows too slowly to reach the embryo sac before it degenerates.

FRUITING

Fruit set

The objective of pollination is fruit set. The term fruit set is vague but refers to the population of flowers that are pollinated and fertilized and that develop into fruit remaining on the tree until harvest, unless they meet a disaster along the way. Research shows that the major factor in reducing fruit set may not be pistil abortion, but rather the intense competition among perfect flowers on an inflorescence. Usually only one fruit is retained per inflorescence, and the winner cannot yet be determined in advance. There remains a great deal to be learned about fruit set for olive and all other crops. For no evident reason, some orchards fail to set crops 2 subsequent years, perhaps due to extreme environmental conditions. Other orchards may produce large crops for 2 or 3 years before having a small crop. The latter situation must arise from the coincidence of several environmental and physiological factors.

Cultivars vary, but most abscission occurs soon after full bloom and final fruit set nearly always occurs within 6 weeks of full bloom. Further fruit abscission can result from pest infestation and environmental extremes. When trees have an inflorescence at nearly every leaf axil a commercial crop occurs with 1 to 2 percent fruit set; with a small population of inflorescence, a commercial crop may require 10 percent fruit set.

Shotberries (parthenocarpic fruit) occur randomly and for reasons not clearly understood. When shotberries occur they may be seen in clusters on each inflorescence (fig. 9.3). Here the inter-fruit competition for raw materials differs from that of normal olive fruit. Shotberries mature much earlier than normal fruit and may be more prevalent when conditions favor a second large crop in succession.

Factors that reduce fruit set. Fruit set results from the interaction of olive tree physiology with the environment. Several tree factors that can reduce fruit set are known. The absence of viable pollen results in no crop as parthenocarpic olives are useless. Incompatible pollinating cultivars, as mentioned earlier, also result in no fertilization. Fortunately, there are numerous compatible combinations for olive. In many situations olives are self-compatible, but Manzanillo has special problems. In most years and areas of the world Manzanillo pollinates itself successfully. In hot weather during bloom, however, Manzanillo pollen grows slowly, resulting in no fertilization. The unfertilized ovary is viable for a very short period after full bloom.

Numerous environmental or management factors can influence fruit set; proper nitrogen management is the greatest. Except for special local problems, nitrogen is the only nutrient supplement required annually. Fruit thinning, in combination with judicious pruning, helps manage better fruit allocation throughout the tree. Some localities by virtue of the microclimate—local temperature, moisture, and wind—have better fruit set than others. High winds consistently reduce fruit set. Pest and disease management are a must, as without control these additional stresses always reduce fruit set.

Fruit growth

Olive fruit growth occurs in a typical sigmoidal fashion (see figure 4.7). The importance of the last period of fruit growth in October must be clearly understood. Research shows that the profit or loss pivots around fruit growth as the premium value for California black-ripe or green-ripe processing is reached in mid-October (see fig. 20.1 in chapter 20). These data show that harvesting too early or too late costs orchardists hundreds of dollars per acre. Delaying harvest too long results in heavier, more valuable fruit but also results in losses due to black fruit and frost damage. For oil olives, the value based on oil continues to increase into January. The endocarp (pit) enlarges to full size and hardens by 6 weeks after full bloom. At that time the endosperm begins to solidify and embryo development takes place, leading to embryo maturity by September. The mesocarp (flesh) and exocarp (skin) continue their gradual growth as

Figure 9.3. Clusters of shotberries on each inflorescence.

shown in figure 4.7 in chapter 4. The environmental and management factors important for fruit set also optimize fruit growth. The fruit begin changing from the green color to yellow-white (straw) and accumulate anthocyanin from the distal or base end. This purple to black color eventually bleeds into the mesocarp, signaling fruit overmature for the California black-ripe or green-ripe processing. As has been reported for most other fruit crops, trees with few fruit mature their crops earlier than trees with many fruit.

ALTERNATE BEARING

Olive, along with numerous other fruit trees including apple, pear, mango, orange, pistachio, and pecan, produces a large crop one year followed by a small, noncommercial crop the next year. The evidence shows that large crops reduce carbohydrates; however, when placed in growth chambers with high light, favorable temperature, and high CO_2 from November through February, olive trees increase starch reserves five times over controls but fail to increase inflorescence development on either previously bearing or nonbearing trees. These data indicate that whatever their other roles are, a shortage of carbohydrates or starch from November through February may not be the direct cause of alternate bearing in olive.

Any cultural practices that diminish olive tree vigor (such as lack of nutrients or water or leaving a large crop in until December) add to the burden and extent of alternate bearing. Environmental extremes and lack of pest control, too, are additive and push trees toward alternate bearing.

Experiments have shown that the presence of seed in fruit may have some influence on alternate bearing. When seeds are killed by 6 weeks after full bloom, branches produce large populations of seedless fruit. These shoots contain viable inflorescences the following year. In shoots with similar populations of seeded fruit, few or no inflorescences are produced in the subsequent year. The question remains: How can one make practical use of this information?

The best technique for avoiding, or at least modifying, alternate bearing is to use naphthaleneacetic acid (NAA) to decrease the fruit population during the cropping year, as described in chapter 14. Pruning is not as effective as fruit thinning in overcoming alternate bearing because leaves as well as fruit are removed. No fertilizer practice can be relied upon to eliminate alternate bearing in olives, although nitrogen fertilization may increase production without greatly changing the long-term patterns of fluctuating yields.

ABSCISSION

Knowledge of how olive inflorescence, flowers, fruit, and leaves abscise from the plant is key to eventually controlling abscission. Most scientists studying abscission have used ethylene-generating compounds to induce abscission. Results to date implicate ethylene as the natural chemical that triggers abscission in all plants. Those interested in technical details about abscission can consult chapter 20. By controlling abscission, fruit populations can be managed as needed. To some extent, this may be done using NAA as a chemical fruit thinner.

Old leaves abscise in April, in a natural process that causes no problems. Leaves that abscise at flower bud sites during the growing season are, however, a great problem as this decreases flower quality and fruit production. Good management maintains good foliage. Infestation by pests and lack of nitrogen or water can induce leaf abscission. Leaf abscission among younger leaves usually results in outbreaks of olive knot and diploidea.

10

PRUNING MATURE BEARING OLIVE TREES

G. S. SIBBETT

Bearing olive trees are pruned to complement other cultural practices in producing annual crops of large fruit. Pruning, in conjunction with fruit thinning, irrigation, fertilization, and pest control, is a valuable contribution to an olive orchard's annual productivity. This chapter discusses pruning bearing trees to produce annual crops of high-quality olives.

To understand pruning in olive production, one must first understand the olive's fruit-bearing habit and pruning's effect on tree growth.

FRUITING HABIT

Olives are produced on 1-year-old shoots in the presence of sunlight. Thus, production is mainly confined to a shell of new shoots 2 to 3 feet (60 to 90 cm) thick on the tree's periphery (fig. 10.1). Few fruit are produced in the shaded interior or within dense clumps of shoots.

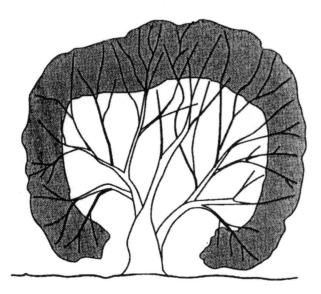

Figure 10.1. The producing "shell" of the tree.

The most productive olive shoots are 8 to 12 inches (20 to 30 cm) long. Short or excessively vigorous shoots are often unfruitful. An important objective of pruning is to develop new, moderately vigorous, well-lighted shoots on the tree periphery.

Pruning decreases the number of current-season shoots but stimulates subsequent shoot growth for cropping. Pruning also reduces insect and disease development by eliminating dense brush. Well-pruned trees have thin canopies that allow better penetration of spray materials.

PRUNING'S EFFECT ON TREE GROWTH

Pruning is a dwarfing practice. It physically removes stored carbohydrates while also removing potential carbohydrate-producing leaf surface. Reduction in leaf surface causes reduced root growth as food materials become more of a limiting factor. Unpruned trees grow larger in total leaf area than pruned trees.

Pruning induces new growth close to the cut primarily by increasing the amount of nitrogen available to each remaining growing point. A few cuts on large-diameter wood cause excessive localized growth of shoots. Well-distributed cuts on small-diameter wood spread the stimulus over the entire tree. "Heading" cuts generally stimulate more buds to grow than "thinning" cuts (fig. 10.2) because cutting the apexes of shoots or branches removes natural growth-control hormones that prevent lateral shoots from developing on unpruned branches. Understanding how pruning influences tree growth is essential to maintaining optimal olive production.

WHEN TO PRUNE

Prune mature olive trees in spring and summer, once winter rains have passed. Pruning then provides the opportunity to

Figure 10.2. Thinning (left) versus heading (right) cuts.

manage production at minimum risk of disease infection and insect attack.

Pruning to manage production

Pruning in spring or early summer, during bloom and young fruit development, can help manage crop size. If bloom is light, pruning can be confined to nonproductive parts of the tree, preserving as much bloom and potential crop as possible. In years of heavy bloom, pruning can be more severe without excessive crop removal. Pruning to thin heavy crops does not result in larger fruit; fruit size is largely determined locally on branches by an adequate leaf-to-fruit ratio, and pruning that removes entire shoots, both leaves and fruit, does not change this ratio.

Pruning for disease and insect control

Olive knot. Olive knot disease is caused by a bacterium dispersed throughout the tree in moisture, commonly rainfall. The bacterium only infects the tree through openings such as leaf scars, pruning wounds, or cracks caused by freezing temperatures. Pruning before or during the wet season unnecessarily opens wounds for olive knot invasion. Also, pruning during winter thins out the tree's canopy, making it vulnerable to freezing temperatures and subsequent bark injury. Pruning in spring and summer avoids these problems and can be used to cut away established olive knots, which supply inoculum for future infection.

Black scale. The black scale insect prefers dense shade. It is sensitive to heat and light and does not survive well with exposure. Pruning to thin the tree canopy before warm summer temperatures arrive effectively minimizes this pest without using insecticides.

OBJECTIVES OF PRUNING

The main objective of pruning is to manipulate tree growth to produce maximal crops of large fruit annually. Olive trees are also pruned for other reasons.

Pruning for harvest

Hand harvest. Hand pickers use ladders to harvest olives. For safe hand picking, tree height should not exceed 15 to 18 feet (4.5 to 5.4 m). Tall, upright limbs that extend beyond this must be removed. If trees are taller than the safe limit at harvest, growers often cut the tall limbs at picking time and harvest them on the ground rather than from an unsafe position on the ladder.

Mechanical harvest. Olive removal by machine requires that energy from a trunk or limb shaker be transmitted from the shaker to the fruit with enough force to break the fruit stem. Unlike many fruit species, olive trees are not well suited for this process. The fruit are small, weighing 3 to 7 grams, and have little inertia. The long, willowy shoots do not transmit energy well, and the brushy clumps of shoots, natural to the tree's growth habit, absorb the shaker's energy before it reaches the fruit. Also, energy is poorly transmitted to fruit on limbs growing at angles greater than 45° from vertical. The result is reduced fruit removal.

Proper pruning is essential to maximize fruit removal. First, the tree's normal shape must be modified for machine harvest. The Manzanillo tree's low, rounded shape must be changed to one that is more upright, with a few stubby limbs and branches of thinned clumps of shoots that transmit energy well. Ascolano, Sevillano, and Mission trees grow more upright than Manzanillo and usually require less modification. Also, the shaker must be able to operate quickly and efficiently in the orchard to economically harvest olives. Most older olive trees must be limb shaken. A maximum of five well-spaced upright scaffold branches should be left on each tree; more limbs will congest the operating area and slow harvest (color plate 10.1).

Restructuring for mechanical harvest should be done gradually, several years in advance. This will avoid both immediate production loss from severe pruning and the resulting profuse, unfruitful vegetative growth. A good rule of thumb is to use saw cuts, removing no more than one-fourth of the leaf surface in any one year.

Once the tree has been restructured, annual maintenance pruning is needed for best fruit removal. Fruit wood must also be renewed and should be attached as directly as possible to the scaffold branch to receive the most energy. All suckers on the trunk and limbs must be continually removed.

Controlling insects and disease

Black scale (*Saissetia oleae*) and the fungus disease peacock spot (*Spilocea oleaginea*) prefer dense trees and humidity for best growth. Pruning to produce thin, airy trees that allow access to heat and light and dry out quickly after rainfall precludes their development and is an excellent cultural method of pest control. Open trees also allow thorough penetration and coverage of pesticides, which enhances chemical control when it is necessary.

Confining trees

Crowded olive trees decline in production as fruiting shoots become shaded. First, the tree's lower parts die out, followed by higher fruitwood. Eventually, production becomes confined to the top of the tree, and the side canopies are lost.

The olive tree must be confined to its allotted space to give it enough light for productive shoots to develop. Pruners should remove or shorten longer branches that interfere with or congest adjoining trees. Undercutting nonproductive branches and pruning older, dead wood from brushy clumps accomplishes this (fig. 10.3).

The lower canopy of crowded, shaded trees cannot be restored to productivity by heavy top pruning. This removes highly productive parts of the tree that quickly fill in again, blocking light access to the lower canopy. Top pruning causes substantial loss of production.

Rejuvenating old trees

As olive trees age, their capacity to produce productive shoots declines, and they must be rejuvenated to regain productivity. Usually, these trees are well spaced but have become so large that they shade out lower shoots and cause production to become confined to the top, which is difficult to pick. To rejuvenate trees, it is necessary to cut scaffold branches back to a height of 6 to 8 feet (1.8 to 2.4 m), preferably to a lateral branch, and to thin any scaffolds congesting the tree, leaving three to five for the main framework (color plate 10.2). Once such heavy pruning is completed, exposed limbs must be protected from sunburn with a whitening agent.

Profuse growth develops along limbs and at cuts after rejuvenation pruning. These shoots need judicious spacing and thinning to rebuild the tree's secondary framework. Once shoots are thinned and spaced out, further pruning should be minimized to allow trees to return to productivity as soon as possible; continued severe thinning of shoots delays bearing. Also, nitrogen fertilizers should be withheld from healthy rejuvenated trees to discourage excessive growth. Once trees regain bearing, normal fertilization should be reestablished.

Alleviating alternate bearing

Olive trees characteristically bear heavy crops one year and light crops the next. This alternate bearing results when the heavy crop suppresses shoot growth and exhausts food reserves (see color plate 14.1 for an example). Flowering and fruit set the following year are then reduced.

Figure 10.3. Undercutting.

Fruit thinning is the only effective method of reducing olive crops to prevent overcropping and subsequent alternate bearing. Fruit thinning improves the leaf-to-fruit ratio by reducing crop but not leaves, which remain to manufacture food for vegetative growth. Pruning, on the other hand, removes both leaves and fruit indiscriminately and is only partially effective because the leaf-to-fruit ratio is not altered. Pruning does stimulate new shoot growth that can be partially fruitful the season after a heavy crop.

The best use of pruning to alleviate alternate bearing is in crop management. Prune heavily in a heavy-bearing year and remove clumps of fruit with relatively few leaves. In a light crop year, wait to prune until the bloom is present, and prune to leave as much bloom as possible for maximum crop. Such a strategy does not eliminate alternate bearing but minimizes it by physically controlling crop size each year.

Pruning frost-damaged trees

The olive is a subtropical tree. Freezing temperatures of 15°F (–10°C) to 22°F (–5°C), depending on cultivar sensitivity, cause the bark to split, leaves to fall, and, occasionally, limbs to die. On damaged trees, profuse growth occurs from uninjured buds, as if the trees had been severely pruned. Injured trees should be left unpruned until new growth reveals the extent of damage. Then prune to remove dead shoots and branches and lightly thin out new shoots early in the growing season. Avoid heavy pruning until normal bearing is restored.

OLIVE IRRIGATION MANAGEMENT

ROBERT H. BEEDE AND DAVID A. GOLDHAMER

Water management in orchards is critical for tree uniformity and sustained high yields of superior quality. Unfortunately, the often laborious task of irrigation is sometimes delegated to people without the technical skills to assess water use, soil moisture content, and application uniformity. Poor water management places an orchard at risk and can have a significant negative effect on revenue. This chapter discusses the importance of good irrigation practices to olive culture and provides guidelines for implementing them.

Olives are considered drought tolerant. Their small leaves are thick and leathery, with a waxy cuticle on the upper surface and hairs on the lower surface to limit water loss (transpiration). The stomata are located primarily on the lower surface in depressions that also reduce water loss. Although these adaptations allow them to survive dry conditions, olives do not produce well without proper irrigation.

WATER AND OLIVE PERFORMANCE

Unlike deciduous trees, which are dormant in winter, olives retain their canopy and use water year-round. However, like other tree crops, olives have certain developmental periods that are especially sensitive to low soil moisture (table 11.1). The bloom period is very sensitive to dry soil conditions, particularly in warm, dry weather. These conditions also cause excessive fruit thinning when naphthaleneacetic acid (NAA) is used.

July and August are typically the months when olives need the most water. Insufficient soil moisture during these months reduces shoot growth and carbohydrate production and, if severe enough, causes fruit shrivel. Shriveled fruit recover with irrigation but may shrivel again during processing. Final fruit size may also be affected by limited carbohydrate production.

Mature orchards require substantial shoot growth to replace old fruitwood and maintain high yields. Shoot growth is also of major importance to young developing orchards as early production depends upon tree size. Olive shoot growth, most noticeable in June and July, is known to be reduced by low soil moisture. Therefore, shoot growth can be used as a visual indicator in determining if water is sufficient in both bearing and nonbearing orchards.

Another, less obvious, effect of poor water management is a reduction in nutrient absorption. Nitrogen and

Table 11.1. Critical periods for adequate soil moisture in California olive orchards.

Period	Growth events	Effect of low soil moisture
February to June	1. Flower bud development 2. Bloom 3. Fruit set 4. Shoot growth	1. Reduced flower formation 2. Incomplete flower 3. Poor fruit set 4. Increased alternate bearing 5. Decreased shoot growth
June to July	1. Stage 1 of fruit growth due to cell division 2. Shoot growth	1. Small fruit size due to decreased cell division 2. Fruit shrivel 3. Decreased shoot growth
Late September to harvest	1. Stage 3 of fruit growth due to cell enlargement 2. Shoot growth	1. Small fruit size due to reduced cell expansion 2. Fruit shrivel 3. Decreased shoot growth

potassium could become deficient in marginal soils with poor irrigation.

Too much irrigation is as detrimental to olives as too little. Poorly drained or layered soils can become waterlogged, resulting in poor aeration and root deterioration. This is more common in winter and early spring, causing poor shoot growth, yellow foliage, and ultimately tree loss. Saturated soil after fruit set contributes to fruit shrivel. Olives suffering from root damage do not tolerate winter cold as well, presumably because they have lower amounts of stored carbohydrates. Phytophthora is also a greater problem in overly wet orchards.

A second, equally significant soil pathogen in olives is *Verticillium dahliae*, a soilborne fungus (see chapter 18). The link between soil moisture and infection by this disease is not well understood, but observations suggest a greater incidence during cool, wet springs in places where excess water persists (such as the field end to which water drains). For this reason growers in high-inoculum soil often fill the root zone to near field capacity in January and then avoid excessive irrigation from February through May.

OLIVE WATER REQUIREMENTS

Until recently, little research information existed on the specific water requirement for olive, possibly because much of the world's acreage is not irrigated. Where irrigation is practiced abroad, the water supply is so limited in most producing areas that only a small fraction of the potential orchard water need is met. In California—where irrigation water is relatively plentiful and inexpensive, excellent distribution systems serve the state, and high-intensity agriculture is practiced—irrigation designed to meet the water needs of trees is practiced on virtually all olive acreage. As competition for California's water increases from the municipal and industrial sectors, however, maximizing the beneficial use of applied water is an increasing priority for olive growers.

The concept of ET

Olive orchard water use depends on two processes: evaporation (E) of water from the soil around the tree and transpiration (T) of water from the tree's foliage. Crop water use is the sum of these two and is called evapotranspiration (ET).

Weather conditions largely determine ET rates. Because both processes that make up ET involve water vaporization, the energy status of the atmosphere determines water loss. Components of this energy status include solar radiation, temperature, humidity, and wind speed. Bare ground upwind of an orchard can also markedly increase ET rates since warmer air (and more energy) can move horizontally from it into the orchard.

Rainfall can supply a significant part of the olive tree's water requirement. Not all rainfall is stored in the soil; depending upon its intensity and duration, up to 50 percent of the rainfall can evaporate or run off the end of the Weld. A practical method of evaluating effective rainfall is augering into the soil at the beginning of the season to determine wetted depth.

Evaporation from the soil is important only when the soil surface is wet. After irrigation, wet soil can evaporate water at the same rate that trees transpire. As the soil dries out, surface evaporation decreases quickly. Thus, the amount of water evaporated depends on the wetted orchard floor area and irrigation frequency. Research shows that localized irrigation, including drip, can lower evaporation significantly and save water in young orchards, but not in mature orchards.

Although cover crops can have many benefits, they use considerable amounts of water. Cover crops or uncontrolled weeds can increase ET by up to 30 percent in mature deciduous orchards and by much more in young trees. Therefore, the cost and availability of water should be taken into account when choosing cover crops.

The most significant plant factor affecting ET is the total leaf area intercepting solar radiation. Thus, tree canopy size, planting density, and leaf development stage all influence crop water use. The degree of orchard floor plant cover (shade) is known to correlate well with the area exposed to sunlight. This relationship between shaded area and ET is key to estimating the water requirement of developing orchards. The relationship between percent ground cover and ET, shown for almond in figure 11.1, is not one to one. Almond ET is greatest when about 55 to 60 percent of the ground is shaded by tree canopies at midday. Full cover is not required to reach maximum ET, presumably because the orchard floor area receiving direct sun heats up and transfers energy to the tree canopies, which increases ET. While the relationship for olive trees has not been established, the results with almond can be taken as a first approximation.

Estimating ET

Two main techniques are used to estimate baseline ET or reference indexes of evaporative demand. There are two indexes of evaporative demand, the potential of the atmosphere to vaporize water. One index is based on measuring water lost from a round metal pan 4 feet (1.2 m) across and 10 inches (25 cm) deep placed in irrigated close-cut grass. Water loss is measured daily in the pan using a depth gauge. This index of ET, referred to as Epan, is commonly reported by weather stations and local newspapers.

The other, more recent, ET index uses weather data and meteorological mathematical models. The data come from a network of about 70 automated weather stations—

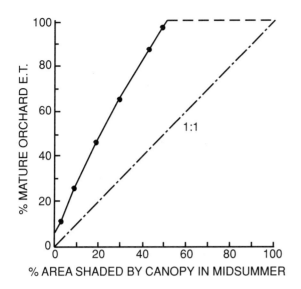

Figure 11.1. Relationship developed between ET and percent shaded area of the orchard floor. SOURCE: Fereres et al., "Drip Irrigation Saves Money in Young Almond Orchards," *Calif. Agric.* (Sept.–Oct. 1982): 12–13.

developed by the University of California and operated by the California Department of Water Resources—called the CIMIS (California Irrigation Management Information System). Each station measures solar radiation temperature, relative humidity, wind speed, and wind direction. These are used in a formula (a modified Penman equation) to yield

an estimate of water use for a close-cut grass, referred to as ETo. This index correlates better with short-term crop water use than Epan, because it is based on parameters that are directly related to the physiology of transpiration rather than simple evaporation from a free water surface. Also, automated weather stations allow rapid estimates of ETo as their data are readily accessible electronically. The remaining discussion considers only ETo and how to use it. To convert Epan data to ETo, divide Epan by 1.24.

Current weather information and ETo estimates are available to growers by dial-up computer modems. For information on the CIMIS, contact the California Department of Water Resources Office of Water Conservation (P.O. Box 942836, Sacramento, CA 94236-0001). Though a less precise guide to irrigation scheduling than real-time data, long-term historical average monthly ETo data have also been compiled for all locations in California in the University of California's ANR Publication 21426, *Determining Daily Reference Evapotranspiration (ETo)*. Table 11.2 provides average ETo information for California's major olive-growing countries.

The crop factor (Kc)

As described above, ETo provides an estimate of crop water use for close-cut grass. For many crops, field research has been conducted to determine their actual water requirement (ETc). Information derived from such studies is site

Table 11.2. Average reference evapotranspiration (ETo) for major olive-growing counties in California, shown in inches per month.

	Jan	Feb	Mar	Apr	May	June	July	Aug	Sept	Oct	Nov	Dec
Sacramento Valley												
Butte (Oroville)	1.22	1.65	2.81	4.72	6.10	7.56	8.54	7.32	5.31	3.66	1.65	0.98
Glenn (Orland)	1.22	1.65	3.05	4.84	6.71	7.44	8.79	7.32	5.79	3.78	1.65	1.10
Shasta (Redding)	1.22	1.43	2.62	4.13	5.61	7.09	8.54	7.32	5.31	3.23	1.42	0.85
Tehama (Corning)	1.22	1.76	2.93	4.49	6.10	7.26	8.06	7.20	5.31	3.66	1.65	1.10
Average	1.22	1.62	2.85	4.55	6.13	7.34	8.48	7.29	5.43	3.58	1.59	1.00
Total 51.1												
San Joaquin Valley												
Fresno (Reedley)	1.10	1.54	3.17	4.72	6.35	7.68	8.54	7.32	5.31	3.42	1.42	0.73
Kern (Shafter)	0.98	1.65	3.42	4.96	6.59	7.68	8.30	7.32	5.43	3.42	1.54	0.85
Kings (Kettleman City)	0.98	1.76	3.42	5.31	7.20	7.91	8.42	7.44	5.91	3.66	1.65	0.98
Madera (Madera)	0.92	1.43	3.17	4.84	6.59	7.80	8.54	7.32	5.31	3.42	1.42	0.73
Tulare (Porterville)	1.22	1.76	3.42	4.72	6.59	7.68	8.54	7.32	5.31	3.42	1.42	0.73
Average	1.04	1.63	3.32	4.91	6.66	7.75	8.47	7.34	5.45	3.47	1.49	0.80
Total 52.3												
Southern California												
Riverside (Riverside)	2.07	2.87	4.03	4.13	6.10	7.09	7.93	7.57	6.14	4.15	2.60	1.95
Total 56.3												

SOURCE: University of California Division of Agriculture and Natural Resources Publication 21426, *Determining Daily Reference Evapotranspiration (ETo)*.

Table 11.3. Average estimated water requirements for clean-cultivated olives grown in the Sacramento and southern San Joaquin valleys.

Month	ETo[*] (in.)	Kc[†]	Crop ETc (in.)	ETc[‡] (in./day)	ETc[§] (gal/tree/day)
		Sacramento Valley			
January	1.2	0.75 (1.05)	0.9	0.03	17
February	1.6	0.75 (1.05)	1.2	0.04	24
March	2.9	0.75 (1.05)	2.1	0.07	39
April	4.6	0.75 (1.05)	3.4	0.11	64
May	6.1	0.75 (1.05)	4.6	0.15	83
June	7.3	0.75 (1.00)	5.5	0.18	103
July	8.5	0.75 (1.00)	6.4	0.21	115
August	7.3	0.75 (1.00)	5.5	0.18	99
September	5.4	0.75 (1.00)	4.1	0.14	76
October	3.6	0.75 (1.00)	2.7	0.09	48
November	1.6	0.75 (0.95)	1.0	0.04	22
December	1.0	0.75 (0.95)	0.8	0.02	14
TOTAL	51.1		38.3		
		San Joaquin Valley			
January	1.0	0.75 (1.05)	0.8	0.03	14
February	1.6	0.75 (1.05)	1.2	0.04	24
March	3.3	0.75 (1.05)	2.5	0.08	45
April	4.9	0.75 (1.05)	3.7	0.12	69
May	6.7	0.75 (1.05)	5.0	0.16	90
June	7.8	0.75 (1.00)	5.8	0.19	108
July	8.5	0.75 (1.00)	6.4	0.20	115
August	7.3	0.75 (1.00)	5.5	0.18	99
September	5.5	0.75 (1.00)	4.1	0.14	76
October	3.5	0.75 (1.00)	2.6	0.08	47
November	1.5	0.75 (0.95)	1.1	0.04	21
December	0.8	0.75 (0.95)	0.6	0.02	11
TOTAL	52.4		39.2		

[*]To derive Epan, multiply by 1.24.

[†]Numbers in parentheses are suggested Kc values for orchards with active cover crop. To derive Kp (crop coefficient, using pan as a reference), divide by 1.24.

[‡]Determined by dividing the monthly ETc by the number of days per month.

[§]Based on large, mature trees spaced 30 × 30 ft. The following equation can be used to calculate individual tree water use for other spacings:

gal/tree/day = ETc (in./day) × spacing (ft^2) × .622 (gal/in. – ft^2).

and time specific and is not accurate under different weather conditions; however, the relationship between ETo and ETc has been found to be relatively constant. Thus, researchers have used this ratio to develop crop factors, or coefficients (Kc's) that allow growers to relate crop ET to ETo. In California's interior valleys, Kc's are relatively independent of location and vary primarily with the tree species and its stage of growth. From the ETo for an olive-growing region, one can apply the Kc for the specified period of the season and obtain an estimate of olive ET.

Recent research in California indicates that irrigating mature trees with a Kc of 0.65 or less results in tree water stress based on predawn leaf water potential. No stress was observed when Kc's of 0.75 and 0.85 were used. Moreover, there is a strong correlation between crop revenue and Kc's

between 0.16 and 0.75: irrigating at less than 0.75 significantly reduces revenue. This is due to a combination of lower yield and fruit size (and therefore value). We suggest that a Kc of 0.75 should be used for conservation irrigation scheduling in California.

Table 11.3 lists monthly Sacramento Valley and southern San Joaquin Valley Kc values and ETc estimates for olives grown under clean-cultivated conditions during a normal year. Table values apply to mature orchards (60 percent shaded area or more). Note that there is very little difference in seasonal crop water requirements between the Sacramento Valley (38.3 inches) and the southern San Joaquin Valley (39.2 inches). Cover crops increase crop ET rates significantly, especially during spring, and require the higher Kc values shown in parentheses.

Long-term average ETo data can be successfully used for irrigation scheduling, even though a normal year seldom occurs. Common sense should be used to modify irrigations if temperatures or wind conditions are quite different from normal.

SCHEDULING IRRIGATIONS

The most common method of water management is to schedule irrigation based on past experience. However, rising water costs, decreasing availability, high energy prices, and the potential to improve orchard productivity now call for more scientific irrigation scheduling based on sound agronomic principles.

There are several different approaches to improving irrigation scheduling. One is to monitor soil moisture levels by hand (the "feel method") or with various instruments and to replenish soil water in a timely fashion. This strategy, if applied on a regular basis, can be effective. Another is to estimate crop water use, as previously discussed, and then irrigate to match that water requirement. This is known as the water budget method.

Newer methods (primarily in the research phase for trees) measure the plant's water status with specialized equipment such as the pressure bomb and infrared gun. These devices measure the tension of water in leaf tissue and canopy temperature, respectively; predetermined thresholds are used to decide when to irrigate. This technique is used for scheduling the irrigation of cotton in California, but more work is needed to determine if such plant-based measurements can be relied upon for tree crops.

The water budget method is the most comprehensive management technique now available; it uses information on crop ET, rainfall, irrigation system efficiency, and, in some cases, soil water-holding capacity to guide an irrigation program. It also answers the two most important questions for effective irrigation: when to irrigate and how much water to apply. The following discussion focuses on the water budget method.

Determining available water content (AWC)

Furrow, basin, and sprinkler techniques of irrigation rely upon the soil to serve as a reservoir between irrigations. Knowing the size of the soil water reservoir and the rate of water being used (ETc), one can determine when to irrigate and how much water to apply to refill the reservoir.

The ability of soil to store water depends primarily upon its texture. Fine-textured soils hold more water than coarse-textured soils. A soil's capacity to hold water for plant use is defined by three terms. The first, field capacity (FC), is the water remaining in the soil 2 or 3 days after being saturated.

This is the amount of water a soil can hold without appreciable loss due to drainage. The second term is permanent wilting point (PWP), the point at which the water remaining in the soil pores is held so tightly that plants cannot extract it. The third term, the difference between the first two, is available water content (AWC). This is the soil water (commonly expressed in inches per foot of soil) that is available for plant use. Table 11.4 gives estimates of AWC for various soil textures.

Table 11.4. Estimates of available water content for different soil textures.

Soil texture	Range (in./ft)	Average (in./ft)
Coarse-textured sand	0.50–1.25	.90
Sandy loams	1.25–1.75	1.50
Silty clay loam	1.50–2.30	1.90
Clay	1.60–2.50	2.30

Sandy soils hold less water than loams and clay loams. This is related to both total pore space and the size of individual pores. Coarse-textured sands have larger pores and less total pore space than silty clay loams; the result is a lesser ability to hold water. Hence, most of the water in coarse-textured soils is easily removed by plant roots. Clay soils possess a large total pore space and hold the most water. However, a large percentage of their pores are small and do not easily give up water; this must be taken into account in making irrigation decisions.

The wide range in AWC for each soil texture indicates that factors other than texture affect water-holding capacity. However, precise AWC determinations are generally not necessary to improve irrigation scheduling. Using the averages provided, growers can obtain a rough estimate of the total water available to their olives by multiplying the AWC for their soil(s) by the depth of the root zone.

Determining the root zone

An accurate estimation of rooting depth is essential for determining the potential AWC. The olive root zone is commonly 3 or 4 feet (0.9 to 1.2 m). An excellent method for evaluating root depth is to backhoe along the drip line at three or four sites in the orchard. These excavations also provide valuable information on soil texture and the existence of compacted layers or hardpans limiting water intake. Based on the average AWC estimation of 1.5 inches per foot for a medium-textured soil (see "sandy loams" in table 11.4) and an estimated olive root depth of 4 feet (1.2 m), 6 inches of water (1.5 in./ft × 4 ft) should be applied to fill the soil reservoir to capacity if it was initially at the PWP.

Establishing allowable depletion

As soil water content decreases from FC, roots must work harder to extract water even though it is well above the PWP. This is because after water is extracted—first from the larger soil pores, then from the smaller—the pores assume two functions: both storage and conduction of water moving between the soil and plant roots. Small pores hold less water, and they hold it more tightly; thus, conduction to the roots is slower. Together, these factors limit water uptake as soils dry out. This falloff in water extraction decreases crop growth before the entire root zone reaches the PWP. Therefore, olive growers should irrigate before the soil water is depleted to a point that restricts growth. An exception may be spring irrigations, when root rot or verticillium wilt could be aggravated by soil water contents near FC.

No single soil water level can be recommended for all situations. Allowable depletion (AD) or yield threshold depletion (YTD) is the target percentage or amount of the total available water in the root zone that indicates irrigation is needed. It depends on several factors including rooting depth, soil texture, weather, and the season. Providing that infiltration does not limit the amount of water effectively applied per irrigation, olive growers typically irrigate when the AWC has reached about 50 percent depletion. In the previous example, assume a 50 percent AD. Since the total AWC was estimated at 6 inches (1.5 in./ft × 4 ft root depth), the next irrigation would be applied when ETc indicated that 3 inches had been used (6 inches × 0.5 AD) since the last irrigation. In stress-sensitive periods such as during flower and fruit development, they should be irrigated at relatively small depletion levels (30 to 40 percent AD).

The AD and AWC concepts are important only for surface and sprinkler irrigation systems. Localized systems (drip, micro-sprinklers) are designed to replenish ETc from daily to weekly, hence the soil is not being used for water storage to the same degree as with surface or conventional sprinkler systems.

APPLICATION EFFICIENCY

The previous information can be used to estimate how often to irrigate and the amount of water required to refill the soil water reservoir. However, when water is applied to an orchard, some losses occur, and they must be considered in calculating the actual amount of water to be applied. The type of irrigation used, soil, wind conditions, and water management practices largely determine application efficiency.

Water applied to a field can be lost by runoff, percolation below the root zone, and (with sprinklers) spray evaporation and drift. The goal of water management is to minimize these losses. For instance, runoff can be minimized by designing an irrigation system that prevents it or reuses the collected tailwater. Application efficiency (Ea) is a term commonly used to describe how efficiently growers irrigate. It is defined as the percentage of applied irrigation water that is stored in the root zone (and thus available for crop use).

Ea is directly related to how uniformly water can be applied to the orchard. Therefore, the irrigation method is of prime importance. Most olive orchards use surface (basin, furrow, and border strip) irrigation methods, although sprinkler and drip/low-volume systems are becoming more popular. Each method differs in its application uniformity. With surface irrigation, the water intake properties of the soil and the rate that water advances over the surface determine uniformity; it is greatest when irrigation water is applied rapidly. With sprinklers, uniformity depends largely on system design—nozzle spacing, type, and size; riser height; and operating pressure. The efficiency of drip/low-volume systems depends on their design, operation, and maintenance. In general, sprinkler and drip/low-volume systems can be operated with higher efficiencies than surface methods. Because application efficiencies vary, Ea must be estimated for each orchard. Cooperative Extension, the Soil Conservation Service, and private irrigation consultants offer assistance in evaluating systems. Some general application efficiency estimates for different systems are shown in table 11.5. An Ea estimate is necessary to determine how much water must be delivered to the orchard (the gross irrigation requirement). For example, assuming a 75 percent efficiency (0.75), the amount of water that must be delivered to achieve an effective 3-inch irrigation would be 3/0.75 = 4 inches. Irrigating 12 acres at this rate would require 4 inches × 12 acres = 48 acre-inches (4 acre-feet).

Table 11.5. Irrigation efficiency (Ea) of olive orchard systems.

System	Ea (%)
Basin	70–80
Border strip	70–80
Furrow	65–75
Sprinkler	75–85
Drip	85–95

A major component of the water budget irrigation method is the amount of water actually being delivered to the orchard. This is more difficult to estimate with ditch water than with wells, but not impossible. Many ditch tenders are quite good at estimating water delivery, usually expressed in second-feet; one second-foot is equal to 1 acre-inch per hour (27,154 gallons). Inexpensive flow measurement devices can be installed to help determine delivery rates. The Soil Conservation Service or Cooperative Extension can assist growers in their selection.

Pumping stations can be tested easily for discharge by contacting the local power company; this free test provides data on pump efficiency, standing and pumping water depths, and the cost per acre-foot of water delivery. Knowing actual pump capacity, one can determine the time required to apply the desired amount of water. Assuming a pump capacity of 1,000 gallons per minute, the running time necessary to apply 48 acre-inches to the 12-acre example would be

$$(27,154 \text{ gal/ac-in.} \times 48 \text{ ac-in.})/1,000 \text{ gal/min}$$
$$= 1,303 \text{ min} = 21.7 \text{ hr}$$

IRRIGATION PROGRAM EVALUATION

It is obvious from this discussion that an accurate estimation of several factors is the key to providing optimal soil moisture. Timely evaluation of soil moisture status is essential to determining the accuracy of water budget–based scheduling; some soil water monitoring is a component of any comprehensive irrigation management program.

The most valuable information from soil moisture monitoring is gained just before and 3 to 4 days after irrigating. Preirrigation monitoring assesses whether irrigation timing and amount achieves the desired allowable depletion (AD). For example, too low a soil moisture (depletion greater than that desired) requires more frequent irrigations or, in the case of well-drained soil, the application of more water at the existing frequency.

The simplest method of evaluating soil moisture is to sample the soil directly with an auger and assess its water content by feel. Guidelines for relating the feel of various soil textures to water content are available through local offices of the Soil Conservation Service or Cooperative Extension. Although time-consuming, direct soil sampling can be effective in determining soil moisture levels and irrigation requirements.

Another method of monitoring soil moisture is with a tensiometer, a vacuum gauge connected to a piece of PVC tubing with water in it and a porous cup at its tip. Tensiometers come in various lengths to reach different soil depths. As soil water is depleted, soil moisture tension increases. This creates a vacuum that is registered on the tensiometer gauge. The drier the soil, the higher the gauge reading. Tensiometers are better suited to sandy soil than clay because they are not mechanically capable of measuring the high tensions at which water is still available in fine-textured soils. Tensiometers are also most valuable when two or three are placed at different depths in a single location. This provides information on the rate and depth of depletion. Used in combination with the water budget method, tensiometers can be helpful in evaluating soil water status.

A third instrument used for soil water measurement is the gypsum block. It consists of a small block of gypsum containing two separate wires; the blocks are installed at different depths in the root zone using a device similar to a soil push-tube. The wires leading up to the surface are attached to a stake or to the tree trunk to avoid damage. A hand-held meter is used to measure the electrical resistance between the wires in the block. Resistance increases as the soil becomes drier. Most gypsum blocks are less accurate in the wet soil moisture range and therefore are more suited for use with surface irrigation systems. Table 11.6 shows the relationship between percent of AWC depletion and tension for several soil textures.

Table 11.6. Percent of available water depleted at various soil moisture tensions.

Tension (bars*)	Loamy sand	Fine, sandy loam	Sandy loam	Loam	Clay
0.3[†]	55	50	35	15	7
0.5[†]	70	62	55	30	13
0.8[†]	77	70	63	45	20
1.0[‡]	82	75	68	55	27
2.0[‡]	90	82	78	72	45
5.0[‡]	95	93	88	80	75
15.0[‡]	100	100	100	100	100

*1 bar = 100 centibars.
[†]Tensiometers operate within this range.
[‡]Gypsum blocks operate within this range.

Soil salinity should be considered when using gypsum blocks. Salt-affected soils will give lower resistance readings, which suggest higher soil moisture levels than are present.

Another soil water measurement device increasingly used is the neutron probe. It consists of a radiation source and a recording unit. The radiation source is lowered into a narrow PVC or metal tube carefully installed in the soil throughout the root zone. Measurements are usually taken at 1-foot increments. The readings are interpreted from a calibration curve that relates the instrument readings to soil water levels.

The neutron probe is primarily used by large farms and by irrigation consultants providing service for a fee. Because the probe is radioactive, it is strictly regulated by state agencies and requires a license for operation. Like all devices installed in the soil, it is site-specific; the access tubes must be placed in soils representing the average texture and infiltration.

CONCLUSION

The actual task of irrigation is relatively simple. However, evaluating existing practices and implementing improved methods can be challenging. Considering such issues as increasing water and energy costs, water allocations to agriculture, groundwater overdraft, and pollution of drinking water, growers realize that scientific water management pays off ecologically, politically, and financially. Applying the principles presented here can significantly improve olive orchard quality and productivity. Knowledge of crop ET throughout the season, along with often simple modifications of irrigation procedures, can bring the olive grower substantially greater returns.

12

MINERAL NUTRIENT AVAILABILITY

MARK FREEMAN AND R. M. CARLSON

Soil is a complex mixture of soil particles, soil solution, organic matter, and biological organisms. Plants obtain most of their mineral nutrients from the soil solution, but each of the other components affects how easily nutrients are absorbed by roots. An olive tree found deficient in a mineral nutrient does not always simply need fertilizer. The cause of that mineral imbalance should be investigated before a solution is attempted.

Olives are more tolerant of high soil boron levels, high soil calcium levels, and less fertile soils than are most other commercial tree crops. In fact, highly fertile soils and high nitrogen levels are undesirable, as excessive shoot growth and many small fruit are produced. Olives do not tolerate poorly drained soils, however.

Only three mineral nutrient imbalances (deficiencies) have been observed in commercial California olive orchards—nitrogen, potassium, and boron—and these are treated with annual fertilizer applications. However, not all olive orchards require annual fertilizer additions, and nutrient imbalances other than nitrogen, potassium, and boron can occur. This chapter was written to help growers understand how mineral imbalances occur.

ESSENTIAL NUTRIENTS

For normal growth and optimal production, most plants must obtain 14 nutrients from the soil. They are separated into two groups, based on the relative amounts needed by the plant. The macronutrient group includes nitrogen, phosphorus, potassium, calcium, magnesium, and sulfur. The micronutrient group includes boron, manganese, zinc, iron, copper, chlorine, cobalt, and molybdenum. The most important management factor regarding all 14 elements is balance. Growth and production are limited by the element that is most deficient (or, in some cases, too abundant or toxic). Until that element's concentration is increased (or decreased when a toxicity occurs), growth will be subnormal.

The concentration of nutrients needed for normal development in a particular part of the plant and time of year also changes. For example, 1-year-old olive leaves store nitrogen, releasing it in response to demands from developing fruit and leaves. However, tree needs do not require that all essential nutrients be added by a regular fertilizer program. Most essential elements are adequate in most soils. Also, only small amounts of some essential nutrients are removed through harvesting, pruning, and other orchard practices. Finally, the leaves of fruit trees recycle much of these essential nutrients back into the tree before they fall off.

Nutrients in the soil can be contained in the soil solution or attached to particles of minerals or organic matter, but plant roots absorb most of their mineral nutrients from the soil solution only. Nutrients exist in solution as molecules with a positive electrical charge (called cations), with a negative electrical charge (anions), or with no electrical charge (neutral species). Some nutrients, such as nitrogen, occur in both negatively and positively charged forms. Table 12.1 summarizes the forms of the elements in the soil solution. Cations added to the soil tend to be fixed onto the surfaces of particles and thus become unavailable to roots until returned to the soil solution. In addition to these simple inorganic forms, several nutrients are found in the soil solution, together with dissolved organic substances in loose combinations called complexes. Some nutrients, such as calcium and magnesium, have much higher concentrations in the soil solution than other nutrients, including phosphorus, potassium, and micronutrients.

SOIL REACTION OR PH

Soil pH refers to the relative concentrations of hydrogen (H^+) and hydroxyl (OH^-) ions in the soil solution. Soil pH is measured on a scale from 0 to 14. This measurement is important because it indicates whether a soil is acidic (pH less than 7), neutral (pH about 7), or basic (pH greater than

Table 12.1. Forms of nutrient elements found in soil solutions.

Class of nutrient	Element	Cationic forms	Symbol	Anionic forms	Symbol
Primary nutrients	nitrogen	ammonium	NH_4^+	nitrate	NO_3^-
				nitrite	NO_2^-
	phosphorus	—	—	hydrogen phosphate	HPO_4^{2-}
				dihydrogen phosphate	$H_2PO_4^-$
	potassium	potassium ion	K^+	—	—
Secondary nutrients	calcium	calcium ion	Ca^{2+}	—	—
	magnesium	magnesium ion	Mg^{2+}	—	—
	sulfur	—	—	sulfate	SO_4^{2-}
Micronutrients	iron	ferrous ion	Fe^{2+}	—	—
		ferric ion	Fe^{3+}	—	—
	manganese	manganous ion	Mn^{2+}	—	—
	zinc	zinc ion	Zn^{2+}	—	—
	copper	cupric ion	Cu^{2+}	—	—
	boron	—	—	borate	$H_2BO_3^-$
				neutral boric acid	H_3BO_3
	molybdenum	—	—	molybdate	MoO_4^{2-}
	chlorine	—	—	chloride	Cl^-

7). The lower the pH, the more acid a soil is, having a higher concentration of hydrogen ions in solution. The higher the pH, the more basic a soil is, having a higher concentration of hydroxyl ions. Soil pH greatly influences the extent to which most nutrients are bound to soil particles, which in turn affects nutrient concentrations in the soil solution. Thus, pH has a definite effect on nutrient availability to tree roots (fig. 12.1). For most plants, a soil pH range between 6.5 and 7.5 is best for overall nutrient availability.

Three processes are largely responsible for orchard soil acidification: leaching of cation bases (such as Na^+, Ca^{2+}, Mg^{2+}, and K^+), removal of those bases by the crop, and the repeated application of acid-forming fertilizers, such as those containing ammonium. Fine-textured soils (like clay or silt) or those containing free lime (calcium carbonate), as many California soils do, have a considerable buffering capacity that reduces the acidification effect. However, sandy soils without free lime may also acidify rapidly, especially with the use of acid-forming fertilizers. Soil pH should be monitored regularly.

The optimal soil pH for olive is not known, although olives grow poorly on soils with a pH above 8.5. Some California soils have a pH higher than 7.0 and high levels of calcium. Olive trees grow well in these calcareous soils.

SOIL BUFFER SYSTEMS

Soil contains many chemical mechanisms, called buffer systems, that limit or buffer against drastic changes in pH or nutrient concentrations. These systems help ensure that a steady supply of nutrients is available, but if a major imbal-

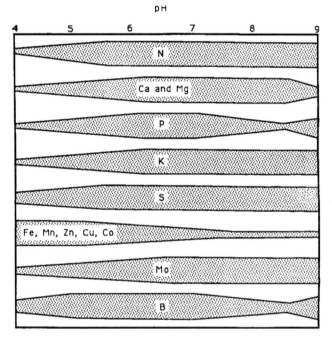

Figure 12.1. Effect of pH on mineral nutrient availability.

ance occurs over time, these buffer systems make it difficult to make quick corrections. Soil minerals (like clay) and organic matter tend to buffer the composition of the soil solution. For example, adding acidic fertilizers over many years lowers soil pH. A clay soil requires much more lime than a sandy soil to raise its soil pH by the same amount. Three important processes in the buffer action of soils are cation exchange, specific adsorption, and the precipitation of compounds having limited solubility.

Cation exchange capacity (CEC)

Cation exchange capacity (CEC) expresses a soil's ability to hold onto cations against leaching. Many cations are mineral nutrients that olive roots can absorb from the soil solution. Mineral soils with a higher CEC are typically more fertile as they have a greater "storage capacity" for mineral nutrients. Cation exchange, the exchange of one cation for another, occurs primarily on the surface of clay mineral particles and on active sites of organic matter (fig. 12.2). The exchange occurs because clay particles and organic matter have negative electrical charges that must be balanced by positively charged cations.

Concentrations of calcium, magnesium, potassium, and sodium are controlled primarily by cation exchange. The extent to which these nutrients are held depends on the amounts of clay and organic matter in the soil. Very sandy soils have little capacity to hold these nutrients; thus, loss of nutrients by leaching can be a problem in them. On the other hand, nutrients added to sandy soils can be readily washed down to the plant roots. In clay soils, penetration of certain fertilizer nutrients (such as potassium) presents a problem in managing deep-rooted crops because the negatively charged soil particles bind to them, removing them from the soil solution. Cation exchange also plays a role in buffering soils against pH changes. Soil particles hold some cations more tightly than others; however, any cation in solution can replace any cation held on a soil particle's surface (exchangeable cation) to some extent.

CEC is important because cations are retained by soil particles with different intensities based on the type and concentration. Generally, calcium and magnesium predominate, and calcium can displace sodium. This is significant when correcting soils high in sodium.

Specific adsorption

Specific adsorption is a highly selective phenomenon. Nutrients are held on the soil particle's surface—adsorbed—by forces much stronger than the electrical attraction forces that bind exchangeable cations (fig. 12.3). Adding water is not enough to overcome these forces and put these nutrients back in solution.

Specific adsorption helps control phosphorus in the soil solution. In neutral-to-acid soils, phosphorus is specifically adsorbed onto the surface of iron and aluminum oxide particles and, to some extent, clay mineral particles. It is not appreciably displaced from them by other components of the soil solution. This effect becomes more pronounced as the soil becomes more acid; hence, one problem with acid soils is the unavailability of phosphorus. Specific adsorption also appears to help control the availability of copper and zinc; thus, they are less available in basic soils. Fortunately for olive growers, deficiencies of these three nutrients have not been observed in California olive orchards.

Precipitation and dissolution of compounds

Some nutrient compounds dissolve only to a small extent in the soil solution. When such a compound comes to exceed its solubility, usually due to a change in pH, the excess forms into solid particles and precipitates. Thus, it is taken out of solution and becomes unavailable to plant roots. Calcium phosphate compounds precipitate in neutral to basic soils as their solubility decreases and as soil pH rises. On the acid side, iron and aluminum phosphates may precipitate (in addition to the specific adsorption of phosphate on iron and aluminum oxide surfaces). These phosphates become less soluble as soil pH falls. Iron and manganese are controlled partly by the solubility of their oxides, which decreases rapidly as soil pH increases.

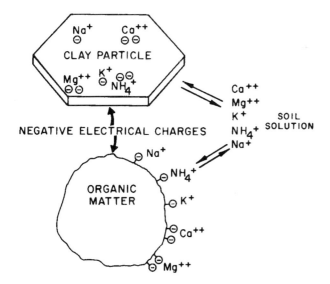

Figure 12.2. Cation exchange. SOURCE: David E. Ramos, ed., *Walnut Orchard Management*, UC Division of Agriculture and Natural Resources Publication 21410, p. 111.

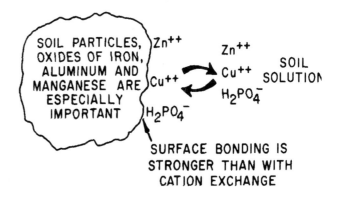

Figure 12.3. Specific adsorption. SOURCE: See figure 12.2.

SOIL TEXTURE

Soil texture, or proportions of sand, silt, and clay, also affects nutrient availability to roots. Many California soils planted to olive are layered, and nutrient availability varies depending on the soil's parent material and the different soil layers present. Clay mineral particles are the smallest, but they have the greatest capacity to store and exchange cations. With their higher CEC, clay soils lose fewer nutrients to leaching than sandy soils. Clay particles can also store more available water in the same volume of soil than silt and sand.

Many olive orchards are planted on two or more soil types. This spatial variation mainly affects water infiltration rates. Nonuniform irrigation can lead to waterlogging, which decreases root health and nutrient availability.

Much of California's olive acreage is planted on foothill soils (in Butte County) or terrace soils (in Tulare and Fresno counties), which are less fertile than deeper valley soils. Trees on shallow soils exhibit more growth and yield in response to nitrogen fertilizer applications than those on valley soils. Too much nitrogen can lead to increased fruit set, small fruit size and alternate bearing. Some of these shallow soils are low in boron. Land leveling, especially within the "cut" areas, can cause potassium deficiency where the surface soil is removed. Shallow soils, however, can yield more fruit than deeper, more fertile soils as they do not promote excessive vegetative growth.

ORGANIC MATTER

Soil organic matter plays a major role in controlling the availability of nitrogen, phosphorus, and sulfur. Those nutrients are released to the soil solution when organic matter is decomposed (mineralized) by microorganisms (fig. 12.4). Conversely, they may become unavailable to plants when microbes, decomposing materials poor in these elements (such as straw), incorporate them from the soil into their own cell bodies.

Organic matter benefits the soil by increasing its cation exchange capacity and water-holding capacity (especially in sandy soils). It can also act as a chelate, making certain micronutrients more available to roots in the form of complexes. In addition, under some conditions it can increase air and water movement into soil and help moderate soil temperature. Unfortunately, most California soils have less than 1.5 percent organic matter, which is low. Summer heat oxidizes much of the organic matter that is added each year.

BIOLOGICAL ORGANISMS

Plants act as a pumping system, continually cycling to the soil surface nutrients. The nutrients added to the soil sur-

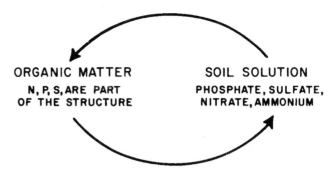

Figure 12.4. Organic matter cycling.

face tend to be bound by soil particles, from which they replace nutrients removed from the soil solution. Plant roots extract nutrients from throughout the root zone and transport them to the plant tops. As plants die and decompose, their nutrients are released to the soil surface again (fig. 12.5). Thus, in undisturbed soil most nutrients are concentrated near the surface. When surface soil is removed by land leveling or erosion, a major part of the nutrient pool is also removed.

Roots also excrete many substances, including carbon dioxide (which forms carbonic acid in the soil solution) and organic materials, that tend to lower the pH of the soil adjacent to them. Except in acid soils, this tends to increase the availability of nutrients to the plant. Some of the excreted organic materials can form complexes with micronutrients such as zinc and iron (natural chelates); this, too, can help roots extract nutrients from soil.

Microorganisms contribute to nutrient availability by decomposing organic materials and oxidizing certain nutrients, which then become available for root uptake. Oxidation is important with nitrogen, iron, and sulfur. Microbes can tie up nitrogen, making it less available, when materials added to the soil are high in carbon but low in nitrogen (like straw). Some soil bacteria can convert atmospheric nitrogen directly into soil nitrogen. In

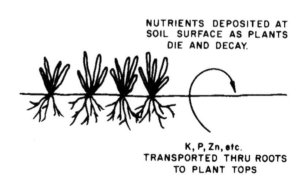

Figure 12.5. Movement of nutrients to soil surface by plant cycling.

72

addition, certain fungi called mycorrhizae aid root uptake of nutrients for many plants when soil nutrient levels are low. Soil microorganisms are a significant aid to soil nutrient availability.

SOIL MOISTURE LEVELS AND NUTRIENT AVAILABILITY

Nutrients in the soil solution move to roots in different ways. Roots can receive nutrients through the soil water that the plant needs for transpiration. This process is called mass flow (fig. 12.6). In some soils and for some nutrients, mass flow can supply the plant's needs. Where mass flow is inadequate, the balance of the plant's needs must be supplied by diffusion (fig. 12.7). As the root depletes the nutrient supply at its surface, a gradient in concentration develops in the soil solution near the root. The nutrient diffuses down this gradient toward the root surface. If both mass flow and diffusion are inadequate, the plant becomes deficient in the nutrient.

The amount of nutrient delivered to the plant root by mass flow and diffusion increases with the nutrient's concentration in the soil solution. However, these delivery mechanisms are also sensitive to the soil's moisture content and temperature. Delivery by both processes slows as soil moisture and temperature decrease. Little can be done to alter soil temperature, but maintaining adequate soil moisture can enhance the supply of nutrients to a plant. Conditions that promote new root growth also increase nutrient availability, because more nutrients become available as roots explore new areas of soil.

TOXIC SOIL CONDITIONS

Plant growth is limited when soils contain excessive (or inadequate) soluble salts, are too acid or too basic, or lack adequate oxygen. High levels of soluble salts reduce the amount of soil water roots can absorb. Excessive sodium, boron, and chloride are toxic to plants. Accumulated sodium also displaces exchangeable calcium and magnesium from soil particles, imparting undesirable physical properties to the soil, such as low water infiltration rates.

Water with high or low levels of soluble salts can adversely affect plant growth. When irrigation water adds soluble salts to soil and tree roots then extract the water, or it evaporates from the soil surface, most of the soluble salts are left behind. These salts concentrate in the soil profile unless irrigations and rainfall in excess of evapotranspiration leach the salts below the root zone. Water with low levels of soluble salts can create different problems. Canal water originating from the Sierra Nevada has a very low salt concentration; it also removes calcium from the soil over time and adds a small amount of sodium. These three factors combine to cause surface infiltration problems.

Acid soils may occur naturally or may develop over time with the addition of acidic fertilizers. In excessively acid soils, aluminum oxides dissolve to leave toxic concentrations of aluminum, and manganese may reach toxic concentrations as insoluble manganese dioxide is converted to the soluble manganous form. Treatment for acid soils is lime (calcium carbonate) to neutralize the acidity.

Excessively basic soils are usually the result of accumulated sodium carbonate or a large percentage of the ion exchange sites being occupied by sodium. Chapter 13 discusses problems related to soil and water quality.

When the supply of oxygen is restricted by waterlogging, soil microorganisms may make chemical transformations that produce toxic levels of certain substances including hydrogen sulfide, methane gas and other toxic organic materials, and manganous ion. Production of these toxins depends on temperature—it occurs much more rapidly in warm soil. In addition, root growth is poor under saturated conditions and nutrient uptake is reduced. Olive trees are sensitive to poor drainage and waterlogging.

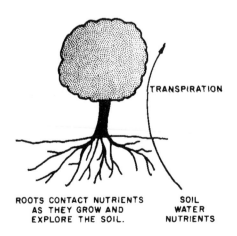

Figure 12.6. Root exploration and mass flow.

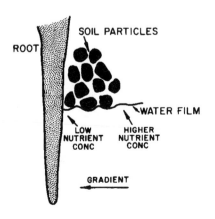

Figure 12.7. Nutrient diffusion to roots.

73

NUTRIENT BEHAVIOR IN SOIL

The behavior in soil of each nutrient or group of similar nutrients is summarized below. Individual nutrient elements may occur in more than one form in the soil solution and may be involved in more than one buffering process. Nutrients added as fertilizer behave exactly the same way as nutrients from organic sources when they enter the soil solution; plant roots cannot distinguish whether a nutrient is derived from organic or inorganic sources.

Nitrogen

Most nitrogen in soil is stored as organic forms that are unavailable to tree roots. As soil organisms and organic matter break down, nitrogen is slowly released to the soil solution where roots can absorb it. The amount released, however, is usually insufficient to replace nitrogen lost by the tree to harvests and prunings. Nitrogen occurs in the soil solution primarily as nitrate (NO_3^-), ammonium (NH_4^+), and urea (NH_2–CO–NH_2). Nitrate, being an anion, is very soluble and is not adsorbed by soil particles, so it can readily move to the plant roots. It can also be leached out of the soil as water moves past the root zone. Urea, too, is mobile. Ammonium, on the other hand, has a positive charge and is adsorbed as an exchangeable cation on the surface of the negatively charged clay minerals. Thus, its mobility is restricted. Ammonium at the soil surface decomposes to ammonia gas, which can be lost to the atmosphere. Ammonium applied to the soil surface as fertilizer does not move far into the soil except in very sandy soils. Incorporation of ammonium fertilizer into the soil minimizes ammonia gas loss.

Nitrogen is constantly recycled through different forms in the soil, air, and plants. Some soil microorganisms break down complex organic forms of nitrogen to water-soluble forms that roots can absorb. Microorganisms also convert ammonium to nitrate by nitrification; optimal soil temperatures for this process are from 80° to 90°F (27° to 32°C). Adequate moisture is also necessary. When the oxygen supply in a soil is low (as in waterlogged soil), other microorganisms can convert nitrate to nitrogen gas, which is lost to the atmosphere. This process, called denitrification, occurs most rapidly at higher temperatures.

Phosphorus

Phosphorus availability depends on soil pH as well as on the amount of phosphorus present. A neutral to slightly acid pH (pH 6 to 7) is most favorable for phosphorus availability. In more strongly acid soil, phosphorus is tied up by specific adsorption on the surfaces of iron and aluminum oxide particles, and by precipitation of poorly soluble iron and aluminum phosphates. On the basic side, low-solubility calcium phosphates form. Phosphorus removed from the soil solution by roots is replaced from these phosphates. But if phosphorus fertilizer is added to soil, most of it becomes unavailable to roots.

Fortunately, phosphorus deficiency in California deciduous tree crops, including olive, is practically nonexistent. These crops do not respond to phosphate fertilizers even when grown in soils that need additional phosphorus for annual crops. Generally, there is no reason to apply phosphate to deciduous orchards other than to supply the needs of a cover crop. Only two cases of phosphorus deficiency have been found in tree crops in California (walnuts near Clear Lake and pears in the Sierra foothills); however, phosphorus deficiency has been reported on olive in Europe.

Potassium

Potassium and ammonium ions behave similarly. Certain clay minerals in soils bind potassium tightly. The concentration of potassium in the soil solution is very low, typically only one-hundredth as much as there is on clay mineral surfaces. Plants require a good deal of potassium, and they can accumulate it from the soil solution if the concentration of potassium at the root surface can be maintained. Soil particles near the roots release their potassium to the soil solution as the plant roots absorb potassium from it. Some soils contain minerals (notably the micas) that break down as they release their potassium. Because the mobility of potassium is quite low, fertilizing deep-rooted crops in clay soils with it can be difficult. Potassium applied to the soil surface tends to be held in the top few inches. As potassium levels in the soil tend to be higher near the surface, a deficiency may occur if much land leveling and soil removal are done.

Calcium and magnesium

Calcium and magnesium are closely related elements, and their soil chemistry is similar. Of the 14 essential plant nutrients, calcium and magnesium occur in the soil solution in the greatest abundance. Their availability is largely controlled by the cation exchange process. They typically occupy 80 to 90 percent of the exchange sites on soil particles of productive soils. Calcium ions can occupy up to 80 percent of those sites. In very acid soils, calcium and magnesium are usually leached out, and sites previously occupied by calcium are replaced with other cations like hydrogen and aluminum. Calcium held in exchange sites promotes good soil structure. Treating acid soils with lime (calcium carbonate) or dolomitic lime (calcium magnesium carbonate, $CaMg(CO_3)2$) neutralizes the acidity and replenishes calcium and magnesium. Occasionally, magnesium deficiency is seen in orchards growing in sandy, neutral soils. Fertilization with Epsom salts (magnesium sulfate) corrects this deficiency.

Sulfur

Sulfur occurs in the solution as sulfate ion (SO_4^{2-}). There is a small tendency for sulfate to be adsorbed by soil particles in certain acid soils, but generally it is mobile. Sulfur deficiency is not a problem in California orchards. Many commonly used fertilizers contain sulfur (as ammonium sulfate, superphosphate, mixed fertilizers). Considerable sulfur is also delivered to the soil in rainfall. Sources of this atmospheric sulfur include stack emissions from industrial plants, automobile exhaust gases, and volcanoes.

Iron and manganese

Iron and manganese availability are largely controlled by the solubilities of their oxides. These elements also undergo transformations called oxidation-reduction reactions. For iron, the transformation from the ferrous (Fe^{2+}) to the ferric (Fe^{3+}) form is the oxidation reaction; the reverse is reduction. In well-aerated soils, the oxidized ferric form, which is of low solubility, is dominant. The manganous (Mn^{2+}) ion oxidizes after precipitating, yielding manganese dioxide.

Solubilities of both ferric oxide and manganese dioxide are pH dependent: the solubilities decrease rapidly as soil pH increases. Most soils contain enough iron and manganese for plant growth. Deficiencies occur because these elements are unavailable to plants at a higher soil pH; thus, their availability can be increased by lowering soil pH. The easiest way to do this is to amend the soil with sulfur, which is then converted to sulfuric acid by microorganisms.

Depletion of soil oxygen (most often by waterlogging) causes reducing conditions in soil. When this happens, ferric oxide and manganese dioxide can be reduced to produce high concentrations of ferrous and manganous ions. Excesses of these ions are toxic to plant roots.

Zinc and copper

Specific adsorption processes probably dominate the availability of zinc and copper. Their amounts in soils are much less than those of iron and manganese, but like those elements they are very strongly adsorbed at a higher pH, less so at a lower pH. A soil pH of 6.5 is more or less the dividing point—at a higher pH, availability of copper and zinc may be severely limited. The amounts of these elements present and the extent of surface that can specifically adsorb them also affect their availability in a given soil. When deficiencies occur, it is often difficult to correct them by adding copper or zinc materials because of their immobility in soil. As with iron and manganese, acidifying the soil may help.

Boron

Boron occurs in the soil solution as neutral boric acid (H_3BO_3) and, to some extent, as the borate anion ($H_2BO_3^-$) in soils on the basic side. Boron is held to some extent on soil particles, but the mechanism involved is not clearly understood. The concentration range of boron that produces good plant growth is narrow. If the concentration in soil solution is below this range, deficiencies occur; if it is above this range, toxicity is a problem. Boron toxicity has not been observed in California olive orchards.

Molybdenum and chlorine

The amount of molybdenum required by plants is very small. It occurs in soil as the molybdate ion (MoO_4^{2-}). In acid soils, it is removed from soil solution by specific adsorption, like phosphate. Molybdenum deficiency is unknown in California orchards. Olive's need for chlorine also is very small. It occurs in the soil as the highly mobile chloride ion (Cl^-). Chlorine is added to the atmosphere in the salt spray from ocean waves. Enough chlorine to meet plant needs reaches the soils in annual rainfall. Chlorine toxicity is a more serious problem than deficiency, but as the chloride ion is quite mobile, it is easily leached out of the root profile with adequate water.

10.1 Mature olive pruned to ideal of five upright scaffolding branches

10.2 Old olive pruned back for rejuvenation

13.1 Potassium deficiency as reflected in leaf appearance

13.2 Boron deficiency as reflected in misshapen, "monkey-faced" fruit

14.1 Overabundant fruit set evident in "on" year of alternate bearing cycle

14.2 Results of trial postbloom application of naphthaleneacetic acid (NAA) to thin fruit; unsprayed sample on left

15.1 Example of herbicide strip treatment in tree rows

17.1 Adult female black scales, showing "H" on back

17.2 Black scale eggs, cast egg shells, and first-instar nymphs, or "crawlers," underneath the adult scale

A

17.3 Sexually immature adult black scales in "rubber" stage, showing very distinct "H" on back

17.4 Sooty mold growing on the honeydew secreted by black scale

17.5 Dense, closed canopies favoring development and survival of black scale

17.6 Open, well pruned canopy promoting higher temperatures (thus increasing the mortality of black scale)

17.7 Young female olive scale

17.8 Purple spotting on fruit caused by second-generation infestation of olive scale

17.9 The parasite *Aphytis maculicornis* developing from egg stage to pupa beneath olive scale

17.10 Cluster of oleander scale on olive leaves and twigs

17.11 Adult latania scale, showing characteristic ridges (the exuvium) forming to a point on one side

17.12 Latania scale damage on fruit

17.13 Cluster of greedy scale (on acacia branch)

B

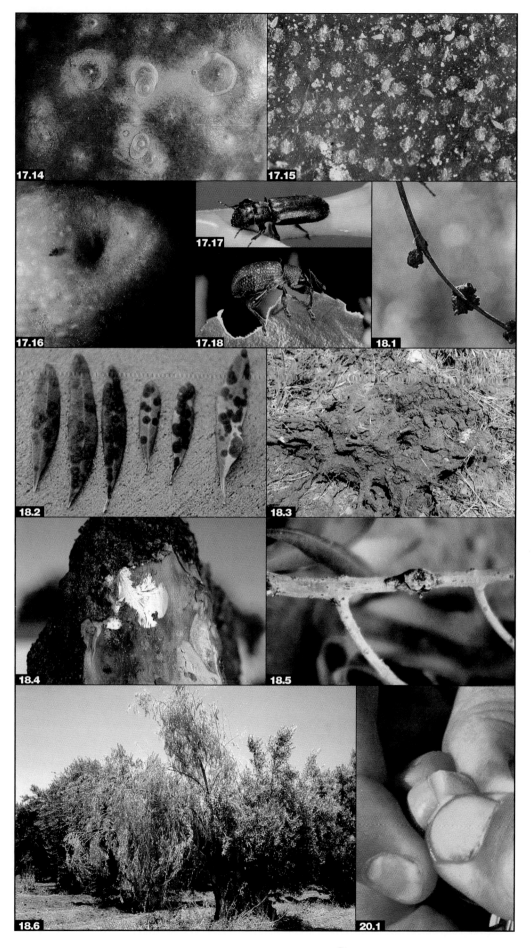

17.14 Surface of olive fruit infested with California red scale

17.15 Olive mites and "silvering" damage on leaf undersurface

17.16 Fruit scarred and dimpled by western flower thrips

17.17 Adult branch and twig borer

17.18 Adult black vine weevil (on euonymus leaf)

18.1 Olive knots on twig

18.2 Lesions of olive leaf spot (peacock spot, bird's eye spot) on leaves

18.3 Evidence of phytophthora root rot in heavy, saturated soil

18.4 "Plaques" of fungal mycelium between bark and wood, due to armillaria root rot

18.5 Typical elliptical diplodia canker on twig

18.6 Verticillium wilt in 80-year-old orchard

20.1 Characteristic white juice of mature olive fruit

C

20.2 Quality (as judged by color) of Manzanillo fruit at harvest time

20.3 Quality (as judged by color) of Mission fruit at harvest time

20.4 Quality (as judged by color) of Ascolano fruit at harvest time

20.5 Quality (as judged by color) of Sevillano fruit at harvest time

20.6 Relative olive color change, from green to black, throughout the harvest season

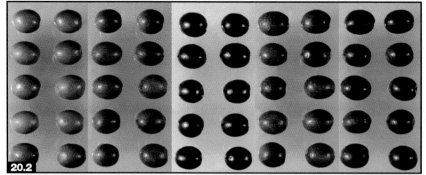

20.2

MANZANILLO	MANZANILLO	MANZANILLO	MANZANILLO	MANZANILLO
Early season	Early season	Early season	Late season	Late season
Pale green to straw	Light red blush	Black	Light red blush	Dark red
Optimal	Acceptable	Unacceptable	Borderline	Unacceptable

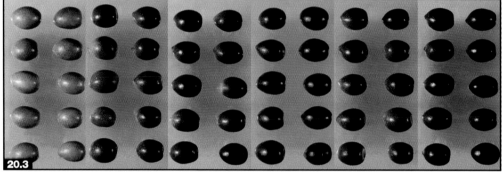

20.3

MISSION	MISSION	MISSION	MISSION	MISSION	MISSION
Early season	Early season	Early season	Early season	Late season	Late season
Pale green to straw	Light pink to dark red	Dark purplish	Black	Light pink to dark red	Dark purplish
Optimal	Acceptable	Borderline	Unacceptable	Borderline	Unacceptable

20.4

ASCOLANO	ASCOLANO	ASCOLANO	ASCOLANO
Early season	Late season	Early season	Late Season
Pale green to straw	Pale green to straw	Slight blush	Slight Blush
Optimal	Optimal	Unacceptable	Unacceptable

20.5

SEVILLANO	SEVILLANO	SEVILLANO	SEVILLANO
Early season	Early season	Late season	Late season
Slight blush stem end	Half or more dark red	Straw	Slight blush stem end
Acceptable	Unacceptable	Optimal	Unacceptable

20.6

D

13

DIAGNOSING AND CORRECTING NUTRIENT PROBLEMS

MARK FREEMAN, KIYOTO URIU, AND HUDSON T. HARTMANN

Diagnosing a nutrient problem involves two basic techniques: careful observations and asking the right questions. Three general diagnostic categories of observations can be used: (1) visual symptoms (on the tree and in the environment), (2) tissue analysis, and (3) soil and water analyses. All three categories have their strengths and weaknesses; the category to be used depends on the problem to be solved.

VISUAL SYMPTOMS

One approach in diagnosing nutritional problems is to look for abnormal symptoms in foliage or growth. Visual diagnosis is the quickest way to identify deficiencies or toxicities. On the other hand, a tree may have already suffered in growth or yield by the time visible symptoms appear. Also, it takes experience to recognize the symptoms of all the deficiencies and toxicities. Borderline deficiencies or deficiencies of more than one element may be hard to diagnose; moreover, problems other than nutrition may cause similar symptoms. Thus, diagnosis from visual analysis alone may be difficult. However, visual symptoms can be an invaluable aid when interpreting soil or leaf analyses. And there is no substitute for observing the field situation on a regular basis.

Successful diagnosis depends on observing symptoms continually. One deficiency may cause symptoms early in the season, whereas another may show up later. One must be aware of environmental factors and their effects on trees. For example, abnormal fruit and foliage can reflect poor irrigation practices or a soil problem. Too much water can induce an iron deficiency; too little can adversely affect growth, leaf color, and yield. Olive trees survive for centuries on poor, rocky hillside soils in the Mediterranean region, but to achieve economic crops under California conditions, management of soil and water must be optimal for good nutrient availability. Fertilizer may not correct a prob-

lem if the real limiting factor is not found and dealt with—in fact, adding too much nitrogen causes heavy crops of small fruit and leads to alternate bearing.

In California, field observations have recorded deficiencies for only three nutrients: nitrogen, potassium, and boron (see indications—in percentages or parts per million—in table 13.1). Potassium and boron deficiencies are illustrated in color plates 13.1 and 13.2. Other nutrient deficiencies have been noted in the field outside California, however, and could occur here in the future. Table 13.2 describes the visual symptoms of olive trees grown experimentally without six different nutrients.

PLANT OR TISSUE ANALYSIS

Tissue analysis involves testing plant parts for actual concentrations of nutrients. Olive leaves are sampled and chemically analyzed for mineral deficiencies and toxicities. A leaf's mineral composition depends on its maturity, current climatic conditions, the availability of mineral elements in the soil, cultural practices, and other factors. The mineral nutrient level in the leaf integrates all these factors and thus reflects the nutrient status of the tree.

Optimal concentrations of different elements, the critical levels below which deficiency occurs, and the levels above which toxicity can develop have all been established for olive (table 13.1). Results of leaf analyses can be compared with these standard values to determine current nutrient status and future fertilization needs. Leaf analysis can help confirm a visual symptom or identify a potential problem that is not yet showing visual symptoms. Results from leaf analysis are best used in a long-term fertilizer program or to prevent a developing problem.

Seasonal use and level of mineral elements

In interpreting leaf analyses, knowledge of the seasonal use pattern of mineral nutrients is helpful. At bud break in the

Table 13.1. Critical nutrient levels (dry-weight basis) in July olive leaf samples.

Element	Nutrient concentration	Occurrence of deficiency in California	Visual deficiency symptoms in field
Nitrogen (N)		Uncommon (due to routine fertilizer applications)	Small, yellowish leaves; shoot growth of less than 8 in.
Deficient below	1.4%		
Adequate at	1.5–2.0%		
Phosphorus (P)		Unknown	
Adequate at	0.1–0.3%		
Potassium (K)		Occasional (Butte County)	Light green leaves, tip burn; dead areas in tree
Deficient below	0.4%		
Adequate over	0.8%		
Calcium (Ca)		Unknown	
Adequate over	1.0%		
Magnesium (Mg)		Unknown	
Adequate over	0.1%		
Sodium (Na)		Unknown	
Excessive over	0.2%		
Chlorine (Cl)		Unknown	
Excessive over	0.5%		
Boron (B)		Occasional (Butte County)	Misshapen fruit — "monkey face"; short, branched growth; limb dieback; rough bark; small leaves with tip dieback
Deficient below	14 ppm		
Adequate at	19–150 ppm		
Excessive over	185 ppm		
Copper (Cu)		Unknown	
Adequate over	4 ppm		
Manganese (Mn)		Unknown	
Adequate over	20 ppm		
Zinc (Zn)		Unknown	Visual deficiency not observed in field, even at very low levels of zinc
Deficient below	Unknown		

spring, when root activity is minimal, many elements that have been stored in the stem and roots become available to the rapidly developing buds. Much of the nitrogen, phosphorus, zinc, and perhaps potassium initially required comes from the stored supply (for instance, in older leaves) and is redistributed to the growing points. Stored nitrogen then becomes important. The more nitrogen stored, presumably, the more available for fruit set. As root activity increases in spring, nitrogen, as well as other mineral elements, is increasingly taken up from the soil. Most of the phosphorus and zinc that accumulates in the leaves has done so by the time the leaves reach full size. This means that these elements, like nitrogen, must initially come from storage tissues. On the other hand, calcium, essential in cell wall formation, is not redistributed but comes directly from the soil by root absorption. Thus, it accumulates in the leaves as the season progresses and reaches its highest level at summer's end. Magnesium,

boron, chloride, and sodium also all tend to increase, but to a much lesser extent than calcium. If boron and chloride exist in toxic amounts in the soil, they continue to increase rapidly during the season and reach their highest levels in the leaves at the end of the summer, as does calcium.

A single leaf analysis does not show the use pattern of mineral nutrients. Concentrations are determined for those elements and expressed as percentages (or parts per million) in a given weight of dried leaves. The concentration of mineral nutrients in leaves changes as the leaves first emerge and then expand to full size. For many elements the smallest change in concentration occurs from late June through early August. Olive leaf samples should be taken then, because critical levels have been established for that time period. The optimal concentration level (or range of values) is known, along with critical levels below which fertilizer should be added.

Table 13.2. Visual symptoms of mineral nutrient deficiencies in Manzanillo olives under experimental conditions.*

Nutrient withheld	Trees	Shoots	Leaves	Fruit
Zinc	Normal.	Normal.	Young leaves slightly lighter green than older leaves.	Fruit appearance and amount are about the same as trees receiving full nutrients, but they mature earlier.
Nitrogen	Small tree size; sparse foliage; heavy defoliation; light crop.	Individual shoots less than 8 in.; very little shoot growth; dieback of shoots.	Small, yellow leaves; heavy defoliation.	Few fruit but normal in appearance.
Calcium	Small tree size, similar to trees without nitrogen.	Terminal dieback, with subsequent lateral growth (early growth); many lateral shoots; finally whole shoot dies.	Terminal leaves curl, turning yellow; then tips become necrotic and leaves drop. Basal leaves on shoot normal in size and color. Terminal leaves small; some basal leaves turn yellow.	Fruit production was sparse but fruits normal in size, with no chlorosis evident.
Magnesium	Same size as normal; good crop.	Long shoot growth; no terminal bud necrosis.	Basal leaves on shoot become chlorotic, turn yellow, and drop; terminal leaves normal in size and color. Just before leaves drop, banding appears: tips yellow, midsection somewhat green, basal area yellow.	Fruit has a yellowish, chlorotic appearance, but not to the extent found in iron-deficient trees.
Potassium	Tree has weeping willow appearance (not upright); branches may lack strength. Total tree size normal.	Short internode (space between leaves on shoot) very characteristic. Short shoot growth. Total node number may be normal.	Pale, yellowish green similar to start of nitrogen deficiency. Slightly smaller-than-normal leaf size; no excess defoliation. Basal leaves show more yellowing than terminal leaves.	Color normal.
Iron	Tree size normal. Moderate crop associated with trees having slight leaf symptoms.	Shoot growth normal.	Small leaf size. Whitish, bleached-out appearance in all leaves, especially terminal ones. Finally, terminal leaves drop, with shoot dieback. Symptoms more severe each year. No leaf necrosis. Midrib and veins more green than interveinal areas. Network of small green veins appears.	Fruits develop a pronounced chlorotic, yellow appearance.

*Nutrient deficiencies were induced over 5 years by withholding a specific mineral element from a nutrient solution added to trees potted in sand. This does not mean that an element is not essential if the tree exhibited normal growth. Studies done by Kiyoto Uriu and Hudson T. Hartmann, UC Davis.

There are exceptions. For example, sampling to compare the nutrient status of a healthy tree with an unhealthy one can be done at any time, provided one is aware of how the concentration of each element changes during the season (fig. 13.1). Concentrations of nitrogen, phosphorus, zinc, and potassium start off high early in the season, decline rapidly, reach a fairly steady state after mid-June, and then (except for potassium) drop in the fall. Concentrations of magnesium, manganese, boron, and chloride do not start high, but remain fairly constant or increase slightly during the season. Boron and chloride levels, however, increase steadily if excessive amounts are in the soil. Calcium levels start low and increase noticeably.

Sampling procedure

Remove mature leaves from the middle of nonbearing, current season shoots from late June through early August. A sample of 80 to 100 leaves is sufficient. Ideally, a sample should be taken from a uniform block of trees. This means that trees of different varieties or different ages, trees on different soil types, and trees under different irrigation systems should be sampled separately.

Samples should consist of a few leaves from as many trees as possible, selected at random from throughout the orchard. Avoid any leaves that are abnormal in appearance or leaves from abnormal trees, unless that is the problem to be solved. In that instance, the abnormal leaves or trees should become a separate sample.

Interpretive guides

The correlations between leaf analysis levels and the expression of deficiency symptoms are shown in table 13.1. Leaf

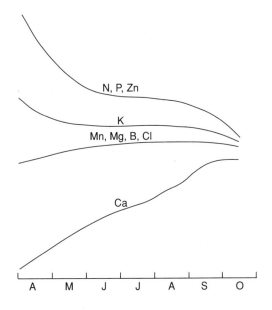

Figure 13.1. Generalized shapes of concentration curves of mineral nutrients in the leaf during the growing season. Curves show trends, not actual values.

analysis is very useful for all the nutrient elements when their levels can be interpreted together with visual symptoms.

SOIL ANALYSIS

Tree crops, including olives, have extensive root systems that occupy a larger volume of soil than do those of most annual crops. Soil can vary widely within such a large area; thus, it may be difficult to take a soil sample that accurately represents the root area and nutrient levels that the roots extract. Furthermore, reliable soil standards for mineral nutrient levels are lacking for fruit trees. Therefore it is difficult to diagnose most nutrient imbalances from soil analysis alone. Soil analysis, however, does help in diagnosing toxicities from excessive concentrations of such elements as sodium, chlorine, and boron. Soil analysis also is useful in locating where these elements occur in excess, which helps in planning corrective treatments.

Sampling procedure

In general, soil samples can be taken for analysis at any time, as soil nutrient levels are relatively stable. Some precautions should be taken for a few of them. Under prolonged wet soil conditions, for example, nitrogen is subject to loss from denitrification. Thus, nitrogen levels in the soil after a lengthy rainy season can be lower than before. In many soils nitrate, chloride, and to some extent boron can be leached by winter rains and irrigation. A new source of water could change the soluble salt content of the top foot of soil fairly quickly. Interpretations of soil analyses for mineral elements need to account for these changes.

The sampling procedure depends on the problem and area involved. Is one tree affected, or many? Is there a pattern in the orchard—down the row, by soil type, in the low areas? Because olive tree roots occupy a large volume of soil and soil variability can be high, 3 to 10 spots in a site should be sampled. Because soils differ in composition at different depths, it is desirable to keep the surface 6- to 12-inch (15- to 30-cm) sample separate, as well as each subsequent foot downward. Samples taken from different distances from the trunk may be combined, but different soil depths should be kept separate. Samples should represent the effective rooting zone (where most of the roots are located). Situations will differ; some soils may need to be sampled down to 4 or 5 feet (1.2 to 1.5 m) if roots are that deep.

A soil auger can be used to obtain samples. Usually, a quart (1L) of soil per sample is enough material for a laboratory.

Interpretive guide for soil and water testing

The following three tables and discussion present general guidelines for fruit trees, indicating where specific information applies to olive. Table 13.3 lists laboratory analyses

Table 13.3. Laboratory analyses used to evaluate soil and water quality for olive production.

Laboratory analyses	Reporting symbol	Reporting units	Soil	Water	Equivalent* weight (mg/meq)
Saturation percentage	SP	%	X	—†	—†
pH	pH	—†	X	X	—†
Electrical conductivity	EC_e	dS/m‡	X	—†	—†
	EC_w	dS/m‡	—†	X	—†
Calcium	Ca^{+2}	meq/L	X	X	20
Magnesium	Mg^{+2}	meq/L	X	X	12.2
Sodium	Na^+	meq/L	X	X	23
Carbonate	CO_3^{-2}	meq/L	—†	X	30
Bicarbonate	HCO_3^-	meq/L	—†	X	61
Chloride	Cl^-	meq/L	X	X	35.4
Sulfate	SO_4^{-2}	meq/L	—†	X	48
Boron	B	ppm§	X	X	—†
Adjusted sodium	adj.SAR_e	meq/L	X	—†	—†
adsorption ratio	adj.SAR_w	meq/L	—†	X	—†
Exchangeable sodium	ESP	%	X	—†	—†
Lime requirement	LR	tons/acre	X	—†	—†
Gypsum requirement	GR	tons/acre	X	—†	—†
Lime	$CaCO_3$	%	X	—†	—†

*ppm = meq/L × equivalent weight (mg/meq).
†Not applicable.
‡dS/m = mmho/cm.
§ppm = mg/L.

commonly used for water and soil quality determinations. Some laboratories may use different units, which are also listed. The following text discusses specific laboratory tests and how to interpret and use their results to solve problems. For further explanation of terms and concepts used in this section, refer to chapter 12.

Saturation percentage

Saturation percentage (SP) is a measure of soil texture from which one can estimate water-holding capacity and cation exchange capacity (table 13.4). It is expressed as the grams of water required to saturate 100 grams of soil.

One-half of the SP is approximately the amount of water that soil holds at field capacity (the moisture content of soil in the field 2 or 3 days after a thorough wetting). One-fourth of the SP approximates the permanent wilting point (PWP) of the soil (the soil moisture percentage at which plants wilt and fail to recover turgidity). The available water is the difference between field capacity and PWP; it represents the amount of water the soil can store that is available to the plant. The SP can indicate changes in soil texture with depth; for instance, a large variation of SP with depth indicates a stratified layer or layers within the soil profile. Layering can be visually confirmed with an auger or backhoe. Soil layers may be places where nutrient availability varies or where poor drainage may cause a toxicity.

Soil reaction or pH

The soil pH is indicated on a scale reading from 0 (acid) to 14 (basic, or alkaline). Within the pH range of 6.5 to 7.5,

Table 13.4. Relationship of saturation percentage (SP) to soil texture, cation exchange capacity (CEC), and available water.

SP	Soil texture	CEC k(meq/100 g)	Available water (in./ft)
< 20	sandy or loamy sand	2–7	<0.6
20–35	sandy loam	7–15	0.6–1.0
35–50	loam or silt loam	15–30	1.0–1.5
50–65	clay loam	30–40	1.5–2.0
65+	clay or peat	>40	>2.0

nutrient availability should not be limiting (see table 13.5). Soil pH has not been observed to limit California olive production. Most California soils whose pH exceeds 8.5 have either verticillium wilt or very poor soil structure due to high sodium levels. If pH problems are suspected, soil samples should be taken at 6-inch (15-cm) increments, or where soil layers change, to locate problem areas.

Lime is commonly used to correct acidic soils (below pH 6). The lime required to raise the pH varies with soil texture; it can be estimated by laboratory analysis. The approximate amount of finely ground limestone needed to raise the pH of a 7-inch (18-cm) layer of soil by one pH unit from an initial pH of 4.5 or 5.5 ranges from about ½ ton per acre for sandy soil to about 2 tons for a clay loam. Usually, only the surface foot of soil becomes acidic enough to require liming. Research on tree crops under drip irrigation has documented very low soil pH levels, but their effect on tree growth or yield is not known.

Cation exchange capacity

The cation exchange capacity (CEC), measured in the laboratory, indicates the ability of the soil to hold cations against leaching. Many soil cations are mineral nutrients that olive roots absorb from the soil solution. Soils with a higher CEC are typically more fertile, as they have a greater "storage capacity" for mineral nutrients. Usually expressed in milliequivalents per 100 grams of soil, the CEC of a soil depends directly on its clay and humus content. Fertilizer should be applied more frequently and in smaller amounts to soils with lower CEC.

Salinity

Salinity is a measure of all the soluble salts present in a soil solution. Salinity damage to trees may be due to specific ions or the total salt content. Specific ions that constitute salinity such as sodium, chloride, and boron can cause damage by themselves if levels are high enough. Damage to

olives from high soil levels of these three elements has not been observed in California. High total soil salinity reduces the amount of soil water available to roots.

Soil salinity is measured in a laboratory from a saturated extract of soil. The soil water is analyzed for water-soluble compounds formed by three cations—sodium, calcium, and magnesium—with the anions chloride, carbonate and bicarbonate, sulfate, borate, and nitrate nitrogen. Total salinity is measured in terms of electrical conductivity, as salts in solution conduct electricity. As salt concentration increases, so does the conductivity.

A saline soil is defined as having an electrical conductivity of the soil-saturated extract (EC_e) of more than 4 decisiemens per meter (dS/m) at 25°C. In water, 1 millimho per centimeter (mmho/cm) of electrical conductance corresponds to about 640 ppm of salt (1700 lb of salt per acre-foot). Olive trees can experience a 10 percent yield loss if soil salinity reaches 4 dS/m (table 13.6). Yields and tree growth are substantially reduced as EC_e increases to 8 dS/m. Most of the saline soils used for agriculture in California have grown annual crops that carry verticillium wilt. Olives would not grow well there for that reason.

Orchards are usually located on well-drained soils and are irrigated with good-quality water; thus, winter rainfall is adequate to leach out annual salt accumulations. However, when soil analysis indicates excessive salt accumulation in the root zone, additional irrigation in spring or fall or heavier irrigations are necessary. For proper leaching, irrigation distribution and uniformity may need to be improved by changing the field level or the system design, or soil structure may need to be modified by ripping an impervious hardpan or mixing a stratified soil. Drainage lines may be required when a high water table is present. Soil amendments, such as gypsum, are generally not necessary to correct saline conditions unless excess sodium is present.

The amount of extra water needed (above evapotranspiration)

Table 13.5. Irrigation water quality guidelines for olives.

Irrigation problem	Degree of problem		
	None	Increasing	Severe
Salinity (affects crop water availability) EC_W (mmho/cm)	<2	2.5–4	>5.5
Permeability (affects soil infiltration rate) EC_W (mmho/cm)			
if SAR = 0–3	>0.7	0.7–0.2	<0.2
if SAR = 3–6	>1.2	1.2–0.3	<0.3
Specific ion toxicity Boron (ppm or mg/L)	1–2		

to leach soluble salts from the soil profile depends primarily on the initial soil salinity, the technique used for applying water, and the soil type. This extra water needed, or leaching fraction, can be calculated for specific orchards; a general rule of thumb is that 1 foot of extra water reduces the salinity of the upper foot of soil by 70 to 80 percent. Most olive orchards in California are not located on saline soils, however.

Salinity can be a problem in the irrigation water. Saline water values are listed in table 13.5. The best remedy to saline water is to find another water source; otherwise, the soil salinity will increase.

SODIC (ALKALI) SOILS

Soils that contain excessive amounts of exchangeable sodium in proportion to calcium and magnesium are termed sodic or alkali soils. Sodic soils are characterized by a dispersion of soil particles that reduces a soil's permeability to water and air. By definition, a sodic soil has an exchangeable sodium percentage (ESP) of greater than 15. That means that 15 percent of the soil's cation exchange capacity is associated with sodium and the remainder with calcium, magnesium, and other cations. Olive trees are affected when ESP levels reach 20 to 40 (table 13.6). Most California soils with this problem that are used in agriculture are planted to annual crops.

When a sodic condition is identified, a laboratory analysis can be performed to determine the gypsum requirement. This indicates the amount of calcium required to displace sodium. After an amendment is applied, the displaced sodium must be leached below the root zone. Organic materials such as manure, cover crops, or crop residues may help improve the soil structure for leaching. In established orchards, heavy irrigation during the dormant period to leach sodium minimizes damage to tree roots from lack of aeration.

Some soils are both sodic and saline. The problem is best dealt with by leaching out the soluble salts such as chloride and borate with irrigation water. It will be necessary to apply a source of calcium to displace sodium from the exchange sites on the soil particles and then leach the sodium displaced into the soil solution.

Sodium hazard in water

There is a close association between the composition and concentration of soil salts and those in irrigation water. When used for irrigation, water with high sodium relative to calcium and magnesium is likely to result in a sodic soil. Water's sodium hazard is indicated by the sodium adsorption ratio (SAR). The adjusted SAR (adj.SAR), also commonly used, includes the hazard that carbonate and bicarbonate add to that of sodium by precipitating some of the exchangeable calcium and magnesium.

Water with a low adj.SAR dissolves lime from the soil and increases exchangeable calcium. Water with a high adj.SAR precipitates calcium, decreasing exchangeable calcium, and can lead to sodic conditions. Irrigation water should have adj.SAR values of below 6; when values exceed 9, problems can occur. Gypsum should be used to replace precipitated calcium when using water with a high adj.SAR. It is normally applied to the bottom of furrows or to that part of the soil surface wetted by irrigation water. Two to four tons of gypsum per acre every year or so is a common rate. Soil incorporation is not necessary.

Boron and chloride toxicity

Leaf analysis is the most useful tool for diagnosing salt injury (such as excessive sodium, chloride, or boron levels) in trees. Soil and water analysis may also be needed to determine the source of salts or whether a problem exists before planting.

Table 13.6. Soil salinity guidelines for olives.

Soil problem	Degree of problem		
	Starting	Increasing	Severe
Salinity (affects crop water availability)			
EC_e (dS/m)	4	5	8
Olive yield decrease	10%	25%	50%
Sodium (ESP) Soil permeability and plant toxicity problems stunt growth		20–40	
Boron (ppm)	2		
pH			
Range for most crops: 5.5–8.4			
Optimal range for most crops: 6.5–7.5			
Known harmful in olive: >8.5			

Problems with chloride toxicity often occur in orchards planted on saline soils not fully reclaimed or when high-chloride irrigation water is used. Because it is much more difficult to correct a salinity problem after the orchard is planted, the soil should be completely reclaimed before planting. Chloride toxicity sometimes occurs after fertilizers containing chloride (in the form of potassium chloride, KCl) are applied to poorly drained soils. The problem can easily be corrected by leaching excess chloride from the root zone, but severe damage can occur.

Boron (borate) toxicity problems typically occur on the west side of the Central Valley, where native soils are derived from marine sedimentary material. Both soil and groundwater can be high in boron. The boron levels that affect olives are listed in tables 13.5 and 13.6. Boron-affected soils are reclaimed only slowly, with great difficulty and much water.

Slow infiltration—low salt water

Irrigating with water that is very pure may slow infiltration into sandy loam or fine-textured soils. This can occur when water contains less than 250 parts per million (ppm) of soluble salts ($EC_w < 0.4$ mmho/cm). It is a common problem on the east side of the San Joaquin Valley, where the canal water originates as snowmelt from the Sierra Nevada and contains only 50 to 100 ppm total salts. With certain soils water infiltration can drop to less than 0.1 inch (2.5 mm) per hour, making it difficult to satisfy the orchard's water requirements.

Gypsum applications can help correct this water penetration problem. The infiltration rate can be increased as much as fivefold by applying 1 to 2 tons of gypsum per acre in late spring or early summer, just before peak evapotranspiration. Gypsum is generally beneficial for three to five irrigations. Infiltration can also be improved by mixing gypsum directly into the irrigation water with specially designed equipment. Also, manure applied to the wetted areas can add soluble salts to the irrigation water.

REVIEW OF SPECIFIC MINERAL NUTRIENTS

Nitrogen

Nitrogen deficiency symptoms are not common in California olive orchards now, because nitrogen fertilizer is applied routinely. The visual symptoms and critical leaf nutrient levels are listed in table 13.1. Soil levels of nitrogen do not correlate well with leaf levels or deficiency symptoms. One researcher found that leaf nitrogen content in olives is fairly constant through the fall and winter but drops when vegetative growth starts in the spring. The leaf levels reach a low point in August and then increase. Nitrate nitrogen (NO_3–N) in groundwater can contribute significant amounts of nitrogen toward a fruit tree's nutritional requirement and should be considered when planning a fertilizer program. Nitrogen levels in irrigation water often range from 5 to 50 pounds of nitrogen per acre-foot. Laboratories report nitrate concentrations in parts per million (ppm, or mg/L). This is converted to pounds of nitrogen per acre-foot by multiplying by 2.7.

Nitrogen levels directly affect fruit set, yield, and shoot growth. Many field trials in California (and around the world) have shown yield and growth increases in olive from nitrogen fertilization. In experiments in the 1950s, orchards on a foothill soil (with naturally low fertility) and a fertile valley clay soil received nitrogen fertilizer. The foothill orchard showed increased fruit set, yields, and leaf size and also delayed fruit maturity. (Some trees on low-fertility soils given heavy nitrogen applications have large crops of small fruit and tend to bear alternately.) The valley orchard showed no immediate response in fruit set or yields. Nitrogen was withheld for 3 years, and leaf nitrogen levels were still adequate. Both nitrogen deficiencies and excesses, then, can hurt yields. Nitrogen levels in leaves differed in "on" and "off" crop years, but stayed above critical levels.

Liquid fertilizers, due to their lower cost, are the most common form of nitrogen used to correct deficiency. Many nitrogen fertilizers are available (table 13.7) and can be easily applied if nitrogen levels are approaching a deficiency. However, fertilizing should not be viewed as a specific step used to change nitrogen levels. Even with no added nitrogen, the level in the trees tends to remain adequate, and in deeper soils with less leaching and rainwater, soil nitrogen levels remain fairly stable.

First, leaf analysis should be used routinely to monitor annual changes in the nitrogen levels and help plan the future fertilizer program. Nitrogen must be absorbed into the tree before March 1 to influence the crop set in the spring. Some growers apply nitrogen during winter; however, research with deciduous tree crops indicates that root uptake of nitrogen is slowest in winter. If urea is applied at the soil surface at that time, the ammonia it yields can be lost to the atmosphere. To avoid this loss, it is best to either incorporate urea or to irrigate it into the soil shortly after application.

The goal of using nitrogen fertilizer is maintaining leaf nitrogen levels of 1.5 to 1.8 percent. This results in adequate (but not excessive) shoot growth of 8 to 20 inches per year with optimal bloom and fruit set. It is common practice to apply 1 to 2 pounds of actual nitrogen per tree per year. In the southern San Joaquin Valley, some soils carry over adequate nitrogen, so fertilizer is only applied in alternate years. Manures can supply nitrogen (see table 13.7),

Table 13.7. Nitrogen-containing fertilizers.

Fertilizer	Formulation	Nitrogen (%)	Water-soluble potash K_2O (%)	Equivalent acidity or basicity (in lb $CaCO_3$) Acid	Base
Urea ammonium nitrate solution*	$NH_4NO_3 \cdot CO(NH_2)_2$	32		57	
Calcium ammonium nitrate solution*	$Ca(NO_2)_2 \cdot NH_4NO_3$	17		9	
Ammonium nitrate	NH_4NO_3	33.5–34		62	
Ammonium sulfate[†]	$(NH_4)_2SO_4$	21		110	
Anhydrous ammonia	NH_3	82		148	
Aqua ammonia	NH_4OH	20		36	
Calcium nitrate	$Ca(NO_3)_2$	15.5			20
Manure (dry)[‡]		(10–30 lb/ton)			
Urea	$CO(NH_2)_2$	45–46		71	
Potassium chloride	KCl		60–62	neutral	
Potassium sulfate	K_2SO_4		50–53	neutral	

*Often injected through low-volume irrigation systems.
†Will acidify the soil when used exclusively over a period of time.
‡Also improves soil structure but can contain high levels of salt.
SOURCE: California Fertilizer Association, *Western Fertilizer Handbook.* (7th ed.), Danville, IL:Interstate, pp. 100–101.

though it is not as quickly available as the synthetic sources. Midseason foliar urea applications have not been shown to increase fruit size.

Potassium

Low levels of potassium in olive leaves and deficiency symptoms have been observed only in foothill orchards of Butte County. Soil levels of potassium do not correlate well with leaf nutrient levels or deficiency symptoms (table 13.1). However, potassium levels below the critical leaf level can occur long before leaf symptoms appear. Therefore, it may be important to monitor this nutrient in orchards planted in sandy soils or where much land leveling has been done, because deciduous trees exhibit potassium deficiency symptoms under those conditions. Researchers worldwide find a correlation between high yields and high levels of leaf potassium. Potassium levels in leaves differ during "on" versus "off" crop years, but are always above the critical level.

Potassium deficiency can be corrected more easily in sandy than in clay or silty soils. Applications of potassium sulfate (K_2SO_4), made during early winter in doses of 10 to 20 pounds per tree, should be effective for several years. On heavier soils, it should be shanked in below the surface within the drip line. On lighter soils, it can be shanked in or surface applied. Potassium chloride (KCl) is less expensive, but because of the chloride it should not be used on sandy or sandy loam soils. Possibly, foliar sprays of potassium nitrate could be used, or potassium compounds applied along with irrigation. Guidelines for amounts are not available.

Boron

Like potassium, boron deficiency in olive has only been observed in Butte County. There, the boron content in leaves correlates very well with deficiency symptoms (table 13.1). Trees showing severe deficiency symptoms have 7 to 13 ppm boron in the leaves. Leaves having 19 or greater ppm of boron do not show symptoms. Olive is much less sensitive to high boron levels than most other commercial tree crops grown in California. Olive in high-boron soil apparently does not accumulate much boron in the leaves.

Boron deficiency can be corrected with soil applications of borax at rates of 1 pound per tree. That treatment should be sufficient for many years. Foliar sprays of Solubor may aid the current season's growth, but the effect does not last as long as the soil application.

Phosphorus

Phosphorus deficiency, or a growth response to the addition of phosphorus fertilizer, has not been observed in California olive orchards. A survey of California olive trees found low phosphorus leaf levels to be associated with poor soil drainage. Actual phosphorus deficiency has been reported in Europe.

Magnesium and calcium

Deficiencies of magnesium and calcium have not been observed in California olive orchards. The deficiency symptoms noted in table 13.2 were induced under sand culture. Under sand culture, calcium and magnesium leaf levels increase or decrease together. In olive leaves, low potassium levels are associated with high calcium levels, and vice versa.

Zinc, copper, iron, manganese, and molybdenum

Little information is available about the requirement of olives for these five minor nutrients. Zinc deficiency has not been observed in California olives, and it has not been induced when zinc has been withheld from olive trees grown in sand culture (see table 13.2). Nonetheless, zinc deficiency is common on many other California tree crops.

Sodium and chloride (excess or toxicity)

Compared with most tree crops, olives are very tolerant of saline and sodic soils, which usually contain high levels of sodium and chloride (table 13.6). In many tree crops, these two mineral toxicities cause leaf tip burn that progresses up the leaf. Leaf analysis is used to identify which nutrient is involved. Sodium or chloride toxicity has not been observed in California olive orchards except where potassium chloride was misused.

14

THE OLIVE TREE AND FRUIT

OLIVE FRUIT THINNING

JOSEPH MARANTO AND WILLIAM H. KRUEGER

Olives normally produce crops in alternate-year cycles. In the "on" year, trees produce abundant flowers and set more fruit than can reach profitable size (color plate 14.1). Because fruit are a strong carbohydrate sink, the large fruit population means that little shoot growth develops. Olives develop fruit buds on the previous year's shoots, so repressed shoot growth diminishes the crop potential for the next year, the "off" year. Prices received by growers are often lower during "on" years, when large tonnages of small, low-value fruit occur, and are higher in "off" years, when fruit are in short supply. Alternate-year bearing is therefore disruptive to orderly marketing and grower profitability.

Maturity is late when trees carry large populations of fruit, and losses from early fall frost are more likely. Harvest costs are greater because of the larger volume of fruit to be picked, much of which is of little commercial value.

The ideal crop load varies with cultivar and with tree age and vigor. Fruit density of approximately six fruit per foot of shoot appears optimal to size the fruit while ensuring moderate shoot growth for next year's crop. Fruit thinning is the most effective method of controlling crop size. Its basis is fruit removal, which allows the remaining fruit to grow larger and shoot growth to proceed.

HAND THINNING AND PRUNING

Fruit thinning by hand is effective, but it is not practical, due to high labor costs. However, for a few trees in the home garden, it may be an acceptable alternative. For maximum benefit, thinning should be completed 3 weeks after full bloom. Later thinning contributes less to larger fruit size and does not reduce alternate bearing. The following points should be observed by the home producer when hand thinning.

• Wear heavy rubber gloves or tape the fingers. With both hands, strip fruit from twigs with heavy fruit set. Take care not to damage or remove leaves.

• Thin only those twigs from which at least five or six olives can be removed at one pull. Try to leave an average of six olives per foot of twig. Unless enough fruit are removed from the entire tree, thinning is not useful.

Pruning, the traditional method for moderating alternate bearing, is especially useful if thinning is not practiced. Pruning to thin out fruitwood reduces the crop, thereby promoting shoot growth to bear fruit the following year. Pruning is an expensive cultural practice, however, and is not as effective in moderating alternate bearing as thinning because it removes both fruit and leaves and does not raise the leaf-to-fruit ratio, which is necessary to increase fruit size. Pruning removes entire shoots, and fruit set may still be excessive on remaining shoots.

To control the crop and affect alternate bearing, prune in spring or early summer of the "on" year when bloom and crop load can be seen. Pruning should be detailed, removing branches with heavy bloom or crop and leaving lighter-cropped branches. Pruning for crop control should be done more heavily in "on" years and lightly, if at all, in "off" years.

CHEMICAL THINNING

Postbloom application of naphthaleneacetic acid (NAA), the common method of thinning in commercial crops, effectively regulates crop size to improve fruit quality and return bloom for the next year (see color plate 14.2). Chemical thinning is the most useful tool available to olive growers for crop control. NAA effectively thins Manzanillo, Ascolano, and Mission but not Sevillano. It is the only material registered and recommended for thinning olives.

Chemical thinning has been used by growers for 25 years; however, widespread adoption has been slow, probably because thinning must be done before the crop load can be accurately judged, and the possibility of overthinning or poor thinning always exists.

When to apply NAA

Timing NAA sprays is critical to obtaining desired results. Olives are successfully thinned with NAA between 12 and 18 days after full bloom. Earlier thinning results in excessive fruit removal, and spraying too late causes unsatisfactory fruit removal. In the Central Valley, olive bloom usually occurs during the second or third week of May, and thinning is done between the last week in May and the first week in June. Two methods can be used to time NAA applications: (1) counting the days after full bloom and (2) judging by the size of the fruit.

Days after full bloom. To use this method, the date of full bloom must be established for each orchard and NAA applied 12 to 18 days later. The NAA concentration of the spray solution is raised by 10 parts per million (ppm) per day after full bloom; that is, if NAA is applied 15 days after full bloom, use 150 ppm in a dilute spray, 300 to 400 gallons of water per acre. Only one application can be made per year. For best results, full tree coverage is essential. Normally, fruit drop occurs between full bloom and 6 weeks later. Competition within and between inflorescences for nutrients during the early fruit growth stage appears to be mainly responsible for fruit abscission.

The full-bloom date is determined as follows. As flowers begin to open, a contrast in color between the green leaves and white flowers can be observed in the orchard from a distance. At full bloom, the tree appears to be white: shoots contain 80 to 90 percent open, fresh flowers, with their bright yellow anthers exposed. The remaining flowers include those not yet open and those whose petals have dropped. Pollen release is abundant at full bloom, and it should be possible to collect pollen by shaking bloom into one's hand. Tapping a limb in full bloom should release a puff of yellow pollen and falling petals. These reference points indicate the date to designate as the full-bloom point. Three to four days after full bloom, as the flowers age, the tree develops a yellow-bronze cast.

Fruit size. NAA is applied when young olives are ⅛ to ³⁄₁₆ inch (3 to 5 mm) wide. Measurements should be made at different locations in the orchard and on the trees' north and south sides. This size generally is reached 12 to 18 days after full bloom, but that peak can be delayed by cool temperatures and advanced by warmth. When this method of timing NAA sprays is used, a spray concentration of 150 ppm NAA is recommended.

The number of days after full bloom and the fruit size methods are best used together, as weather affects fruit size development and may make the "full bloom" method inaccurate. Almost daily inspection of the orchard during and after bloom is the best way to determine spray timing.

How chemical thinning works

NAA is absorbed by the leaves and fruit and is translocated to the abscission zone of the fruit stems. Within the first 2 weeks after application, an abscission zone is formed, causing some fruit to drop. NAA enhances the naturally occurring June drop of young olives.

High air temperatures above 100°F (38°C) during and soon after NAA application cause greater fruit thinning than is desirable, especially on stressed trees.

Chemical thinning precautions

Chemical thinning is a sensitive operation, and occasional under- and overthinning occurs with NAA sprays. The response to NAA is influenced by environmental conditions and tree stress during and after the thinning application. Although growers cannot have complete control over environmental conditions, understanding the role of stress minimizes risk. Tree stress tends to accelerate the thinning response, so growers should avoid stressing trees during and after thinning. Only well-watered, healthy trees should be chemically thinned. Young shoot tips may be injured by NAA, but there is no lasting effect.

Should chemical thinning be annual?

Ideally, fruit thinning should be done every year. Annual thinning should remove enough fruit so that shoot growth and return bloom are maximized.

Often the fruit thinning response is not uniform from season to season. Many times enough fruit are removed to increase the fruit's size and value, but not enough to eliminate poor tree bloom and alternate bearing. Sometimes poor or excessive fruit removal occurs, and inversely proportionate bloom occurs next season. In those circumstances thinners may or may not be necessary.

Complete fruit removal

Occasionally it is desirable to remove the entire crop, as when olives are used in ornamental plantings and ripe olives would otherwise drop and create a nuisance. For complete crop removal, a solution of 200 ppm NAA is applied in two sprays, the first 2 to 3 days before full bloom and the second a week later. If the bloom period is short, a second spray may not be necessary. A single spray may be applied at full bloom, but often crop removal is incomplete. For large trees, a power sprayer is required; 10 to 15 gallons of solution per tree give good coverage.

Note that spraying with NAA when the temperature exceeds 100°F (38°C) may injure new growth and may also cause some leaf drop. Tender ornamentals nearby should be covered, and drift should be avoided by spraying only under calm conditions and by using moderate pressure to apply a coarse spray.

15

PEST MANAGEMENT

WEED MANAGEMENT IN OLIVES

CLYDE L. ELMORE

Weed management in an olive orchard should reduce the negative impact of weeds on trees, prevent buildup of hard-to-control weeds, and reduce plant debris around the base of the tree for ease of harvest. Permanent cover crops or sod cultures may be desirable in an olive orchard, particularly on sloping ground. Their root systems, especially those of annual grasses, can penetrate plow pans and improve water percolation in many soils. Plants can provide a firmer soil surface than cultivated soil for better year-round access in the orchard. They also help reduce soil erosion and soil surface sealing.

If not properly managed, weeds can create problems in an orchard. They can compete with trees for water, nutrients, and sunlight, especially in newly planted orchards and shallow soils. Young orchards infested with weeds may take longer to come into production. Weeds are less competitive with trees when the orchard is 3 or 4 years old and has become established, but many weeds—especially such perennials as bermudagrass, dallisgrass, and johnsongrass—can still lower orchard productivity.

Weedy orchards may enhance the activities of other pests by providing shelter or overwintering sites for insects, rodents, and snakes. When winter vegetation such as wild oat, mustard, or radish dries, these weeds can also create a fire hazard.

GROWTH HABITS

Plants found in an olive orchard can be grouped as annuals, biennials, or perennials. Annuals germinate, grow, flower, and produce seeds in one season. The cycle may be completed in several months at any time of the year, depending on the weed species, but most annuals are classified generally as winter or summer annuals. In California's mild climate, certain annuals may behave as biennials or short-lived perennials; an example is cheeseweed (little mallow). Biennials, such as bristly oxtongue, complete their life cycle in two growing seasons, producing vegetative parts in the

first season and flowers and seeds in the second. Perennials live 3 years or longer, often dying back in winter and regrowing in spring from underground parts.

MANAGEMENT GUIDELINES

Management differs for each orchard and depends upon the weed species present, the irrigation method used, and the amount of control desirable. For example, winter annuals are least troublesome because in that season there is usually enough moisture to support both trees and weeds. These can be managed in spring by cultivating, mowing, or using herbicides. Summer annuals, biennials, and perennials, however, require stricter management to reduce their competition. Perennial weeds should be removed outright to reduce competition with trees, especially for water use.

Site preparation

Weed management starts before the orchard is planted. Control annuals with discing or with postemergent herbicides. Control perennials before trees are planted, to reduce their competition in the new orchard and to avoid potential injury to young trees from herbicides. Control bermudagrass, dallisgrass, and johnsongrass with repeated discing and drying during summer (if the site is not irrigated); seedlings can be controlled after the orchard is planted. Field bindweed can also be reduced using this method, but it is best controlled by irrigating to produce a vigorous plant and then treating with glyphosate or 2,4-D, followed in 10 days by discing and drying the soil. Field bindweed is not completely controlled with any method, but seedlings can be controlled with cultivation or contact herbicides.

Management in new orchards

Weed management is most critical in new plantings. Weeds around young trees compete for nutrients, water, and light. Weedy orchards may take a year or two longer than weed-free ones to become economically productive.

91

Some growers prefer to manage weeds without herbicides for the first year or two after planting. This usually requires hand-weeding around trees several times during spring and summer as well as cultivating between tree rows. It may be feasible to use polypropylene or polyester mulches around young trees to reduce annual weeds and hand-weeding. It is preferable to cultivate before weeds have gone to seed. Many of these orchards are converted to nontillage after the second year, controlling weeds by mowing or with herbicides.

To control weed seedlings, preemergence herbicides can be applied after planting trees, either in a square or circle around each tree (at least 4 to 6 feet across) or as a strip treatment down the tree row. Weeds between rows can be controlled by mowing or discing. Mowing may be required four to eight times during spring and summer, whenever weeds are 6 to 8 inches high . Discing is frequently required after each irrigation. It is well to keep in mind that discing wet soil can create hardpan, which reduces water penetration.

Management in established orchards

In established orchards, there are many options for weed control. These include the methods discussed for new orchards plus other herbicides that can be safely used on established trees. Options include (1) discing or mowing between rows, with hand-weeding around trees; (2) discing or mowing, with a basal square or circle of herbicide around each tree; (3) strip treatment down the tree row (color plate 15.1); or (4) total reliance on herbicides. Total herbicide treatment can mean either applying preemergence materials across the whole orchard floor with follow-up postemergence spot treatments or chemical mowing (using low rates of postemergence herbicides three to four times during the year to suppress vegetation) between rows with strip treatments down the row.

Certain disadvantages are associated with a total reliance on herbicides. No single herbicide controls all annuals; combinations of herbicides, sequential treatments, or preemergence plus postemergence combinations are needed to maintain a weed-free soil. In orchards on slopes, soil erosion can be a problem if soils are bare. In some soils, compaction and development of a thin, silty surface layer, which impedes water infiltration, may become a problem. Light, shallow cultivating or scratching the soil surface may remedy this.

Preemergence herbicides do not control established perennials. These weeds spread rapidly in the absence of annuals; this is particularly true of bermudagrass, field bindweed, and nutsedge. Some preemergence materials control only certain groups of plants, leaving the tolerant ones to propagate. For example, simazine controls broadleaves but not crabgrass or witchgrass, and oryzalin controls grasses but leaves groundsel, sow thistle, fleabane, and other weeds (table 15.1).

USE OF HERBICIDES

Herbicides are used to control specific weeds that are or can become a problem in an orchard. They may be used in strips, around the bases of trees, or on the entire orchard floor. Select herbicides and time their applications with care.

Preemergence herbicides

Preemergence herbicides are sprayed on the soil to control germinating weed seeds. They must be moved by water (rainfall or irrigation) into the surface 1 to 3 inches of soil, where weed seeds germinate. One of the herbicides, napropamide, must be incorporated within a week; others may stay on the soil surface and wait for rain to incorporate them. Some cannot be mechanically incorporated or weed control is reduced. The label states how soon the herbicide must be incorporated after application or whether incorporation is necessary. Examples of preemergence herbicides are diuron (Karmex), simazine (Princep), oryzalin (Surflan), oxyfluorfen (Goal), and napropamide (Devrinol).

Oxyfluorfen also has foliar activity on certain young, established weeds, and so is selectively more effective against young annual broadleaves and cheeseweed than against annual grasses and perennials. None of the other listed preemergence herbicides controls existing weeds.

Preemergence herbicides can provide control from several weeks up to a year, depending on yearly rainfall, the solubility of the material, soil properties, frequency and method of irrigation, weed species, and dosage applied. Prolonged moist conditions around low-volume emitters promote the breakdown and leaching of herbicides. Splitting a preemergence treatment into two applications (with the same total dosage) can prolong control, particularly in areas with heavy rainfall, in orchards on sandy soils, in orchards treated in early fall, or in orchards with a heavy growth of summer annuals. Treatment can be split by using one-half to two-thirds the amount of chemical in fall and the remainder the following spring.

A given dosage of preemergence herbicide is more phytotoxic in sandy soils or soils low in organic matter than in soils high in clay or organic matter. Herbicides also leach from the surface of sandy soils more readily than from clay soils, which allows weeds to grow above the herbicide. In orchards on sandy soils, split treatments give longer residual control and are safer for trees.

Because preemergence herbicides can persist in soil from a few months to a year or more, their use should be discontinued 1 to 2 years before removing an orchard. Where a tree must be replaced, backfill untreated soil around the roots of the new tree.

Table 15.1. Weed susceptibility to herbicides.

Weed species	Preemergence herbicides					Postemergence herbicides				
	diuron (Karmex)	napropamide (Devrinol)	oryzalin (Surflan)	oxyfluorfen (Goal)	simazine (Princep)	glyphosate (Roundup)	oxyfluorfen (Goal)	paraquat (Gramoxone)	sethoxydim (Poast)	fluazifop (Fusilade 2000)
Annual grasses										
Annual bluegrass	C	C	C	P	C	C	N	C	N	N
Barnyardgrass	C	C	C	N	P	C	N	P	C	C
Sprangletop	C	C	C	N	P	C	N	P	C	C
Jungle rice	C	C	C	N	P	C	N	P	C	C
Lovegrass	C	C	C	N	P	C	N	C	C	C
Crabgrass	C	C	C	N	P	C	N	C	C	C
Wild barley	C	C	C	N	P	C	N	C	C	C
Wild oats	P	C	P	N	P	C	N	C	C	C
Witchgrass	P	C	C	N	P	C	N	P	C	C
Annual broadleaves										
Brass buttons	C	C	P	C	C	C	C	C	N	N
Cheeseweed	P	P	P	C	P	P	C	P	N	N
Chickweed	C	C	C	P	C	C	P	C	N	N
Cudweed	C	C	P	C	C	C	P	P	N	N
Filaree	C	C	C	C	C	P	P	P	N	P
Fleabane	C	P	N	P	C	C	P	P	N	N
Groundsel	N	P	P	C	C	C	C	C	N	N
Henbit	C	N	C	C	C	C	C	C	N	N
Horseweed	C	P	N	P	C	C	N	N	N	N
Knotweed	C	C	C	C	C	C	P	P	N	N
Pigweed	C	C	C	C	C	C	C	C	N	N
Prickly lettuce	C	C	P	C	C	C	P	C	N	N
Puncturevine	P	P	C	C	P	C	P	C	N	N
Purslane	C	C	C	C	C	C	P	C	N	N
Shepherdspurse	C	P	P	C	C	C	C	C	N	N
Sowthistle	C	C	P	C	C	C	C	C	N	N
Speedwell	P	C	C	C	C	C	—	C	N	N
Spurge	C	N	P	C	P	C	P	C	N	N
Star thistle	C	P	N	C	C	C	C	C	N	N
Perennial grasses										
Bermudagrass	N	N	N	N	N	C	N	N	P	P
Johnsongrass	N	N	N	N	N	C	N	N	P	P
Dallisgrass	N	N	N	N	N	C	N	N	P	P
Perennial broadleaves										
Blackberry	N	N	N	N	N	C	N	N	N	N
Curly dock	N	N	N	N	N	P	N	N	N	N
Dandelion	N	N	N	N	N	P	N	N	N	N
Field bindweed	N	N	P (seed)	N	N	P	N	N	N	N
Nutsedge	N	P	N	N	N	P	N	N	N	N

C = controlled; P = partially controlled; N = not controlled.

*Nonbearing only.

Postemergence herbicides

Postemergence (foliar-applied) herbicides are used on young established weeds or (in the case of glyphosate) on rapidly growing flowering perennials.

The two types of postemergence herbicides differ in their mode of action. Contact herbicides kill only the parts of the plant that are actually sprayed; good coverage and wetting are therefore essential. An example is paraquat. A single spray kills susceptible annuals; retreatment is necessary if regenerating perennials are present or if annuals reestablish themselves from seed. A contact herbicide is most effective when applied to seedlings or young weeds, because it is easier to get good coverage and less material is needed.

Translocated herbicides (glyphosate, fluazifop, and sethoxydim) do not require thorough coverage, because the material is transported from the sprayed part to the rest of the plant, including its roots and rhizomes. They are therefore more effective in killing perennials than are contact herbicides. Because different agents work in different ways and on different weeds, herbicide combinations are sometimes desirable, such as oxyfluorfen plus glyphosate for a broad spectrum of annual grass and broadleaf weeds.

Herbicides and application rates are chosen according to the weed species present, soil type, irrigation method, and age of trees. No single material registered for olives controls all weed species; in many instances, combinations or sequential applications of different herbicides provide better control than one compound alone. It is crucial to follow all label precautions carefully.

Table 15.1 is a list of currently registered herbicides in olive orchards. For an update contact your University of California Farm Advisor, Pest Control Advisor, or County Agricultural Commissioner.

COVER CROPS

In some orchards, cover crops are being planted rather than using resident (weed) vegetation. These cover crops can be winter annual, fall-seeded cereal crops such as wheat, oat, cereal rye, or barley, or winter annual Blando bromegrass, Zorro fescue, or subterranean clovers. These are seeded into a prepared seedbed in late September through mid-November as winter cover. The latter plants reseed themselves if mowed in January or early February and then allowed to regrow and seed in April and May. Mowing after the seeds mature ensures seeds for the next season. These cover crops should be combined with a strip treatment down the tree row so that the plants do not grow around the trunks. For more information on cover crops, consult UC Division of Agriculture and Natural Resources Publication 21471, *Covercrops for California Agriculture*.

MONITORING

Monitoring is essential for selecting a weed management program, especially for selecting the proper herbicides. It should be done three times a year, in November, February, and May.

In November, after the first rains have begun, look for winter annual seedlings in the tree row to determine whether the preemergence treatment was adequate. Also, check the ground cover for perennial seedlings. In February, the full spectrum of winter weeds should be present. If a few species were not controlled by the postemergence treatment, note them for possible changes in next season's treatment. This happens when the preemergence herbicides used in the tree row are ineffective against the dominant weeds in the orchard. If weed growth is heavy, consider a postemergence treatment. By May or June, summer annuals have germinated. Monitoring at this time reveals whether the preemergence treatment was effective against summer annuals and what species of perennials are present.

When tillage is the main method of weed control, monitoring before tilling allows the grower to treat perennials with the correct translocated herbicide so that the equipment will not spread the underground parts of the plant.

Records are essential in weed management. Weed survey information collected over several years is valuable in identifying changes in weed populations and in planning weed control programs. A sample format for recording weed data is given in figure 15.1. Perennials deserve special attention; it is useful to sketch a map of the orchard and mark where they occur. These records should be part of the permanent orchard history.

Weed records can be stored on computer using a form similar to figure 15.1 to record the species found in individual orchards, the herbicides used, and whether or not control was achieved. Species can also be recorded by year or, for perennials, by location in the orchard. Knowing which weeds are present and their susceptibility to registered herbicides enables the grower to select effective herbicides for the following season. A scale from 1 to 5 can indicate the level of infestation: 1 = very few weeds; 2 = light infestation; 3 = moderate; 4 = heavy; 5 = very heavy. Weed species in treated and untreated areas, as in strip weed control, should be recorded separately.

ORCHARD LOCATION _____   CONTROL METHODS _____

CONTROL DATES _____

COMMENTS _____

	NOV _____		FEB _____		MAY _____	
	% of total weeds		% of total weeds		% of total weeds	
	treated	untreated	treated	untreated	treated	untreated
ANNUAL GRASSES						
annual bluegrass						
barnyardgrass						
crabgrass						
sprangletop						
wild barley						
wild oat						
_____						
_____						
_____						
ANNUAL BROADLEAVES						
cheeseweed (mallow)						
clovers						
groundsel						
filaree						
fiddleneck						
knotweed						
lambsquarters						
mustards						
pigweeds						
puncturevine						
purslane						
_____						
_____						
_____						
_____						
PERENNIALS						
bermudagrass						
dallisgrass						
johnsongrass						
curly dock						
field bindweed						
nutsedge						
_____						

Figure 15.1. Sample form for recording weed species.

95

16

PEST MANAGEMENT

NEMATODES OF OLIVE

M. V. MCKENRY

Nematodes are microscopic, true roundworms; plant-parasitic nematodes are those that derive their nutrition directly from plants. Of concern to olive growers are nematodes that feed on olive roots and increase to high populations. The three nematode genera of particular concern, based on experiences with other crops, are: root lesion nematodes (*Pratylenchus* spp.), citrus nematode (*Tylenchulus semipenetrans*), and root knot nematodes (*Meloidogyne* spp.). Almost no nematode pathogenicity data are available for olives.

Growers should expect variability in nematode damage and incidence, depending on soil texture and seedling or rootstock variability. Unthrifty trees in localized areas of the orchard are among the most obvious symptoms of nematode damage. To determine whether nematodes are present, a soil sample must be taken for nematode analysis.

ROOT LESION NEMATODES

Several species of root lesion nematode can occur in olive orchards. A species that commonly damages olive is *Pratylenchus vulnus*. Infected trees may be characterized by poor growth and dieback of small branches. Young trees planted in infested soil frequently fail to make satisfactory growth and are dwarfed or stunted. Larger roots of infected trees have symptoms of longitudinal cracking of the root cortex, and the area underneath these cracks is darkened and necrotic. Necrotic lesions are typical of root lesion nematode attack, and nematodes are normally present in root tissue immediately adjacent to the dead area. Nematodes also attack and frequently kill small feeder roots.

This nematode is more prevalent in warmer regions of California, but it may be found in northern olive-producing regions. Its favored hosts are most woody perennials including walnut, almond, stone fruit, citrus, and grape.

Other root lesion nematodes can occur in olive orchards. *Pratylenchus penetrans* has a very wide host range, including roots of woody perennials, clovers, and grasses. It is most common in the northern United States and the northern half of California, but it also occurs south of the California delta region, especially at higher elevations, on crops such as cherry and apple. Generally speaking, northern California olive growers deal primarily with *P. penetrans,* whereas growers in the southern San Joaquin olive district deal primarily with *P. vulnus.* The extent of damage by these two species is unknown.

A third root lesion nematode, *Pratylenchus neglectus,* occurs in orchards on roots of grasses and weeds but probably does not feed on olive roots.

It is important to know which of the three species of root lesion nematode is present when attempting to diagnose a field problem as nematode related.

Citrus nematode

The citrus nematode, *Tylenchulus semipenetrans,* attacks olive roots in localities where trees are adjacent to or planted on land previously occupied by citrus or grape. Its effects on olive tree growth and production are incompletely known, but infected root systems are characterized by considerable disintegration of small feeder roots.

Host species for the citrus nematode include citrus, grape, persimmon, and olive. It can be prevalent in a wide variety of soils including those with 50 percent or more clay particles. It occurs in both southern and northern California olive orchards.

An impressive characteristic of this nematode is its ability to develop to very high population levels. Infested olive orchards have responded to nematicide treatment with increased flower development and subsequent yield. Trees infected with citrus nematode can be expected to lack vigor and have a thin foliar canopy.

Root knot nematodes

Root knot nematodes, *Meloidogyne* spp., sometimes attack olive, causing the formation of galls or knots on the roots;

heavily infected roots cannot carry on normal functions. Infected trees may have reduced vigor and show symptoms of decline.

There are no methods to control root knot nematode infestations on roots of established olive trees. Preplant soil fumigation and use of nematode-free planting stock are the best methods to avoid future nematode injury to young trees. A clonal olive rootstock, Allegra, developed and patented by the University of California, shows high resistance to *Meloidogyne* spp. in laboratory tests. All own-rooted olive cultivars grown in California are susceptible to attack.

This nematode is very common in California and is especially problematic in sandy soils south of the delta region. It is not known which or how many species of *Meloidogyne* infest olive.

SOIL SAMPLES

Soil samples taken from the planting site for examination in a professional laboratory help show which nematode species are present. This information is needed to decide on soil fumigation and possible rootstock selection. High nematode populations are common in soils previously planted to woody crops, and preplant fumigation is recommended.

Some laboratories collect samples, or growers may collect their own (consult a county Farm Advisor for the nearest commercial analytical laboratory). Growers who collect samples should make sure the laboratory will process them as soon as they are received. Processing usually takes several days to 2 weeks. Laboratory reports should be kept as part of the permanent orchard history.

To collect samples, visually divide the orchard site into sampling blocks that represent differences in soil texture, drainage patterns, or cropping history. Take a separate sample for each block so that problems unique to that block can be identified. A sample for nematode analysis consists of about 1 quart of soil taken from a mixture of 5 to 20 subsamples. Nematodes are harder to detect when soil has been fallow or recently planted to nonhost crops such as cereal grains. In these situations, taking as many as 20 subsamples from several locations increases the likelihood of detecting any nematode present.

In an established orchard, separate subsamples should be taken for comparison from around trees that show symptoms and around adjacent, healthy-looking trees. Subsamples should include feeder roots when possible and should be taken in frequently wetted zones at the edge of the tree canopy.

Sampling can be done at any time of the year. It is best to sample when the soil is moist, preferably within a week after rainfall or irrigation. Take samples to a depth of 36 inches (90 cm) using a soil auger, a sampling tube (Viehmeyer, Oak Field, or the like), or a shovel. The amount of root collected with a sampling tube is much smaller than with a soil auger.

For each sample, collect subsamples at various depths from 6 inches to 3 feet (15 cm to 1 m). Thoroughly mix the subsamples in a bucket, and take 1 quart as a representative sample for the sampling block. Pour the soil and roots into a durable plastic bag or other moisture-proof container, seal it tightly, and keep it in the shade. Label each bag with your name and address, location of the orchard, sample block, soil type or texture, cropping history (crops for last several years, current crop, anticipated crop), and notable symptoms; this information is critical for a meaningful analysis. More than one sample from each sampling block improves the precision of the estimate and the information on nematode distribution in the field, but processing samples is costly.

Any diagnosis of nematode samples must distinguish the three root lesion nematode species. Send or deliver the samples to the laboratory as soon as possible, using a cardboard box insulated with newspaper or, in summer, a styrofoam ice chest. If any delay occurs, keep the samples in a cool place, at 40° to 55°F (4° to 12°C).

Damage thresholds have not been established for the different nematode pest species in olive. If soil samples indicate that root knot, root lesion, or citrus nematodes are present and the land to be planted has a crop history of woody perennials or broadleaf plants, the soil needs to be fumigated before planting.

SOIL FUMIGATION

Nematode pests cannot be eradicated completely over a large area. Their populations gradually rebuild over time, and no postplant eradication treatments are available. Preplant soil fumigation allows an orchard time to develop a healthy root system that can ultimately withstand or tolerate future nematode damage.

The quantity of chemical applied is only one factor that determines effectiveness of soil fumigation. Equally important is soil moisture content, soil texture, and soil temperature. Each of these must be considered before fumigation.

Old roots larger than ½ inch (1.25 cm) in diameter and tree stumps harbor nematodes and protect them from fumigation; these must be removed before fumigating.

The best time to fumigate is usually from September until mid-November, but this can vary regionally and with soil texture; greater flexibility is possible in the sandiest soils. Less-than-optimal soil conditions result in a faster return or repopulation by nematodes and can reduce the extent of protection from 6 years to 6 months.

APPLICATION

The top several inches of soil are the most difficult to fumigate, because the fumigant volatizes most readily through this porous part of the soil. Cultipacking, rolling, or dragging the soil immediately after fumigation can provide an adequate seal for fumigants. Some soil fumigants are toxic to plants and, depending on the dosage, must be applied several weeks or months before trees are planted. The pesticide label indicates any potential phytotoxicity of the soil fumigant to the tree. Follow the specific directions on the fumigant label for placement and depth of chisels. Observe the suggested waiting period before replanting.

17

PEST MANAGEMENT

INSECT PESTS OF OLIVE

W. W. BARNETT, C. KENNETT, K. DAANE, AND JOHN E. DIBBLE

Pest insect populations in California olive groves are generally kept below levels of economic damage by their natural enemies as well as by proper pruning and irrigation techniques. If treatments are needed, selective programs can achieve control without disturbing the biological control of other potential pests. Monitoring pest and beneficial species lets the grower avoid unnecessary pesticide treatments that could lead to outbreaks of secondary pests.

BLACK SCALE

Black scale, *Saissetia oleae,* is the major pest of olive in California. During the 1950s and 1960s, it was generally controlled by chemical treatments used against the then-more-serious pest, olive scale (*Parlatoria oleae*). When the biological control of olive scale became fully effective during the late 1960s, annual treatments for it were discontinued, and black scale reemerged as the predominant olive pest.

Thought to be native to South Africa, black scale is distributed throughout California. Hosts include almond, apple, apricot, mountain ash, fig, fuchsia, grape, grapefruit, orange, plum, prune, and rose. It only causes serious economic losses to olive and citrus, however.

Description. Adult females are brown when young, becoming black as they age. Mature females are 2 to 5 mm long and nearly hemispherical, with a plainly visible elevated ridge resembling the letter "H" on the back (color plate 17.1). Black scale eggs, which are laid under the female scale covering, are 0.2 to 0.3 mm long and light colored when first laid, becoming pinkish after 2 or 3 days. A few days before hatching they assume a reddish orange color, and nymphal eyespots become visible within the eggs.

First-instar nymphs, called crawlers, are 0.3 to 0.4 mm long and pale yellow to light brown, with dark eyes (color plate 17.2). After emerging from the eggs, crawlers search for a suitable feeding site for up to 7 days before they insert their mouthparts and begin to feed. The nymphs double in size

before their first molt, which occurs 3 to 8 weeks after hatching (depending on temperature and host plant conditions). Second-instar nymphs are from 1 to 1.3 mm long and 0.3 to 0.7 mm wide when the "H" becomes distinct. After the second molt, nymphs migrate from the leaves to twigs.

The next stage, the sexually immature adult, is drastically different in appearance. It is dark, ashy gray to brown and 1.5 to 2 mm long, with its legs hidden beneath it. The "H" becomes quite distinct. This stage is referred to as the rubber stage (color plate 17.3). Chemical control efforts against this and the adult stage are much less effective than those used on earlier instars. Adult scale size varies greatly from 2 to 5 mm long, 1 to 4 mm wide, and up to 2.5 mm high. During this ovipositional or last stage, the scale darkens, turning completely black. The mean number of eggs per female is about 1,200, but 4,000 have been reported.

Male and female black scales are identical until after the first molt. During the early second instar, male scales, which are rarely seen in California, elongate and eyes become visible near the front of the body. This stage lasts about 4 weeks, and the male scale molts again to a prepupal stage that lasts from 5 to 8 days in warm weather. Prepupae are dark brown with visible antennae and legs. The male molts again to the pupal stage, which has a red head with black eyes. Antennae, legs, and wing pads become conspicuous and minute. Light yellow, winged males emerge in 10 to 15 days.

Field biology. Black scale typically overwinters as second- and third-instar nymphs and completes its development in early spring. Egg deposition begins in April or May, and crawler emergence is completed by late July in most areas. Crawlers may settle on shoots or leaves and, in rare cases, on fruit. In fall, some scales migrate to more favorable overwintering sites on twigs, where they spend the winter. Black scale normally has one generation per year in most interior areas of California, but where the development pattern is influenced by cultural practices and weather, a second or partial second generation may occur.

Damage. Black scale inserts its mouthparts into the plant to extract carbohydrates. This can reduce fruitbud formation, cause leaf drop and twig dieback, and reduce the next year's crop. Indirect damage also occurs. The sticky honeydew secreted by developing scales may make harvesting difficult and reduce fruit quality. Sooty mold, which develops on the honeydew, shades leaves and thus depresses photosynthesis and respiration (color plate 17.4).

Monitoring. The first indication of black scale is usually the presence of honeydew on the leaves. Twenty-five to 30 trees should be checked during April and October, the two periods of greatest honeydew accumulation, to get an idea of population levels.

Sample for adult scales in May, focusing on two to three areas in each block, particularly those that have had scale problems in the past. First select 10 trees in each area. Count the number of adults on the terminal 18 inches (45 cm) of 10 branches on each tree; be sure to include the lower, inner, and outer sections of the tree. Sum the numbers of black scale in each 10-branch sample and divide by the number of branches sampled to determine the infestation level. Infestations fall into one of four levels: light (0 to fewer than 1 per branch sampled), moderate (1 to 4), heavy (4 to 10), and severe (more than 10).

Light infestations typically do not require treatment in open-canopy orchards. Closed-canopy orchards should be pruned and an application of a dormant oil considered.

Moderate infestations may occur following a cool summer or within a closed orchard canopy. This level of scale typically does not cause damage; however, it presents the potential for substantial damage and economic losses the next year. In trees with open canopies, the scale population should decrease or remain stable, depending on summer temperatures. After a mild summer, a dormant oil should be applied. Orchards with closed canopies should be pruned, and use of a dormant oil or chemical treatment applied.

Heavy infestations can cause economic damage; if left untreated, the next generation will inflict substantial crop loss. Heavy infestations are rare in open canopies, but orchards with closed canopies must be pruned, chemically treated, or both.

Severe infestations occur in closed-canopy orchards in which treatment of moderate or heavy scale infestations is delayed. Economic loss can be extensive. The orchard should be pruned (removing severely damaged branches) and treated with an insecticide.

Cultural controls. Environmental conditions have a marked effect on black scale populations. Hot, dry weather commonly kills crawlers and reduces scale populations. Cool, humid conditions encourage black scale; such conditions are favored in low, bushy trees with dense, continuous canopies (color plate 17.5). Regular pruning exposes the scale and maximizes mortality. An open or airy canopy (color plate 17.6) is the best cultural control. When not pruned, the canopy closes and summer heat is moderated. In this protected environment, black scale can survive hot summers and develop outbreak populations in mild summers. Different irrigation and ground cover management practices affect the orchard's environment and may affect the severity of black scale outbreaks.

Natural control. About 70 species of natural enemies have been introduced to control black scale in California. Less than 15 have become established, and none has proved to be an effective control agent on olive. In the Central Valley, dominant biological control agents are wasp parasites: *Metaphycus helvolus, M. bartletti,* and *Scutellista cyanea.*

Unfortunately, climatic factors that limit scale also limit these control agents, because the parasites cannot develop and survive without suitable black scale host stages during certain periods of the year. Although insect predators such as green lacewings (*Chrysoperla* sp.), convergent ladybird beetles (*Hippodamia convergens*), and a black ladybird beetle (*Hyperaspis* sp.) feed on young black scale, only the last species has been found to significantly lower black scale populations.

Chemical control. Dormant oil treatments are effective against light to moderate infestations, especially when used in conjunction with pruning to open the orchard canopy. However, for heavy or severe infestations, chemical pesticides should be applied. Pesticides are most effective against first- and second-instar nymphs found in summer. Postharvest treatments are also possible, until the rubber stage is reached the following spring.

OLIVE SCALE

The olive scale, *Parlatoria oleae* (Colvée), is widely distributed throughout the world's olive-growing regions, including the Mediterranean and Middle East, England, India, Russia, Turkey, and Argentina. In the United States, it was first noted on privet in Maryland in 1924, although it may have been in Phoenix, Arizona as early as the 1890s. In California, it was first found near Fresno in 1934. It spread rapidly through olive-growing areas in the Central Valley and was south of the Tehachapi Mountains by 1961. It became a major pest of olives and required annual pesticide treatments to protect fruit from economic damage. Today it ranges from San Diego to the northern Sacramento Valley.

Olive scale is a pest of many other crops and has been collected from over 200 plant species, but it is now controlled by natural enemies and chemical treatments are rarely needed.

Description. The adult female cover is almost circular, about 1.25 mm across, slightly convex, and light to dark gray, with a brownish nipple or exuvium. The young female's body under the scale cover ranges from a reddish to a deep purple as eggs develop (color plate 17.7). The male's covering is elongate, white, and flat; the exuvium is to one end rather than central, and is brownish or blackish.

Field biology. There are two generations a year. The scale overwinters as an immature mated third-instar female.

Overwintered females mature and begin laying eggs in late April and early May. Crawlers begin emerging in May and wander for a short time, then settle on twigs, leaves, and, in some cases, newly set fruit. Emergence of first-generation crawlers is usually completed by late June or early July. Both male and female scales are produced during the first, or summer, generation. Females from this generation mature during July and lay eggs during August and early September. These eggs of the fall generation hatch, and crawlers settle on leaves and twigs, but to a much greater extent on fruit. Males complete their development in fall and fertilize immature female scales before winter.

Damage. Extremely heavy infestations of olive scale cause defoliation and twig death and frequently reduce tree productivity. Major damage results from scales settling on fruit. Fruit infested by the first generation become badly misshapen. Infestation by the second generation causes pronounced purple spotting of the green fruit, rendering it worthless for pickling (color plate 17.8).

Monitoring and control. Two species of introduced parasites provide excellent control of olive scale. *Aphytis maculicornis* (DeBack & Rosen) (color plate 17.9), introduced in 1952, provided good control in some groves but was less successful in others because it is inhibited by the hot, dry summers of interior California. *Coccophagoides utilis* (Doutt) was introduced in 1957; the two parasites in combination provide widespread biological control of olive scale. Chemical treatment to control olive scale is rarely needed unless biological control is disturbed by treatments for other pests.

If olive scale was detected in the previous season or if chemicals are used in the orchard or on nearby crops, watch closely to detect crawlers moving onto the fruit in spring and summer. If treatments are needed, control the first generation in late May, June, or late July. A postharvest treatment is also effective. Usually only one treatment during a year is needed to control this pest.

OLEANDER SCALE

The oleander scale, *Aspidiotus nerii* (Bouche), also known as ivy scale, occurs throughout the warmer parts of the United States and is among the most common scale insects in California. It attacks a wide range of plants including acacia, aloe, avocado, azalea, Boston ivy, boxwood, cactus, camellia, cherry, grape, grapefruit, lemon, magnolia, mistletoe, Monterey pine, orange, rose, sago palm, and yucca. It rarely requires treatment on other hosts, but on olive, infestations occasionally become sufficient to damage fruit.

Description. Oleander scale resembles greedy scale (see page 104) except that its scale covering is less convex and the exuvium is almost central. Oleander scale is 1 to 2 mm across, flat, and gray with yellow or light brown exuvium (color plate 17.10).

The male covering is smaller than the female and more elongate, with the exuvium at one end. The mature scale body under the covering and the crawlers are yellow.

Field biology. Little is known about the life cycle of oleander scale. The majority of overwintering individuals are adult females. Either eggs are laid or young are born alive beginning in April. Females continue producing progeny for almost 2 months, causing an overlap of generations. A second generation is produced in July and August.

Damage. Oleander scale is generally found on leaves and to a lesser extent on twigs in the tree's lower inner part. Leaves and twigs can tolerate heavy populations before any reduction in crop occurs. When populations are heavy, oleander scale infests olive fruit. Infested fruit are characterized by green spots on purple fruit, as scales delay maturity of the tissue around the scale. Early infestations seriously deform fruit, and later fruit spotting renders olives worthless for pickling.

Monitoring and control. Biological control agents sometimes keep oleander scale in check. The best way to decide whether a treatment is needed is to examine the previous season's grade sheet and determine the amount of cullage caused by this pest. When required, treat first-generation crawlers in late May and June when crawlers are first seen moving onto fruit. Oleander scale can also be monitored with double-sided sticky cellophane tape placed around branches near heavy populations to detect crawler emergence.

LATANIA SCALE

Latania scale, *Hemiberlesia lataniae* (Signoret), has been found on a wide range of hosts in tropical and subtropical areas. It is very common in California, being recorded on such diverse hosts as acacia, avocado, bramble, cedar, euonymus, fuchsia, gladiolus, Kentia, kiwifruit, philodendron, rose, willow, and yucca.

Description. The adult scale covering is gray or white, with a darker exuvium. The covering is quite convex, with the exuvium toward one side (color plate 17.11). The body of the female under the scale cover is yellow to orange, in contrast to the purple color of the olive scale. Apparently male scales do not occur in California, although they have been observed in other parts of the United States. The crawler and second-instar bodies are orange.

Field biology. Latania scale overwinters as second-instar nymphs. In early spring they mature; the female scale initially lays eggs in batches of 15 to 20, and then 3 to 5 a day until she dies. Eggs are laid beneath the scale covering; on hatching, the young crawlers migrate a short distance, settle down, insert their mouthparts, and begin feeding.

The legs of the crawlers become functionless after they settle. The first generation may complete its development in as little as 2 months. Crawlers are reported to be active in May, July, and September, indicating that at least two and maybe three generations a year occur in California.

Damage. Latania scale feeds on leaves, bark, and fruit. If the population is heavy on twigs, dieback may occur. Most damage occurs when scales develop on the olive fruit (color plate 17.12), rendering it worthless for pickling.

Monitoring and control. Parasites play a significant role in the management of latania scale. If the grade sheet from the previous season indicated an economic infestation, a treatment is needed. Time the application to the emergence of the crawler in May or June. Double-sided sticky cellophane tape is useful to determine when crawlers are active.

GREEDY SCALE

Greedy scale, *Hemiberlesia rapax* (Comstock), is the most common and most widely distributed species of armored scale in California. It infests innumerable hosts in most parts of the United States and may attack almost any woody plant. However, it is not as damaging to its host as are many other scale species.

Description. This scale is easily confused with latania scale and can be distinguished only after microscopic examination in the laboratory. The scale covering is usually light gray, circular, very convex, and thin (color plate 17.13). It measures about 1 to 1.5 mm across when fully grown. The exuvium is yellow to dark brown and slightly off center. The body of the mature female under the scale cover is yellow and circular or pear shaped. Adults resemble ivy or oleander scale but are less convex, with an almost central exuvium.

Field biology. Little is known about the biology of this insect. Most overwinter as adult females, although other development stages may also overwinter. As this scale may be found in various stages of development, it presumably has several overlapping generations a year.

Damage. Greedy scale may become abundant on the bark of branches, especially on older suckers. However, like other armored scales, little damage occurs unless it develops on the fruit.

Monitoring and control. Parasites and predators play a prominent role in regulating greedy scale populations. If grades indicate that greedy scale is causing fruit loss, monitor crawlers with double-sided sticky cellophane tape and apply treatments when crawlers are present.

CALIFORNIA RED SCALE

Although California red scale, *Aonidiella aurantii* (Maskell), is a significant pest of citrus, infestations on olive only occasionally require treatment. It is widely distributed throughout central and southern California on citrus, and it attacks other diverse hosts such as fruitless mulberry, grape, nightshade, rose, and walnut.

Description. The adult female has a thin, round scale covering about 2 mm across. The body color beneath the cover is reddish and shows through the scale covering. The exuvium is located centrally or subcentrally. The male scale covering is gray and elongate.

Field biology. Female scales give birth to young that remain under the scale covering for 1 or 2 days before emerging as crawlers. Crawlers seek a favorable site to settle, insert their mouthparts, and begin feeding. The female molts twice before becoming mature. Male and female development are similar until after the first molt, when the male covering becomes elongate rather than round. The male passes through a prepupal, pupal, and winged adult stage. There are two or three generations a year, and any stage in the life cycle may be found at any time of the year.

Damage. All parts of the olive tree can be infested, but only on rare occasions are treatments needed. California red scale does not discolor fruit, which distinguishes its damage from that of the olive and oleander scales. However, infested fruit are worthless and are culled before processing (color plate 17.14).

Monitoring and control. Depending on the climate, growing season, and treatment for other pests, biological control can be effective against California red scale in some areas of the state, though not in the San Joaquin Valley. Red scale can be monitored by examining fruit, twigs, and leaves, or by using double-sided sticky cellophane tape or pheromone traps. If treatments are required, treat first-generation crawlers in June or the second generation in late July and August.

OLIVE MITE

The olive mite, *Oxyenus maxwelli* (K.), is a native of the Mediterranean and is found worldwide in olive-growing districts. Ascolano is the most susceptible cultivar, followed by Sevillano, Manzanillo, and Mission.

Description. Olive mites are tiny, four-legged eriophyid mites with yellowish to orange bodies (color plate 17.15). Females are broadest at the front of the body and taper to the rear. They are 140 to 160 micrometers long and difficult to see without at least a 20-power lens.

Field biology. Olive mites overwinter as adults in bark crevices. Egg laying begins in late winter or early spring and continues until summer. Sudden periods of relative humidity below 20 percent and high temperature cause high mortality. The mite estivates in various stages of development during summer and resumes activity again in fall until cold weather.

Damage. Olive mite is normally found on the surfaces of immature terminal olive leaves. Usually it causes no damage; when present in large numbers on young leaves, it "silvers" them and causes longitudinal curling, but this does not damage the tree or its productivity. In spring, the mites collect on the developing inflorescence, and heavy populations there cause pistil abortion and subsequent crop losses. Dead and discolored floral buds, bud drop, "blossom blast," and inflorescence abscission are also symptoms of bud damage associated with olive bud mite.

Monitoring and control. Treatment is not recommended unless fruit set and crop have been below normal for several years and large numbers of mites are found. However, if poor cropping has occurred several years in a row, examine shoot tips and developing bloom for the presence of olive mites. If heavy populations occur on developing inflorescence, treatment is recommended.

WESTERN FLOWER THRIPS

The western flower thrips, *Frankliniella occidentalis* (Pergande), is widely distributed throughout western North America. It has a very wide host range, including over 139 species of plants in California alone.

Western flower thrips is attracted to olives during bloom. Ascolano is most susceptible, although other cultivars can be injured.

Description. Western flower thrips adults are tiny insects about 1 mm long, with two pairs of fringed wings. Adults vary in color, from white to yellow with slight brown spots on top of the abdomen, to yellowish with an orange thorax and brown abdomen, to completely dark brown. Different color forms predominate according to the time of year.

Eggs are opaque and kidney shaped and are inserted in the parenchyma cells of leaves, flower parts, and fruit.

First-instar nymphs are opaque or light yellow, turning golden yellow after the first molt. Upon completing development, nymphs drop to the ground and pupate in protected places. Pupae are soft bodied, with visible wing pads.

Field biology. Adults overwinter in weeds, grasses, and other sites within or outside the orchard. In early spring, they deposit eggs in shoots, buds, and flower parts of host plants. Eggs hatch in 5 to 15 days, depending on temperatures. Nymphs feed on developing leaves, fruit, or shoots. After completing their development, nymphs drop to the ground where they molt twice before emerging as adults. Populations usually peak in May or June. As wild areas dry up, thrips migrate to cultivated areas, including olive orchards, where additional generations are produced. There are five to six generations of western flower thrips a year.

Damage. Because western flower thrips migrate to olive groves from adjoining grassy areas after they dry up in spring, trees near drying grain fields or near dry weeds within the orchard are most susceptible to damage.

Although thrips feed on leaves and tender shoots, most damage is caused when they feed on fruit. Damaged fruit is scarred and dimpled; it is culled before processing (color plate 17.16).

Monitoring and control. There are no legal chemical controls for thrips on olives, but infestations can be prevented culturally. Avoid discing orchard cover crops while trees are in bloom. Open areas adjacent to groves should be disced as early as possible to prevent thrips' development and migration to olive trees.

BRANCH AND TWIG BORER

The branch and twig borer, *Polycaon confertus* (LeConte), attacks a number of fruit and nut trees in California, but grape, madrone, and oak are its preferred hosts. Damage to olive is generally limited to areas adjoining these hosts. It seldom causes economic injury.

Description. The adult branch and twig borer is a slender brown beetle about 13 to 20 mm long (color plate 17.17). The body is round, with the head and thorax being narrower than the body. Larvae are "C" shaped, white, and covered with fine hairs.

Field biology. The adult lays eggs in dead and dying wood of many native and cultivated trees and shrubs outside the orchard. The larvae bore into the heartwood of the host and feed until development is complete. Pupation occurs inside infested wood, and adults emerge early in spring. Adults fly to adjoining orchards, where they bore into branches and twigs, causing a characteristic injury. There is one generation a year.

Damage. Adults bore into the axil of small twigs and branches or the base of buds. Small branches die and injured branches frequently break off at the holes made by these beetles. Borer damage is sporadic and not usually of economic importance.

Monitoring and control. Branch and twig borers can be minimized by burning all infested wood inside and around the orchard to destroy developing larvae. There are no chemical controls for this pest.

AMERICAN PLUM BORER

On occasion the American plum borer, *Euzophera semifuneralis* (Walker), infests olive trees. This borer also attacks a number of cultivated deciduous fruit and nut trees and ornamental plants.

Description. Adult moths have gray forewings with brown and black markings and a wingspan of about 18 mm. Eggs, oval and white when first laid, turn a dull red shortly after. Eggs are laid singly or in small clusters, usually in cracks or bark crevices. Young larvae are white with large, dark brown heads. Mature larvae are about 25 mm long and are dusky white, pinkish, or dull greenish. Pupae are olive green when first formed, becoming dark brown before emergence.

Field biology. American plum borer overwinters as either immature or mature larvae, depending on the area. Mature larvae pupate in early spring, and adult moths emerge in April and May. There are multiple generations in California. In late fall, larvae construct loose silken cocoons under bark scales, at the entrance to or near feeding sites in which they overwinter.

Damage. The larvae attack the soft, spongy callus tissue that occurs at graft unions, tree wounds, and in galls caused by the olive knot bacterium. They can continue to feed into normal tissue, girdling limbs, which may be weakened or killed. Most damage is caused to new grafts.

Monitoring and control. The borer can be detected by the brownish frass and webbing at feeding sites. No control treatments have been developed for this insect on olive.

BLACK VINE WEEVIL

The black vine weevil, *Otiorhynchus sulcatus* (Fabricius), has been recorded from more than 80 host plants. It has long been a serious pest of grape in Europe and of caneberries, strawberries, and ornamentals (especially container-grown plants) in the western United States. Occasionally it also attacks olives, primarily in the San Joaquin Valley.

Description. Adult black vine weevils are oblong, about 10 mm long, and brownish black, with a somewhat roughened surface (color plate 17.18). The body is covered with dense, short, light-colored hairs with small patches of yellow scale-like hairs on the elytra, the hard front wings. A long, broad snout projects from the front of the head.

The legless larvae, which live in the soil, are about 10 mm long when mature. The body is dirty white with a brownish head.

Field biology. Black vine weevils overwinter as larvae in the soil. Pupation takes place inside earthen cells in the soil, and adult females emerge in March in the San Joaquin Valley and begin laying eggs from 2 to 4 weeks after emergence. The black vine weevil is parthenogenetic, there being no known males. After eggs hatch, young larvae work their way into the soil, where they feed on roots until the following spring. There is one generation a year.

Damage. Damage caused by larval feeding on grape roots in parts of Europe has been described as severe. Little is known about the impact of larval feeding on olive roots, however. Feeding by adults is what most concerns growers in California. Adult black vine weevils are nocturnal: they hide beneath loose bark, in debris, or in other protected places during the day and move up the tree to feed at night. They primarily feed on leaves, and heavy infestations can cause considerable leaf loss. Adults feed along the leaf margin, causing a characteristic notched appearance.

Monitoring and control. Because adults hide under loose bark and debris at the base of the trees during the day, they are difficult to detect. In grape, tree wraps placed around trunks can be used to detect the presence of adult weevils.

There is no specific recommendation for controlling black vine weevil in olives. Insecticides applied to the trunks and the base of the trunk after adult emergence and before egg laying begins have been effective in grape. Bait broadcast around the trunk has also been effective on other crops.

18

PEST MANAGEMENT

DISEASES OF OLIVE

BETH L. TEVIOTDALE

OLIVE KNOT

Since ancient times, olive knot, caused by the bacterium *Pseudomonas syringae* pv. *savastanoi* (Smith) Stevens, has afflicted olive trees. The disease occurs wherever olives are grown and probably was brought to California on cuttings in the last half of the nineteenth century. Olive knot does not kill trees, but it does reduce productivity by destroying twigs and branches, and fruit from infected trees may have off-flavors. All cultivars are susceptible, and damage can be severe when weather favors disease.

Symptoms. Rough galls (the "knots"), usually $1/2$ inch to 2 inches (1 to 5 cm) in diameter, develop on twigs and small branches at wounds—leaf scars, pruning cuts, or injuries that have occurred during mechanical harvest or other orchard operations (color plate 18.1). Galls at harvest injury sites may grow quite large. Galls interfere with the transport of water and sugars, causing defoliation and death of twigs and branches. The disease is restricted to the aboveground parts of the tree and does not affect root tissues.

Disease cycle. The bacteria survive in galls and reproduce inside them all year. During rains, they are extruded to the gall surface and are readily washed about. Infection rarely occurs without moisture, and rain followed by high humidity especially favors olive knot. The bacteria may also be carried on pruning shears and other equipment. Insect transmission of olive knot has not been reported in California.

Olive knot bacteria enter and establish infections only in wounded tissue, not in natural openings such as stomata and lenticels. The most commonly colonized wounds are leaf scars; thus, periods of heavy leaf fall present the greatest threat of infection. Blossom scars, rifts made as shoots emerge from branches, and mechanical injuries are other points of bacterial entry. Cracks in bark caused by freezing injury can become infected, which means that cold winters are conducive to outbreaks of olive knot.

Temperature is not a limiting factor in disease development. The optimal temperature for pathogen growth is 72° to 75°F (22° to 24°C), the maximum 90°F (32°C), and the minimum 40° to 50°F (5° to 10°C). Most natural infections in California happen between October and June, in the rainy season; however, the knots develop when the tree is actively growing, in spring and early summer. Therefore, infections established in late fall are not noticeable until spring, whereas in spring galls are visible 10 to 14 days after infection.

Control. Olive knot is difficult to control. The strategy is prevention. Applications of copper-containing fungicides to protect leaf scars or other injuries minimize disease, but they often must be repeated to protect new wounds as they appear. A minimum of two applications is usually necessary—one in fall, before winter rains begin, and another in spring, when most leaves are shed. Copper may injure trees in areas of low rainfall.

Careful pruning during the dry season, to remove galls that are the sources of bacterial inoculum, is helpful. The material Gallex kills galls, but application is costly in time and labor, and it is appropriate only for infections on limbs or trunks.

OLIVE LEAF SPOT

Olive leaf spot, peacock spot, and bird's eye spot are names for the disease caused by the fungus *Spilocea oleaginea* (Cast.) Hughes. Worldwide, it is known as olive leaf spot; in California, it usually is referred to as peacock spot. The disease occurs in all olive-growing regions of the state. Cultivars vary in susceptibility, but all are subject to infection. Outbreaks are sporadic, and the disease may take several years to become serious enough to cause alarm.

Symptoms. Leaves, fruit, and fruit stems may be attacked, but lesions are observed most often on the upper leaf surfaces. Lesions first appear as small sooty blotches $1/16$ to $1/4$ inch (2 to 6 mm) across; these later become muddy green to black spots (color plate 18.2). Some lesions develop a yellow halo and remind people of the "eye" spot on a peacock's tail feathers; hence, the vernacular names peacock spot and bird's eye spot. Many lesions may occur on a leaf. Most infected leaves fall prematurely, which weakens and kills small wood and eventually reduces productivity. New infections are first seen in late winter and early spring; by summer, most affected leaves have fallen, leaving partially defoliated shoots with healthy leaves on the tree. The disease is usually most severe in the tree's lower part and north side.

Disease cycle. Not all infected leaves fall, and the fungus survives on those leaves. Holdover lesions produce very few conidia (spores) during summer, become crusty and whitish, and may be difficult to find. In fall, margins of those lesions expand and a new crop of conidia is produced.

The conidia are picked up and spread by moving water, which is why the lower parts of trees are most commonly infected. Lateral spread is very limited even adjacent trees may exhibit vastly different amounts of disease.

Conidia germinate only in the presence of free moisture, and germination, infection, and mycelial growth proceed readily over a wide range of temperatures, 70°F (21°C) being optimal. Most infections take hold during the coldest part of California winters; temperatures above 86°F (30°C) restrict germination of the spores. Infections established in winter take longer to become visible as lesions than do those initiated in spring.

Inoculum buildup appears to play an major role in the severity of olive leaf spot. It may take several years for this disease to cause economic loss.

Control. Olive leaf spot is controlled by a copper-containing fungicide applied once in late fall before winter rains begin. A second application is of questionable value; if used, it must be applied before mid-January. Later treatments, as recommended for olive knot, offer no protection against olive leaf spot.

PHYTOPHTHORA ROOT AND CROWN ROT

Root and crown rot of olive trees occurs but is not a common or serious problem in California. The disease is caused by any of several soilborne species of the fungal genus *Phytophthora*. At present, *P. citricola* and two unidentified species of *Phytophthora* have been isolated from olive trees having symptoms of root and crown rot. *Phytophthora dreschleri* is highly virulent to olive in greenhouse tests.

Symptoms. *Phytophthora*-infected trees exhibit reduced growth, have thin canopies, and eventually die. If the disease progresses rapidly, trees may expire in 1 or 2 years. Root systems of infected trees are discolored, but the mycelium of the *Phytophthora* fungus cannot be seen by

the unaided eye. If infection has progressed to the crown, a juncture between healthy, white bark and dark, diseased tissue is apparent.

Disease cycle. *Phytophthora* species require free moisture in the soil to produce mobile zoospores, and these need free moisture to invade olive root tissue. Consequently, root and crown rots produced by *Phytophthora* are associated with heavy soils and prolonged periods of high soil moisture (color plate 18.3). The fungi live independently in the soil and survive long periods of dryness as oospores. Each species has its own particular requirements of temperature, moisture, nutrients, and host susceptibility.

Control. Water management is the basis for control of phytophthora root and crown rot. Cultural practices that avoid prolonged saturation of soil, such as planting on berms, shortening irrigation time, and improving water penetration, lessen root rot. No chemicals are available to control this disease, and resistant olive rootstocks have not been identified.

ARMILLARIA ROOT ROT

Armillaria root rot, also called oak root fungus, is a serious disease of many tree crops but not of olive in California. The pathogen is a soilborne fungus, *Armillaria mellea* (Vahl.) Quel.

Symptoms. Infected trees have slowly thinning canopies and appear weak. This symptom often develops first on one side of the tree and then progresses over several years to involve the whole tree. The bark and outer wood of the upper roots and crown show discoloration. Distinctive white, fan-shaped sheets of fungal mycelium, called plaques, are located between bark and wood (color plate 18.4). Rhizomorphs—flat, stringlike structures of white mycelium with a protective dark, rubbery coating—are sometimes found on the surfaces of infected roots. These, however, are often difficult to find and can be confused with small roots.

Disease cycle. *Armillaria mellea* does not live independently in soil, but resides in dead wood, such as old tree roots, and can survive for decades if not subjected to desiccation. The fungus does not ramify through the soil; instead, a healthy growing root is invaded when it comes in contact with an infected root or through root grafts. The slow, circular pattern of spread through the orchard, from tree to tree, reflects this means of dispersal. Trees with large root systems, such as oak, that are infected by *A. mellea*, leave many sources of inoculum distributed throughout the soil profile.

Control. Removal of roots from infected plants, followed by deep fumigation, can slow the progress of the disease, but fungal eradication has not been achieved. No olive rootstocks are resistant, and infected trees cannot be cured.

DIPLODIA CANKER

Diplodia canker is found in olive orchards in the Sacramento Valley and probably occurs elsewhere. It does not cause direct harm to the tree, but it can aggravate damage resulting from olive knot disease.

Symptoms. The fungus, a species of *Diplodia*, invades olive knot galls and progresses into the twig to form an elliptical canker (color plate 18.5). The canker girdles and kills small shoots or branches, exacerbating the damage caused by olive knot. Diplodia canker is not known to infect wood greater than ½ inch in diameter.

Disease cycle. Details of the epidemiology of the disease are unknown.

Control. No control is recommended.

VERTICILLIUM WILT

The most serious economic disease of olive in the southern San Joaquin Valley's olive-growing region is verticillium wilt. Caused by the soilborne fungus *Verticillium dahliae* Kleb., it kills many young and mature trees each year.

Symptoms. Leaves on one or more branches suddenly collapse and die soon after the first warm weather of summer. Dead leaves and bloom (in the case of early spring death) remain on the tree, indicating the branches that have been infected (color plate 18.6). Internally, there is usually little or no discoloration of the vascular tissues that is seen in other verticillium infected plants. Trees die after repeated attacks over several years. Infections increase with tree age as root systems enlarge and explore larger volumes of contaminated soil.

Disease cycle. *V. dahliae* is found in many agricultural soils around the world. It has a wide host range and is a pathogen of many crops grown in California, including cotton, mel-ons, peppers, pistachio, stone fruits, and tomato. It is also found in the lower San Joaquin Valley in association with indigenous and weed species.

The fungus survives for many years in soil as microsclerotia, dark multicelled structures the size of small grains of sand. Microsclerotia are formed inside infected plants and are released into the soil as tissues decay. They remain quiescent until a plant root grows within a few millimeters, stimulating them to germinate. Once inside the plant, the fungus grows into water-conducting elements, the current year's xylem; this disrupts the plant's water transport system and causes wilt and subsequent death. Many microsclerotia must participate in infection to cause disease.

Most verticillium infections occur in cool, moist soil during late winter and spring, before high temperatures prevail. As temperatures rise, infections decrease until soils cool in late summer or early fall, which may bring another round of infections. During hot summer months, the fungus dies out in the upper parts of the plant and becomes difficult to isolate, although disease is apparent. When cool and moderate spring temperatures persist or summers are mild, verticillium wilt is extremely common.

Control. No reliable methods of control have been developed. Soil fumigation is effective in nurseries but is not reliable for established plantings. Site selection for new plantings should be based on crop history and an assessment of the inoculum level (number of microsclerotia) in the soil. Land previously planted to verticillium-susceptible crops is likely to harbor high counts of microsclerotia. Inoculum levels can be determined by soil analysis, available through private laboratories. Solarization—covering the soil between established trees with plastic sheeting in the affected area for several weeks during summer to raise soil temperature and destroy the fungus—has provided inconsistent control. A resistant rootstock is not available, though some tolerance has been reported in the cultivar Ascolano.

19

PEST MANAGEMENT

SPRAY APPLICATION PRINCIPLES AND TECHNIQUES FOR OLIVES

JOHN E. DIBBLE

Olive trees grow differently than deciduous trees do. The result is heavy, dense foliage, mostly on the periphery of trees. This natural density resists spray penetration and may cause poor coverage within the tree canopy and top center. Essential to good spray coverage, then, is a pruning program that opens up the tree. A pest control program that uses chemicals as well as beneficial insects is far more likely to be satisfactory when olive trees have been periodically pruned.

Given properly pruned trees, the prerequisites for successful high-volume or low-volume spray coverage are the same. One must evaluate tree size and spacing, calibrate equipment in advance, and properly calculate the materials needed. When these prerequisites are met, the pesticide can be applied satisfactorily by either method so that it hits the target pest. Chemical failure or insect resistance is too often blamed when the problem is really poor coverage.

HIGH- VERSUS LOW-VOLUME APPLICATION

High-volume (dilute) sprays are defined as those that deliver 350 to 800 gallons of solution per acre, usually resulting in spray runoff. Low-volume (concentrate) applications apply 20 to 100 gallons of spray solution per acre, resulting in no runoff or drip. Spray rates as low as 15 gallons per acre (gpa), called extra-low-volume or high-concentrate sprays, and mid-volume sprays (150 to 300 gpa) that result in slight drip have also given satisfactory results.

Studies show that coverage and control are reduced when sprayer speeds exceed 2.5 miles per hour (mph) for dilute spray and 2 mph for concentrate. Failures in coverage are most easily seen in scale control, a major problem in olives (see chapter 17). To be efficient, concentrate spraying is necessarily more exacting in its requirements than dilute. High air velocity, a small range in droplet size, and proper travel speed are essential for good coverage and control using concentrates. Simply put, the sprayer must move slowly enough

(remain adjacent to the tree long enough) to penetrate the overall canopy.

Coverage

Spray coverage from a dilute application usually shows a "washy" spray pattern that completely covers surfaces but does not necessarily provide better pest control than the "stippled" pattern from a concentrate application. The total number of gallons of spray per acre is not necessarily the critical factor in obtaining proper spray coverage and pest control. Careful evaluations of most tree crops show that concentrate applications can give coverage equal to dilute; furthermore, fungicides and various chemical plant additives can also be satisfactorily applied as concentrates

In the case of hard-to-control scale insects, there are more failures on deciduous trees with dilute than with low-volume treatments. The great volume emerging from the sprayer may give the operator a false sense of coverage, but volume of spray does not compensate for improper speed of travel, poor nozzling, or a badly directed air pattern. Nozzle wear, in particular, is rapid with the use of wettable powders and can occur in both concentrate and dilute sprayers. This factor may be ignored by operators of dilute sprayers, simply because they have a large number of nozzles, and checking nozzle wear is time-consuming. Nozzle wear affects droplet sizes and gallons-per-minute (gpm) discharge; it is often mistakenly compensated for by increasing travel speed, which only compounds the problem.

Correct nozzling

All spray applications, from dilute to high concentrate, overspray the bottom half of the tree. Spray deposits in the bottom of the tree can be four to five times greater than in the top half. Pest control is similarly affected. Overspraying is due to the height and location of the sprayer in relation to the tree's height and configuration. This imbalance can be largely corrected through proper nozzling: adjusting the gpm discharge of the spray so that approximately two-thirds of the spray is emitted from the top half of the nozzle manifold. This adjustment can be made on most sprayers by putting large nozzle tips at 1, 2, 10, and 11 o'clock on the spray manifold, medium tips at 3, 4, 8, and 9 o'clock, and small tips at 5, 7, and 12 o'clock. Air discharge can also aid coverage if it is adjusted to approximately the same configuration.

In dilute spraying, runoff and dripping from branch to branch counteract the effects of poor nozzle adjustment somewhat, but correct nozzle calibration is necessary for maximum coverage. Although the overspraying that occurs in dilute applications protects the careless operator to some degree, in low-volume spraying there is no such allowance. It is, therefore, good practice for all sprayer operators to ensure proper nozzling, the right speed of travel, careful measurement of insecticides, and accurate calculation of the amount of spray needed per acre.

TYPES OF EQUIPMENT

Dilute (high-volume) spraying

The configuration, function, and performance of dilute air-carrier sprayers are well known to growers. These sprayers are available in many styles and sizes, but they all function in basically the same way.

This type of spray application has been used by olive growers for many years. Although the advent of the air-carrier dilute sprayer greatly redressed earlier problems with high-pressure handgun sprayers, it has not solved all coverage problems. Both systems use large volumes of water. Whereas the handgun's poor coverage resulted from human fatigue, that of the air-carrier sprayer often results from improper nozzling and travel speed. However, if calibrated and operated correctly, the latter can give excellent results.

Drawbacks include the need to refill (and therefore handle) the pesticide often, usually every acre. Many dilute sprayers also have a large number of nozzles, increasing the potential for plugging and wear. Usually larger than concentrate sprayers, dilute units can also be more awkward to handle, and they may create greater soil compaction and maintenance problems. On the plus side, in applying large volumes of water, dilute sprayers produce large droplets, which help counteract winds. The greater volume of water does not necessarily mean, though, that spray reaches higher or deeper into the foliage.

Concentrate (low-volume) spraying

Concentrate spray is commonly applied using older dilute sprayers that have been modified by changing their pump pressure and altering the spray manifold. Newer models of dilute sprayers are designed to convert easily for concentrate spraying. These can be adjusted down to the desired 100-pound spray pressure at the manifold, have 100- to 160-mph air velocity, and feature a second or multipurpose manifold that accommodates the smaller, hollow-cone, disk-type nozzles used for concentrate applications.

A third group of low-volume sprayers is specifically designed for concentrate applications. Most use the same kind of nozzles, pressure, and air velocity used to adapt dilute sprayers. Others use low-pressure systems to move the spray liquid to special nozzles where a high-velocity air discharge (160- to 220-mph) shears the spray liquid into small droplets. In all cases, a narrow range of small droplet sizes is desired for concentrate spraying. This group of sprayers usually cannot deliver spray rates above the concentrate or semiconcentrate range.

Most concentrate spray applications made commercially are in the 25- to 100-gallons-per-acre (gpa) range. Interest in the high-concentrate range of 5 to 25 gpa is rising, as it requires the fewest fill trips and stops, but it may never enjoy wide use in olive groves, given the form and density of the trees.

Sprayer selection

Growers should always check the performance of any sprayer system according to their particular requirements and request a demonstration in the orchard. Depending on the cost of purchase and operation and the severity of pest problems, growers may desire a larger fan (to direct greater amounts of air into particularly dense or tall trees as well as into widely spaced rows) or greater horsepower (to operate a power take-off, or PTO, sprayer). They should also consider the convenience and complexity of the equipment's operation and maintenance.

Concentrate advantages

Because low-volume spraying is popular in deciduous orchards and increasingly in nondeciduous tree crops, the advantages of concentrate spraying are discussed here even though its use is limited in olive groves. Low-volume applications can permit use of equipment that is smaller, initially less costly, and often more easily and cheaply maintained than the equipment used for dilute applications. (PTO units are even more economical than engine-powered units.)

Savings in time per spray operation are notable: there is less downtime, because fewer refills. Using a 400-gallon, low-volume sprayer calibrated for 40 gpa, 10 acres can be sprayed between fills. In a 30-foot row planting at a 1.8-mph travel speed, coverage would take a little over 9 minutes per acre (6.5 acres per hour), resulting in approximately 1.5 hours of continuous spraying for each 10 acres.

Low-volume spraying can also be as effective as dilute while using less chemical per acre—usually 25 to 30 percent less. The reduction is possible primarily because there is none of the spray runoff from the tree that occurs in dilute applications. Deposition is more efficient and can equal that of dilute applications even at the lower rate. The numerous small and relatively uniform droplets from low-volume applications stick on contact to tree surfaces.

In addition, the total spray water used per acre is reduced by 75 to 90 percent over that used in dilute spraying. Transporting less water weight through the orchard means reduced soil compaction, even more desirable when soil is wet.

In summary, low-volume sprays can be as effective as high-volume sprays in reducing pest populations by over 90 percent to an acceptable level, providing the olive trees are opened up by pruning. Scale control, of particular concern to olive growers, poses no greater problem than that of other pests whose control requires complete and uniform spray coverage. The number of gallons of spray per acre, therefore, is not a major factor for coverage and control.

DRIFT PROBLEMS

The drift of minute chemical droplets can be hazardous to people, animals, and wildlife and can contaminate adjacent crops. Pesticides can be carried by air drift or water runoff, and drift cannot be entirely eliminated from ground or aircraft applications. A certain number of tiny droplets, produced by all types of nozzles and application techniques, tend to become airborne and drift downwind. As a proper spray application comes down in spray gallonage per acre, it must come down in droplet size to produce the droplet surface area required for good coverage. Potentially, then, the low-volume technique poses a greater drift hazard due to its lighter spray. Although a great many of these droplets are subject to drift, it has been reported to amount to no more than 2 to 3 percent of the total volume of spray. Also, because of the mechanical design of most low-volume sprayers, air volume (the amount of air) is low, so its force does not usually extend much past tree height. On the other hand, high-volume spray application tends to cast spray far above tree height, where some of it is susceptible to drift.

Most damage by pesticide drift is done within the farm community. More extensive damage, however, can result from the transport of chemicals through water, from soil-water runoff from treated fields, and from high-level airborne drift. Pesticide drift can also produce excessive residues on nearby crops, rendering them unfit for the retail market or for animal fodder. Confining chemicals to their intended field and reducing losses from chemical drift onto untreated fields are objectives that must be met more effec-

tively than ever, if agriculture is to continue using many pesticide chemicals.

SAFETY

The dangers of and precautions for spraying are similar for all application techniques. Operators should keep in mind that the chemical is most concentrated in the container and that the spray is highly concentrated in the tank. They must wear protective clothing—including a spray-repelling hat, footwear, and gloves and an approved respirator—during and between spray runs, and especially when loading, for their greatest protection.

Low-volume spraying can use less toxicant per acre than high-volume spraying, a factor in its favor. The operator also handles the actual pesticide or containers only once every 5 to 10 acres (depending on gallons per tank) rather than every acre, as with high-volume sprays. Furthermore, the operator is not subjected to drenching by the spray, nor is the cover crop or ground saturated with runoff.

SPRAYER CALIBRATION

The actual steps involved in the proper calibration of an air-carrier orchard sprayer are relatively simple and have already been described generally. Following are some formulas you will find useful when calibrating, as well as detailed, step-by-step procedures with a specific example to work through. Refer to tables 19.1, 19.2, and 19.3 as you do so. Figure 19.3 is a general sprayer calibration worksheet to be used in the field.

Formulas useful for calibrating spray applications in orchards

$$\text{gallons per minute (gpm, for one side of sprayer)} = \frac{\text{gpa} \times \text{mph} \times \text{row spacing (ft)}}{1{,}000}$$

$$\text{gallons per acre (gpa)} = \frac{\text{gpm (for 1 side)} \times 1{,}000}{\text{row spacing (ft)} \times \text{mph}}$$

$$\text{miles per hour (mph)} = \frac{\text{gpm (for 1 side)} \times 1{,}000}{\text{gpa} \times \text{row spacing (ft)}}$$

$$\text{acres per hour} = \frac{12 \times \text{mph} \times \text{row spacing (ft)}}{100}$$

$$\text{speed of travel (expressed as tree spaces passed per minute)} = \frac{\text{mph (desired)} \times 88}{\text{tree spacing (ft)}}$$

$$\text{number of trees per acre} = \frac{43{,}560 \text{ (square feet per acre)}}{\text{row spacing} \times \text{tree spacing}}$$

$$\text{EXAMPLE:} \quad \frac{43{,}560}{30 \times 30} = 48 \text{ trees per acre}$$

Calibration procedures for orchard air-carrier sprayers

INFORMATION

Known:
1. gpa (gallons per acre)
2. psi (sprayer pressure at manifold)
3. mph (miles per hour)
4. no. nozzles/side
5. row spacing

Unknown:
1. gpm needed
2. nozzle sizes and placement
3. simple measurement for speed

EXAMPLE

Known:
1. gpa = 400
2. psi = 150
3. mph = 2
4. no. nozzles/side = 9
5. row spacing = 30 × 30 ft

Unknown:
1.

$$\text{gpm/side} = \frac{\text{gpa} \times \text{mph} \times \text{row spacing}}{1{,}000}$$

$$= \frac{400 \times 2 \times 30}{1{,}000} = \frac{24{,}000}{1{,}000}$$

$$= 24 \text{ gpm/side}$$

2. nozzle sizes and placement

If there are nine nozzles per side and 24 gpm are needed,

$$24 \div 9 = 2.7 \text{ gpm/nozzle}$$

However, the best arrangement is to obtain ⅔ gpm from the top half of the manifold and ⅓ from the bottom half; therefore, different size nozzles should be used (fig. 19.1). In the example here, medium-size nozzle tips that discharge approximately 2.7 gpm are selected along with smaller and larger ones that will discharge a total of 24 gpm (fig. 19.2). Use the correct nozzle chart for your sprayer nozzles—select nozzles that would best fit the needed smaller and larger category (table 19.1). After setting up the same nozzle arrangement on the other side of the sprayer, the calibration would be completed.

3. speed of travel (using tree spaces as measuring units and desiring 2 mph)

1 mph = 88 ft/min

$$\text{spaces/min} = \frac{2 \text{ mph} \times 88 \text{ ft/min}}{30 \text{ ft tree spacing}}$$

$$= 176 = 5.9 \text{ trees passed per minute}$$

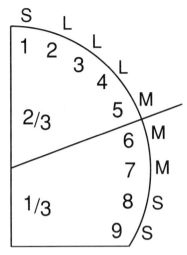

Figure 19.1. Most desirable general division of nozzle tips.

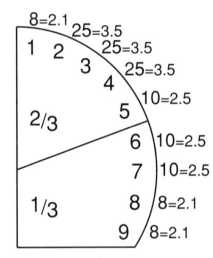

Figure 19.2. Specific desirable arrangement of nozzle tips to discharge total of 24 gpm.

Table 19.1. Example for nozzle chart (showing gpm at 150 psi).

Nozzle size	Gallons per minute				
	50 psi	100 psi	150 psi	200 psi	250 psi
2			1.0		
3			1.2		
5			1.9		
8			2.1		
10			2.5		
15			3.0		

Table 19.2. Orchard sprayer calibration chart for sprayer traveling at 2 mph.

Gallons per minute discharge necessary from each side of sprayer for 50 to 600 gpa at different row spacings

	Row spacing (in feet)						
GPA	**18**	**20**	**22**	**24**	**28**	**30**	**45**
50	1.8	2.0	2.2	2.4	2.8	3.0	4.5
100	3.6	4.0	4.4	4.8	5.6	6.0	9.0
150	5.4	6.0	6.6	7.2	8.4	9.0	13.5
200	7.2	8.0	8.8	9.6	11.2	12.0	18.0
250	9.0	10.0	11.0	12.0	14.0	15.0	22.5
300	10.8	12.0	13.2	14.4	16.8	18.0	27.0
350	12.6	14.0	15.4	16.8	19.6	21.0	31.5
400	14.4	16.0	17.6	19.2	22.4	24.0	36.0
450	16.2	18.0	19.8	21.6	25.2	27.0	40.5
500	18.0	20.0	22.0	24.0	28.0	30.0	45.0
550	19.8	22.0	24.2	26.4	30.8	33.0	49.5
600	21.6	24.0	26.4	28.8	33.6	36.0	54.0

Table 19.3. Orchard sprayer calibration charts for three different spray rates per acre.

Gallons per minute discharge necessary from each side of sprayer at different speeds and planting distances

	Row spacing (in foot)						
MPH	**18**	**20**	**22**	**24**	**28**	**30**	**45**
				100 GPA			
1.00	1.80	2.00	2.20	2.40	2.80	3.00	4.50
1.25	2.30	2.50	2.75	3.00	3.50	3.75	5.63
1.50	2.80	3.00	3.30	3.60	4.20	4.50	6.75
1.75	3.15	3.50	3.85	4.20	4.90	5.25	7.88
2.00	3.60	4.00	4.40	4.80	5.60	6.00	9.00
				400 GPA			
1.00	7.2	8.0	8.8	9.6	11.2	12.0	18.0
1.25	9.0	10.0	11.0	12.0	14.0	15.0	22.5
1.50	10.8	12.0	13.2	14.4	16.0	18.0	27.0
1.75	12.6	14.0	15.4	16.8	19.6	21.0	31.5
2.00	14.4	16.0	17.6	19.2	22.4	24.0	36.0
2.25	16.2	18.0	19.8	21.6	25.2	27.0	40.5
2.50	18.0	20.0	22.0	24.0	28.0	30.0	45.0
				500 GPA			
1.00	9.00	10.00	11.00	12.00	14.00	15.00	22.50
1.25	11.25	12.50	13.75	15.00	17.50	18.75	28.13
1.50	13.50	15.00	16.50	18.00	21.00	22.50	33.80
1.75	15.75	17.50	19.25	21.00	24.50	26.25	39.38
2.00	18.00	20.00	22.00	24.00	28.00	30.00	45.00
2.25	20.25	22.50	24.75	27.00	31.50	33.75	50.63
2.50	22.50	25.00	27.50	30.00	35.00	37.50	56.2

FILL IN (based on your spray operation)

    A. Tree row spacing (in feet):_____

    B. Gallons of spray desired per acre (gpa):_____

    C. Speed of travel selected in orchard (mph): _____

CALCULATE (using orchard sprayer calibration chart if speed of travel is 2 mph; otherwise,
        using following formula)

    A. Gallons per minute (gpm) necessary per sprayer side

$$\text{gpm} = \frac{\text{gpa} \times \text{mph} \times \text{tree row spacing}}{\times 1{,}000} = \underline{\hspace{3cm}}$$

    B. ⅔ of gpm (for top half of manifold) = _____

    C. ⅓ of gpm (for bottom half of manifold) = _____

CHECK (with a pressure gauge)

    Your sprayer pressure at the manifold = _____

SELECT (your proper nozzling)

    A. Obtain a nozzle chart for your type of nozzle tips (orifice sizes). Refer to the column indicating the same pressure (psi) at which your sprayer operates. Working with only one side of your sprayer, first select tips for the top half of the manifold that total approximately ⅔ of the gpm discharge for one side. The balance (⅓) of gpm discharge should come from the nozzles on the bottom half of the manifold. Preferably these nozzle tips should not all be the same size but rather arranged so that those in the 2, 3, and 4 position are the largest; those in the 5, 6, and 7 position are the medium size; and those in the 1, 8, and 9 position are the smallest. This is done to conform to the trees' height and width, the distance the spray must travel, and the density it must penetrate. If your sprayer has more or fewer nozzles than the nine in the example, adjust the gpm per nozzle accordingly, but maintain the ⅔ and ⅓ relationship. In each case, the total gpm discharge of all nozzles should equal the amount calculated.

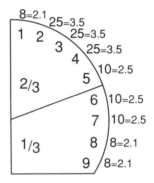

    B. Now set up the same nozzle arrangement on the other side of your sprayer.

CALCULATE (the speed of travel)

    A. Check your desired speed in the orchard by traveling the required number of spaces in one minute.

$$\text{Tree spaces/min} = \frac{\text{mph} \times 88}{\text{tree spacing (ft)}} = \underline{\hspace{3cm}}$$

VERIFY (speed against other measures)

    A. Spray out an acre or part of an acre of trees with plain water to check the pattern as well as the total gallons per acre (gpa) output. If the spray pattern needs to be adjusted based on your observed penetration and deposit, rearrange the nozzles accordingly. For example, the larger nozzles may need to be moved up or down on the manifold to better conform to tall or to low, bushy trees.

    B. If the gallonage per acre is off, check to see whether (1) your original pressure (psi) reading was wrong, (2) your nozzle size selections were off, or (3) your speed of travel was too slow or fast.

Figure 19.3. Orchard sprayer calibration worksheet.

20

HARVESTING

THE OLIVE HARVEST

GEORGE C. MARTIN, KAREN KLONSKY, AND LOUISE FERGUSON

All crops are harvested when they are judged to be horticulturally mature, a stage of development that meets an agreed-upon standard established in the marketplace. For the California processed olive fruit, horticultural maturity occurs about 4 months before physiological maturity. This early harvest allows olive fruit to be processed according to the California black-ripe or green-ripe methods to achieve defined industry standards.

Grower payment for processed olives is based on the size and weight of olives after cullage (see chapter 21); however, size and weight have not been used by the olive industry in determining when to harvest. When to pick has generally been determined by visual and physical factors. An olive is considered mature if it exudes a characteristic white juice when squeezed (color plate 20.1). The color range considered ideal for picking extends from an even pale green with a minimum of whitish spots (lenticels) through a straw color. A red blush is permissible on Manzanillo, Mission, and Sevillano olives early in the season, but color is considered undesirable late in the season (color plates 20.2 to 20.6).

WHEN TO HARVEST

Olive harvests have customarily begun in mid-September, peaked in mid-October, and finished in mid-November. The primary reason for delaying harvest early in the season is to accrue value through weight and size. The primary reason for accelerating harvest late in the season is to decrease losses due to overripeness, drying wind, and cold damage.

Clearly, the traditional method of determining when to harvest olives has been inexact. Generally it has resulted in a too-early rather than too-late harvest. Overripe fruit is usually more obvious to the grower because of fruit appearance and value lost.

From their analysis of the components of value in an olive harvest, UC researchers have generated a method for determining optimal crop value. The components of crop value are shown for 3 years' crops in figure 20.1: the upper portion of each graph shows the crop by size category on each harvest date, and the lower portion depicts the net value of the crop and its total weight on each harvest date. The two components of olive crop value are the weight and size of the crop; however, the weight of the total crop changes little through the harvest season. Weight thus has essentially no relationship to crop value. Also, as figure 20.2 demonstrates, individual olives, within their size classification, do not change weight significantly over the harvest season. This is constant despite tree crop load. Olive sizes, however, particularly the total percentage in the standard canning categories of medium, large, and extra large, are closely related to the crop's net value. In all instances shown, crop value is greatest when these three sizes reach their maximum total percentage.

The second half of the research, determining when this optimal crop value occurs, produced the following procedure for determining when to harvest:

1. Beginning in mid-September, take daily samples from three olive trees (100 randomly selected olives apiece), from each representative orchard area.

2. Determine the total percentage of standard medium, large, and extra-large olives.

3. When 50 percent of the olives are within those categories and the percentage is increasing at the rate of 3 to 5 percent per week, picking should begin within 1 week and last no longer than 2 weeks.

Thus, in California, a 14-day period in October has been identified when olive fruit quality and yield combine for greatest profit. Harvest before or after this period results in substantial losses in income (fig. 20.3).

Growers eager to take advantage of this information have been frustrated by the slow rate of the harvest. The best laborers can harvest 500 pounds of olives a day. Thrifty orchards average about 3 tons of fruit per acre; thus, in this

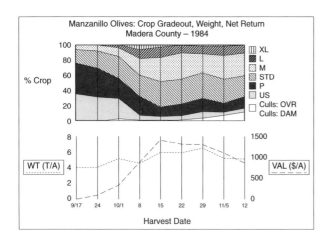

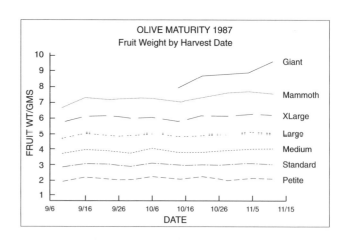

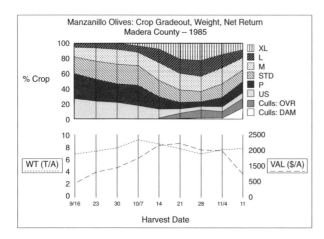

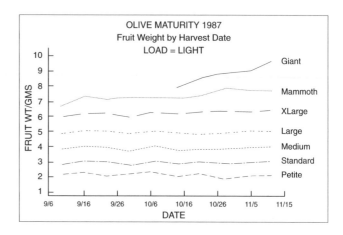

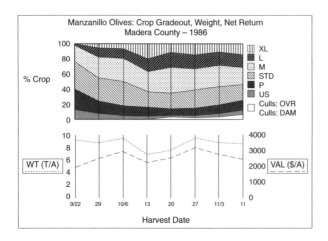

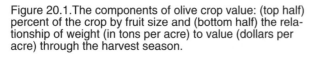

Figure 20.1.The components of olive crop value: (top half) percent of the crop by fruit size and (bottom half) the relationship of weight (in tons per acre) to value (dollars per acre) through the harvest season.

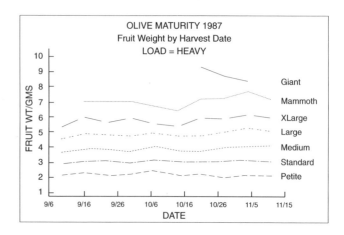

Figure 20.2. The effect of harvest date on individual olive fruit weight within size grades on moderately (top), heavily (middle), and lightly (bottom) cropped trees.

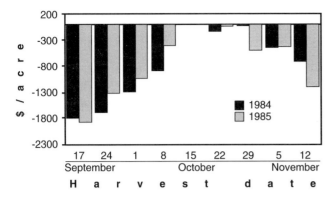

Figure 20.3. Income lost per acre when harvest occurs before or after the optimal time. Maximum profit is shown for October 15; all other harvest dates result in losses of income compared to that date. SOURCE: Adapted from Sibbett et al. (1986).

example 12 worker-days are required to harvest an acre. In California, the defined economic unit is an orchard whose size can support and be managed by a family of four. For olive this is about 100 acres, an orchard that would require 48 workers working 25 days to harvest. These estimates mean that harvest for that 100-acre orchard would exceed the period for maximum return by at least 11 days. Many growers are able to complete harvest in about 21 days, but they still lose much crop value.

HAND HARVEST

In the early years after planting, olives are harvested by hand from the ground; in time, ladders must be used. In both cases the method of olive removal is the same. The fruit are removed by sliding the cupped, gloved hand down the limb in a milking action. The limb is placed so that fruit fall into the picking bag. When the bag is full, the fruit are released into standard orchard bins of 1,000-pound capacity. This process can result in considerable fruit and tree damage. Fruit damage occurs from using a rough technique, dropping fruit from great distances, and including debris with the fruit. Tree damage results from leaves being torn off with the fruit. At each leaf scar, the olive knot fungus can enter.

Ladder use presents another problem for hand harvesting. Where upper limbs extend beyond 14 feet (4.3 m), pickers are less likely to harvest the fruit on them, and in any case the increasing likelihood of laborers falling from ladders makes 14 feet the maximum safe harvesting height. Ladder maintenance is recommended, and weakened ladders should be discarded.

Growers should assume that laborers do not know how to safely use a ladder. Thirty minutes of safety instruction with a new crew is time well spent in terms of decreasing injuries to the work force.

MECHANICAL HARVEST

Developments in labor management and availability in the United States make it less likely that olive growers can achieve optimal harvest by hand. Research in California shows that mechanical devices that position workers in the orchard (such as on picking platforms) do not increase harvest rates. These devices improve the picking speed of only the slowest workers; the best workers may be slowed down because the picking aid moves at the rate of the slowest picker. Unless picking crews are well matched, motivated workers work better without the harvest aid.

Although there is little interest in harvest aids among olive growers, there is great interest in mechanical harvesting. Chief among the predictable reasons are the high cost and the scarcity of labor. To avoid both of these problems, a few olive growers have been motivated to convert to mechanical harvesting.

The goal in mechanical harvest is to conduct vibration from where the machine grips the tree to the point of fruit attachment. The amount of energy reaching the fruit is reduced by such factors as moisture in the wood, internal and external damping forces, bark characteristics, and the natural frequency of the fruit and stem. The shaking energy delivered to the tree is a function of stroke (a length) and frequency (motions per unit of time). Researchers have established an ideal stroke/frequency index for many crops, including olive. If the parameters they describe are applied, 60 to 80 percent of the olives can be shaken from the tree with minimal tree and fruit damage. However, the 20 to 40 percent remaining on the tree after shaking means lost income for 2 years—reduced income for the current year, and reduced flowering and fruiting for the next.

Pruning for mechanical harvest

In their natural growth habit, olive trees extend, in a weeping fashion, cascades of long, pendulous limbs that bear fruit at their extremities (see figure 4.1 in chapter 4). For mechanical harvest, lower branches must be removed to attach the shaker clamps. Without a clear view of the trunk or scaffold limb, the bark will be damaged when the clamp is attached or detached. In the main tree structure, scaffold limbs should be at an angle of 45° or less (that is, more upright) as acute-angled limbs transmit energy more efficiently than do horizontal limbs. Crossover limbs absorb energy and must be removed. Dead limbs and those with too-dense twigs should be thinned out. See chapter 10 for details on pruning.

The shaking machine

Selection. Machine choice depends on orchard size and the economics of the specific site (see chapter 6). About five times more energy is required to mechanically remove olive fruit than other fruit harvested in California. The shaker should feature a 1.5- to 3-inch stroke at 1,000 to 2,000 cycles per minute. What is desired is an abrupt, high-powered shake. Long shakes (5 seconds and longer) damage bark and fruit. Some growers alternate one machine between two rows, each row having a rollout tarp. In such a system, two crews are kept busy with one shaker operator. While one crew is rolling up a tarp with fruit, the other crew has laid out the tarp for the next shaker. Fruit are carefully dumped into standard orchard bins for transport to the processor.

Minimizing bark damage. To avoid bark damage, the shaker operator must have a clear view of the point of attachment between the machine and the tree. This is ensured by specific pruning and by using a properly designed shaker machine. When scaffold limbs are shaken, there must be enough clearance to allow a 90° angle of attachment between the shaker and the scaffold; all other angles induce bark damage.

Trees should not be completely dry at harvest, but at least a 2-week interval between the last irrigation and shaking is recommended. Wet or recently irrigated trees have loose bark that is more readily damaged. Details of the particular orchard site also affect the waiting period between irrigation and harvest.

Clamp pressure must be great enough to prevent slippage on the trunk or scaffold, but not so great as to crush the bark. Here the operator's experience is critical, as the same pressure does not always result in the same effect throughout an orchard or from year to year.

Compared with deciduous fruit tree shakers, olive shakers use extra weights and require greater shaker energy. These features, plus the shaker pattern, must be fine-tuned on the site and during use, as regular attention to details leads to the best results and the least bark damage.

Shaker pads must be serviced on a rigid schedule. One shaker can go through four to six pads a day, and they should be cleaned out, rotated, and have more walnut shells added each day. It is best to turn pads each hour and rotate them from one side of the head to the other every 2 hours.

Finally, the single most important bark injury preventative is to employ a well-trained, well-paid, rested, conscientious operator. Probably the best approach is to pay by the hour with a bonus for quality work as determined by fruit and bark damage. The shaker operator makes or breaks the shaking operation. Sloppy operators damage bark, shake the tree for too long, and bruise the fruit. Overhasty operators both damage bark and increase the need for machine repairs.

Tree training to form a rigid tree helps maintain fruit removal by mechanical shaking at the 70 percent level, but other means for loosening physiologically immature fruit are needed. Several decades of research in testing chemical loosening agents have had minimal success. The problem remains one of balancing fruit removal with leaf loss. Leaf loss beyond 25 percent substantially reduces flowering the next year, and at each leaf scar the olive knot bacterium can enter.

ECONOMICS OF THE OLIVE HARVEST

Harvesting accounts for 45 to 65 percent of the total cash production costs for olive. As crop size increases, so does the total harvest expense; however, the larger the crop, the lower the harvest cost per ton. Excessive brushy growth, dead limbs, heavy weed growth, smut from black scale infestations, and rough ground add to harvest expense. Whether to harvest by hand or by shaker is an economic question with many variables. This section presents some of management's considerations when comparing hand (table 20.1) with mechanical harvest.

Table 20.1. Example of hand harvest costs.

Tons per acre	Costs per ton ($)	Costs per acre ($)
< 1.5	$275	$413
1.5	225	338
2.0	225	450
2.5	200	500
3.0	200	600
3.5	200	700
4.0	175	700
5.0	175	875

There are two kinds of mechanical harvesting equipment: one grabs and shakes individual limbs; the other shakes the trunk. Both can be either pulled by tractor or self-propelled. The fruit may be caught with rollout canvas or other kinds of catching frames. Trunk shakers can be used on smaller trees, but larger trees require limb shakers. A mature tree requires four to six limb-shaker attachments.

The shaker machine can move faster than the catching frames, particularly among smaller trees that require fewer attachments; thus, having two or three catching frames speeds operations. Harvest time ranges from 3 to 5 minutes per tree, depending on the number of shaker attachments and the harvest crew's skill.

Cullage can be higher with mechanical harvesting than with hand picking when shaking time per attachment extends beyond 5 seconds. The primary cause is puncturing of the fruit skin; other bruises tend to disappear in processing. Cullage can be reduced by guarding against fruit pileup in the catching frame and by pre-pruning to remove dead brush. Any brush that lands on the catching frame should be removed quickly by the catching-frame drivers. Padding sharp parts of the shaker and catching frames with carpet or other material also reduces bruising.

As with all fruits, olives increase in size daily as harvest approaches. Thirty percent of their size and weight is gained in the last 6 weeks. The period of optimal picking lasts only about 2 weeks. In theory, there is more flexibility in hand harvest, as it is often easier to hire more pickers than to buy or hire another shaker.

The most serious drawback to mechanical harvesting is the low rate of fruit removal (table 20.2). The removal rate for hand picking is about 95 percent, depending on crew supervision and tree size; removal rates for mechanical harvesting range from 65 to 80 percent. Removal percent decreases as tonnage per acre increases (resulting in smaller, lighter fruit) with larger trees.

Table 20.2. Removal rates for alternative harvest methods.

Harvest	Removal rate (%)	Cullage (%)
Hand picking	95	5
Shaking	65–80	5–20
Shaking using a chemical loosening agent	80–95	5–20
Shaking followed by hand picking	99	5–20

Another drawback to mechanical harvesting is the potential increase in limb breakage. Olives require five times more energy to remove than other fruits, and this intense energy release can damage older trees. Some of the damage may not show up until years later. However, limb breakage is greatest in the first years of mechanical harvesting, when the weakest limbs are eliminated by breakage.

An example of a grower's economic analysis is presented in table 20.3. This analysis is generalized and hypothetical and must be adapted for any given orchard. In fact, it is unlikely that any two orchards could use the same cost figures for determining whether to harvest by machine or by hand.

The analysis assumes that 77 percent of the crop is removed by mechanical harvesting and 98 percent of the remaining crop is gleaned by hand afterward. This means that 22.5 percent is removed by hand and 0.5 percent remains on the

tree. For example, with a 7-ton crop, 5.39 tons are removed mechanically and 1.58 tons are gleaned, for a total harvested crop of 6.97 tons. This means 0.03 ton, or 60 pounds, per acre is left on the trees. As crop size increases, the amount of fruit left on the tree after shaking increases; so gleaning becomes more important. On an average-size crop, more than a ton per acre would be left in the trees if no hand picking were done.

Harvest costs per acre are divided into costs for shaking and costs for hand gleaning. Mechanical harvesting costs include an investment of $75,000 in machine costs, spread out over 42 acres. This includes the expense of a used shaker and two catching frames.

It is difficult to accurately calculate the life of a mechanical shaker or its eventual resale value. Much of the equipment currently used for olives was originally built for almond, prune, or walnut harvesting and converted for olive use. In this analysis, straight-line depreciation is calculated over 10 years with a 15 percent salvage value. Interest is figured at 10 percent to reflect the cost of financing the investment. Maintenance and repairs are assumed to be about $1,700 per year, or $40 per acre.

Increased cullage from mechanical harvesting is calculated at between 5 and 10 percent, an increase of up to 15 percent over hand picking (table 20.2). For a 7-ton crop 77 percent, or 5.39 tons, is removed mechanically. Using a figure of 3.2 percent for the percent increase in cullage over hand picking, about 0.17 ton per acre is lost by mechanical harvesting that would not be lost if the crop were hand harvested. This loss is valued at $85, based on an average value per ton of $500.

Gleaning costs are calculated at $295 per ton. There seems to be a slightly higher cull rate for gleaning than for hand harvesting. An increase of 0.3 percent was used to calculate the additional loss from gleaning over hand harvest costs.

Total costs of shaking and gleaning are shown in table 20.3 at various yield levels on a per-acre and per-ton basis. The larger the crop, the higher the total costs per acre. In mechanical harvesting, the cost per ton decreases with a larger crop, because the overall cost does not vary much with crop size. Thus, cost per ton shaken on a 7-ton yield is $112; cost per ton on a 4-ton yield is $185.

When mechanical harvest is followed by hand picking, the average cost per ton increases because hand-picked olives cost much more per ton. However, it is still economic to glean the remaining fruit by hand if its value exceeds the cost of hand picking. The average cost per ton for all fruit removed is $154 for a 7-ton yield and $210 for a 4-ton yield (table 20.3).

Table 20.3. Mechanical harvesting cost estimates.

Assumptions:	Percent of removal	
	Shaking	77%
	Gleaning	98%
	Number of acres	42
	Harvest equipment cost	$75,000

Tons per acre	8	7	6	5	4	3
Tons shaken	6.16	5.39	4.62	3.85	3.08	2.31
Tons gleaned	1.80	1.58	1.35	1.13	.90	.28
Total tons removed	7.96	6.97	5.97	4.98	3.98	2.59
Harvest costs per acre						
Shaking costs						
Labor	$223	$223	$223	$223	$223	$223
Repairs	40	40	40	40	40	40
Fuel, oil, tarps	17	17	17	17	17	17
Depreciation	152	152	152	152	152	152
Interest	89	89	89	89	89	89
Loss to cullage increase	97	85	72	60	48	36
Total shaking costs	$618	$606	$593	$581	$569	$557
Gleaning cost:						
Hand picking	532	465	399	332	226	81
Loss to cullage increase	3	2	2	2	1	0
Total gleaning cost	$535	$467	$401	$334	$227	$82
Total harvest cost	$1,153	$1,073	$994	$915	$796	$639
Harvest costs per ton						
Tons shaken	$100	$112	$128	$151	$185	$241
Tons gleaned	295	295	295	295	295	295
Total tons removed	145	154	166	184	210	247

These numbers do not mean that maximizing yield creates the greatest overall profit. Heavy tonnage is commonly associated with small fruit size and alternate bearing. Though delaying harvest to increase size pays off with certain crops, usually the delay results in too many black fruit and damage from frost. Marketable product must be balanced with overall yield.

Picked fruit begin to lose moisture immediately. When harvested during hot, sunny weather, fruit should be set in the shade while waiting to be hauled away. Unshaded fruit become sunburned and are graded as culls. Rough handling causes bruises and a reduction in grade.

TECHNICAL CONSIDERATIONS

This section is for those who wish to know more about the technical aspects by which olive flowers, inflorescences, fruit, and leaves separate from the plant and about research on the use of chemical fruit-loosening agents. The discussion covers abscission; treatment with ethylene, the natural chemical that causes abscission; and future directions for research.

The abscission process

The problem of achieving maximum fruit loosening with minimal leaf loss has prompted studies into the abscission process for many organs, from inflorescences and flowers to fruit and leaves, by the Pomology Department at UC Davis. Leaf abscission after treatment with the ethylene-releasing compound 2-chloroethylphosphonic acid (ethephon) has been studied in the laboratory and compared with natural abscission in the field.

Events in the clearly defined abscission zone at the base of mature olive leaves occur much as do those of other crops. For olive, ethephon application induces onset of separation 36 to 60 hours after treatment. In another 8 to 12 hours, separation is evident in the abaxial cortical cells adjacent to the vascular system, which proceeds from these interior cells to the epidermis (fig. 20.4). Next, separation in the adaxial side occurs in the same manner—that is, from inside out.

122

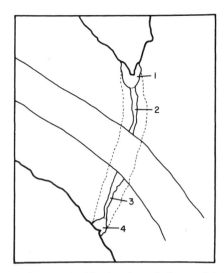

Figure 20.4. Camera lucida drawing of olive petiole base, showing adaxial (1) and abaxial (4) indentations, the adaxial (2) and abaxial (3) separation layer, and the abscission zone (broken lines). SOURCE: Polito and Stallman (1981).

The last point of separation occurs in the vascular region and the epidermal cells of the indentation at the leaf petiole base. During this process there is no cell division in the abscission zone, which contains 10 to 12 rows of isodiametric (round) cortical parenchyma cells. The line of separation during abscission is marked by cell wall swelling and dissolution of the middle lamella.

Histochemical examination of the abscission zone reveals that (1) starch localizes in abundance near the vascular region but does not change in content during abscission; (2) cell protein content increases notably before and after abscission; (3) intercellular pectic substances show loss; (4)

there is little loss of cellulose; (5) there is no tylose formation; and (6) there is no lignification of cells in the abscission zone.

Olive fruit abscission involves two abscission zones, one between the peduncle and pedicel and the other between the pedicel and fruit. The peduncle/pedicel abscission zone is much like that of the leaf, with an easily identifiable separation zone of isodiametric cells that are smaller than the adjacent elongated cells. In contrast, before abscission the pedicel/fruit junction does not have an identifiable zone of abscission layer cells.

Treatment with ethylene-releasing compounds (ERCs), such as ethephon or Alsol, results in fruit separation most frequently at the pedicel/fruit zone, but abscission may occur at both peduncle/pedicel and pedicel/fruit zones. The separation process for fruit is similar to that for olive leaves. Cell plasmolysis occurs first in the pedicel pith and cortical regions and moves toward the phloem. However, no xylem disruption is evident. With time, pectin and cell-wall polysaccharides are lost and starch grains form. As plasmolysis proceeds, cell walls and middle lamellae disintegrate. No cell division is evident in the abscission zone during separation.

In the olive inflorescence, eight abscission zones form in response to ethephon treatment (fig. 20.5). These were identified experimentally by subjecting sampled infloresc-

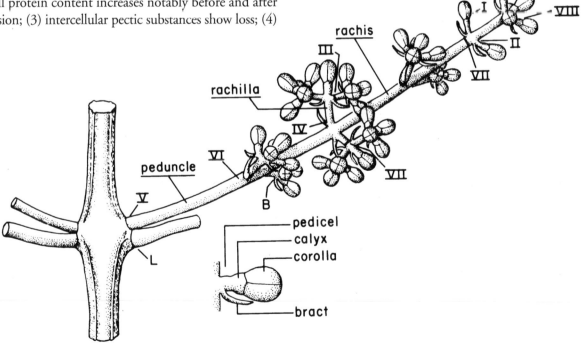

Figure 20.5. Morphology of the olive inflorescence (idealized), showing all possible patterns of branching. Examples of all possible abscission zone types are indicated. Inset shows olive floral morphology. (Inflorescence abscission zones are numbered I to VIII; bract = B, leaf = L. SOURCE: Weis et al. (1988).

ence to ethephon or ethylene gas treatment weekly beginning 8 weeks before and continuing until the time of anthesis. As is the case in the leaf, the abscission zones of the inflorescence axis are preformed early in their development, and they are also similar in their small cell size, dense cytoplasm, and difference in cell wall staining, compared with cells outside the abscission zone. Whereas the leaf abscission zone is two to five cells wide and distinct, the inflorescence abscission zones are many cells wide and diffuse.

The separation characteristics of the inflorescence are similar to those of the leaf. Abscission of the leaf, inflorescence, flower, and fruit, as induced by an ERC, is similar to natural abscission. Treatment with an ERC or ethylene gas accelerates the onset of separation. Treatment with ethephon causes leaf abscission faster than it does inflorescence abscission, but the reverse is true when ethylene gas is used. Also, fruit abscise at about half the concentration of ethylene gas required for leaf abscission. These findings are difficult to explain without determining the amount of ethylene reaching the abscission site.

In the field, fruit respond more rapidly than do leaves to ethephon. Field treatments can be compromised by many factors, including (1) the environmental conditions at treatment time, (2) the length and dosage of ethylene exposure, and (3) the type of ERC. These are discussed next.

Environmental factors affecting ethylene action

Used under field conditions, ERCs yield variable responses. The variability is probably the result of temperature and moisture conditions, which play major roles in the action of ERCs. At 93 percent relative humidity, ethephon decomposition rate is reduced even when temperature is increased from 68° to 86°F (20° to 30°C). However, at 37 percent or 70 percent relative humidity—conditions common in the field—ethephon decomposition rate increases as temperature increases from 68° to 122 F° (20° to 50°C).

Tree moisture status also affects ERC treatments; fruit removal is greater and leaf loss less when the orchard is treated at the end of the normal irrigation cycle. This does not necessarily imply that the trees are stressed, only that irrigation is due. Results have been similar in experiments comparing treatments of nonirrigated and irrigated trees.

Laboratory studies show that partially desiccated olive shoots take up more ethephon and translocate less of it than do shoots with sufficient moisture. In this laboratory system, the fruit take up a similar amount of ethephon, whether partially desiccated or moist. These results show that moist shoots distribute ethephon that may reach target leaf cells better and more easily than desiccated shoots do.

California field experiments show that ethephon application provides the greatest fruit separation with the least leaf loss when the temperature is between 60° and 86°F (16° to 30°C) and when trees require an irrigation. All of these data corroborate the importance of the amount and duration of ethylene exposure at the abscission zone.

Ethylene exposure time and concentration

In the laboratory, excised olive shoots fed an ERC through the stem are convenient for study. Although no experimental laboratory system can completely approximate conditions in the field, this method avoids compromise by the uncontrolled environmental factors previously discussed. Direct comparisons of the excised olive shoot system with field treatments have shown remarkable similarity.

Use of the excised olive shoot system in the laboratory reveals that the effects of ethephon depend on its concentration and the exposure time, regardless of leaf location. Leaves that are first to release ethylene gas after ethephon treatment are the first to abscise. Whereas a 90 percent leaf abscission is induced with a 2-hour ethephon pulse at 250 milligrams per liter (mg/L), only 1 hour is required at 500 mg/L. In these experiments, leaf abscission occurred after a minimum induction period of 50 hours following ethephon treatment. Untreated leaves in the laboratory system are stable and show little or no ethylene evolution for about 7 days. Stem-feeding ethephon offsets the variability found when foliar sprays are used. It appears that ethephon arrives at the leaves long before decomposition, with subsequent release of ethylene. Experiments to verify this work are ongoing.

Other experiments show that leaves are more responsive than fruit to ethephon-induced abscission when fed through cut stems. In field treatments of ethephon foliar sprays, fruit abscission is always greater than leaf abscission, perhaps because more ethephon collects on the fruit than on the leaf. Still, in either foliar- or stem-fed treatments, we do not know the exact concentration of the chemical at the abscission zone. Finally, the amount of ethylene that various plant organs emit after stem feeding with ethephon does not indicate the abscission rate. Leaves and inflorescences evolve similar amounts of ethylene, but leaves abscise far more than do inflorescences. Fruit evolve small amounts of ethylene and show variable abscission responses.

In experiments to correlate field and laboratory results, droplets of equal size and ethephon concentration were applied to the pedicel/fruit cavity on excised shoots and on unaltered shoots in the field. This procedure eliminates the uptake and transport variable inherent in treatments via cut stems in the laboratory. Abscission response curves are similar for the field and the laboratory shoots. Abscission occurs earlier in the laboratory, probably because the temperature there is constant at about 77°F (25°C). In the field, this temperature is reached for about 8 hours a day, but it is much cooler at night. These results agree with other experiments showing increased ethylene release from ethephon at higher temperatures.

The release characteristics from ERCs have been studied in comparisons of leaf and fruit abscission. When ethylene release is measured after applying droplets of CGA-15281 and ethephon, CGA-15281 gives maximum ethylene peaks 2 hours after treatment (perhaps even earlier), whereas the ethylene peak is 13 to 18 hours after treatment with ethephon. Fruit abscission begins 7 to 12 hours after CGA-15281 treatment and 19 to 25 hours after ethephon treatment. These data substantiate field trials suggesting that short, concentrated applications of ethylene might enhance fruit abscission but minimize leaf abscission. A time-concentration constraint does exist, as laboratory work shows that very short ethylene bursts of saturating quantities do not induce leaf abscission.

These data highlight the importance of the duration and concentration of ethylene in favoring abscission of fruit over leaves. Laboratory experiments have systemically explored these two variables using cut olive shoots with fruit inside 10-liter jars through which different ethylene/air mixtures flow for different amounts of time. The data from many trials have been assembled to construct three-dimensional response surface plots.

Ethylene concentrations greater than 10 ppm applied for more than 20 hours lead to excessive abscission of leaves and fruit. For optimizing fruit abscission above 90 percent, more than 3 ppm ethylene is required for at least 28 hours (fig. 20.6). To regulate leaf abscission below 25 percent, ethylene content should be below 7.5 ppm for less than 38 hours (fig. 20.7). From these data an ideal response surface plot can be calculated showing fruit-to-leaf ratios greater than 3.6 (90 percent or greater fruit abscission and 25 percent or less leaf abscission). Ethylene doses of 3 to 5 ppm for 28 to 34 hours yield fruit-to-leaf ratios up to 13.3:1.

Ethylene pulse treatments

In the field, ethylene release from an ERC is affected by temperature, more ethylene being released during a warm day than a cool night. Laboratory results from continuous ethylene treatment (figs. 20.6 and 20.7) thus do not fully represent ethylene release in the field, where much less ethylene is released at night. Experimental systems have therefore been modified to deliver pulses of ethylene: 8 to 16 hours of ethylene, followed by air for 12 to 20 hours, then ethylene again for 12 to 32 hours. The pulse approach allows greater total ethylene exposure and produces far higher fruit-to-leaf ratios

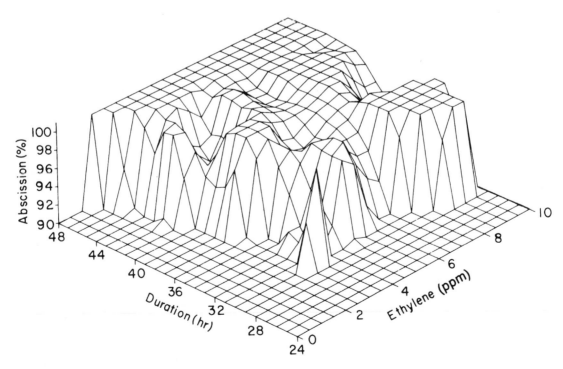

Figure 20.6. Olive fruit abscission response to ethylene concentration and duration: portion of surface depicting doses that induce at least 90 percent fruit abscission. SOURCE: Lang and Martin (1989).

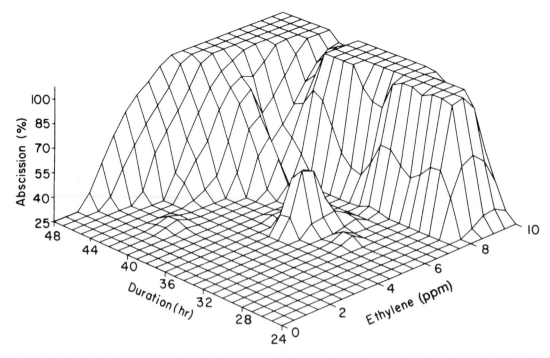

Figure 20.7. Olive leaf abscission response to ethylene concentration and duration: portion of surface depicting doses that induce more than 25 percent leaf abscission. SOURCE: See figure 20.6.

than is the case with continuous ethylene treatment (fig. 20.8). These experiments raise the possibility of designing an ERC with certain release characteristics. The ideal protocol in these experiments is 8 hours of ethylene, 16 hours of air, then 24 to 32 hours of ethylene, resulting in about 98 percent fruit abscission and less than 6 percent leaf abscission (fig. 20.8). The most successful combinations of ethylene concentration and time of exposure give similar results,

whether using continuous or pulse ethylene treatments, but the optimal result—maximum fruit abscission and minimum leaf abscission—is achieved with pulse treatments.

Enhanced ethylene production and leaf abscission

Ethephon generates two peaks of ethylene. It has been suggested that the second ethylene peak is autocatalytic (self-generated) and arises from the initial release of ethylene from

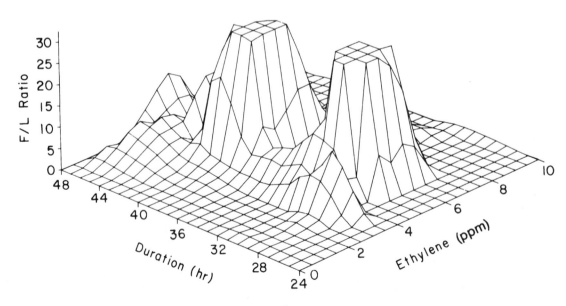

Figure 20.8. Response surface model of olive fruit-to-leaf abscission ratios showing the effect of pulsed ethylene treatments. SOURCE: See figure 20.6.

ethephon; also, as shown here, pulse treatments of ethylene have physiological significance. Experiments with the excised olive shoot system have explored the influence of external ethylene on subsequent endogenous ethylene production and on whether regulation of leaf abscission is involved.

For olive fruit, ethylene production is low, and any rise in ethylene production results from external ethylene trapped in the fruit; thus, there is no ethylene autoenhancement in fruit. By contrast, leaves treated with ethylene show autoinhibition of ethylene production during the first 24 to 48 hours but autoenhancement by 120 hours. The autoenhancement is 100- to 400-fold, irrespective of leaf age or time of year. Autoenhancement of ethylene production in intact or detached olive leaves is positively correlated with external ethylene concentration. Two aspects are particularly interesting. First, the magnitude of autoenhanced ethylene production is greater than that reported for other crops. Second, autoenhancement occurs 24 to 48 hours after leaf abscission (fig. 20.9). These data support the contention that autoenhancement of ethylene may affect leaf senescence but not abscission.

Ethylene sensitivity versus responsiveness

In ERC experiments, stem feeding results in greater abscission of leaves than fruit, whereas foliar sprays lead to greater fruit than leaf abscission. These results bring into question the sensitivity and responsiveness of treated olive organs.

Foliar sprays of 600 ppm of CGA-15281 cause 100 percent fruit abscission and 7 percent leaf abscission. When fed through the stem, the same concentration of CGA-15281 results in 38 percent fruit abscission and 26 percent leaf abscission. Stem feeding of ethephon induces 100 percent leaf abscission and 5 percent fruit abscission. Perhaps spraying ethephon or CGA-15281 causes the treatment chemical to collect in the pedicel/fruit cavity, whereas no such collection basin exists in olive leaves. This possibility is confirmed by treatments with single droplets containing ethephon in the pedicel/fruit cavity, which induces 100 percent abscission.

The issue of sensitivity to ethylene is not resolved by these data. Whether through foliar spray or stem feeding, the amount of ethylene exposure at the abscission zone cannot yet be determined. Ethylene gas treatments show that separation starts first in fruit, well before leaves; still, it may be that the gas penetrates to the abscission zone of fruit faster than it does to that of leaves. Certainly, the fruit are more responsive than leaves to ethylene gas or ERC spray.

Work is in progress on a method to determine where ethephon is transported after stem feeding. Perhaps this proce-

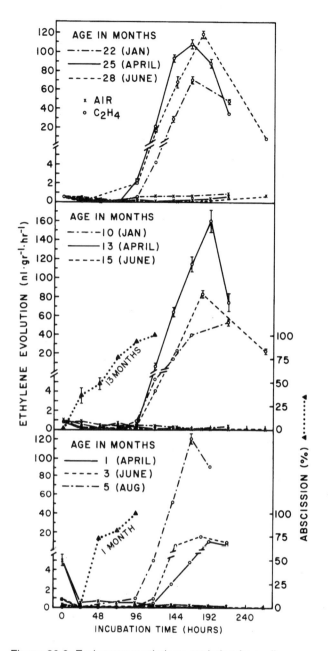

Figure 20.9. Endogenous ethylene evolution from olive leaves and abscission of leaves at different ages following exogenous ethylene treatment at 10 ppm. Bars depict standard error of the mean (n = 12). SOURCE: Goren et al. (1988).

dure can yield data to determine the comparative ethylene sensitivity between olive leaves and fruit.

Future directions for olive abscission research

At this stage in olive abscission research, the search for the "good idea" remains most important. Forty years of empirical studies testing candidate chemicals have given us precious little useful information. We need to understand the plant better first. However, some factors involved in the mechanical harvest of olive are already clear; they are summarized here.

127

The forces that predicate mechanization are the combined problems of labor availability and economics. Mechanical principles require no more than tailoring the solution to the application. These principles demand a tree form, which can be described by engineers, that transmits shaking energy in absolute terms at high efficiency to the fruit. Proper management, however, can only slightly modify tree form, and geneticists have no inexpensive methods available to alter tree form.

The problem of fruit separation rests at the abscission zone. For olive, we can describe some of the anatomy of separation and can elucidate aspects of its histochemistry. We know that similar preformed abscission zones occur on the leaf and at the peduncle/pedicel junction of the inflorescence, and that separation events for both are similar, whether occurring naturally or by ERC treatment. Even so, study of these abscission zones and others in the inflorescence and flower has not revealed a research approach to exploit.

Ethylene is surely a major feature of the abscission process. Application of ethylene via ERCs provides a possible solution, but the problem remains that ERC treatment, though resulting in excellent fruit removal, also leads to excessive leaf loss. The leaf loss results in outbreaks of olive knot and reduced crops.

We have learned a great deal about ERCs and how ethylene release is tempered by moisture and temperature. We know that models for ethylene exposure for specific periods and at prescribed concentrations can yield a solution for complete fruit separation with negligible leaf loss. However, it may be that such solutions are as far from practicality as those of the engineers who model optimal olive tree form or maximum shaker energy conduction. Where do we go next?

The choices should be apparent: We must design the proper tree form to conduct shaker energy, make the tree behave by releasing its fruit on schedule, or design an ERC with specific ethylene characteristics.

Restructuring the olive tree seems to be a formidable task and a project for genetic engineering in the next century. Basic studies in genetic engineering should perfect gene-trait identification, gene manipulation, and controlled expression. Then regeneration of whole plants from genetically altered cells must be brought under control. These problems, though daunting, will yield to time and research effort—probably a great deal of both.

Making the plant release its fruit at a prescribed time may actually be a part of the first alternative—controlling not the structure of the entire tree, but the tree's physiology of separation. Perhaps a fresh outlook is needed for research on the abscission process. In molecular biology, the teaming of natural products chemists, physicists, and physical chemists in the 1930s and 1940s contributed to cracking the genetic code. They entered the research with a fresh approach, as it was a different area of research for them. Perhaps the time is right for a fresh approach in abscission physiology.

The final choice for controlling abscission is intriguing. The dosage/time model of figures 20.6 through 20.8 outlines the conditions for ethylene release that effect maximum fruit removal with minimum leaf loss. An effort should be mounted to tailor an ERC that behaves consistently over several prescribed parameters of temperature, light, relative humidity, and pH. The technology to meet these requirements is available, although the solution may cost more than chemical companies are willing to invest.

Controlling abscission seems to be an overwhelming task as we now begin to understand the problem. Yet we have entered a stage of research capability when we have greater means for finding solutions. The time is ripe and the future bright in abscission control research. As we gradually peel back the layers of our ignorance concerning plant growth, the solution will appear.

REFERENCES

Goren, R., C. Nishijima, and G. C. Martin. 1988. Effects of external ethylene on the production of endogenous ethylene in olive leaf tissue. *J. Amer. Soc. Hort. Sci.* 113:778–83.

Lang. G. A., and G. C. Martin. 1987. Ethylene-induced olive organ abscission: Ethylene pulse treatments improve fruit-to-leaf abscission ratios. *Acta Hort.* 210:43–52.

Lang, G. A., and G. C. Martin. 1989. Olive organ abscission: Fruit and leaf response to applied ethylene. *J. Amer. Soc. Hort. Sci.* 114:134–38.

Polito, V. S., and V. Stallman. 1981. Localized cell growth in ethephon-treated olive leaf abscission zone. *Sci. Hort.* 15:341–47.

Sibbett, G. S., M. W. Freeman, L. Ferguson, D. Anderson, and G. Welch. 1986. Timing Manzanillo olive harvest for maximum profit. *Calif. Agric.* 40:19–22.

Weis, K. G., R. Goren, G. C. Martin, and B. D. Webster. 1988. Leaf and inflorescence abscission in olive. I. Regionation by ethylene and ethephon. *Bot. Gaz.* 149:391–97.

21

GRADING CANNING OLIVES

LOUISE FERGUSON AND GENE WELCH

All canning olives are graded by licensed state inspectors upon delivery to the processor to ensure that established standards are uniformly enforced. Inspection procedures are specified by Federal Marketing Order 932, administered by the California Olive Committee. The inspection service is maintained by a cooperative agreement between the U.S. Department of Agriculture's Agricultural Marketing Service and the California Department of Food and Agriculture's Division of Inspection Services and Fruit and Vegetable Quality Control (Federal-State Inspection Service). Processors pay the state for this service.

Returns to growers are based on total weight and quality of olives within each size classification. The inspector's job is to ensure that weighing and sizing are correctly done, either personally or, more usually, by the processor's personnel. However, it is the inspector who is accountable to the California Olive Committee for proper implementation of procedures and accuracy of dates, weights, counts, and records of the same. The California Department of Food and Agriculture *California Fresh Olive Inspection Circular* (1987) details the procedures and documentation required of olive inspectors.

The initial inspection request of a season generally requires a minimum of 48 hours' notice. If there has been a layoff during the season, 24 hours' notice is sufficient for resumption of inspections. Before grading any lot, the inspector verifies its identity and confirms that it is consistent with accompanying documentation—generally a weighmaster's receipt, company receipt, or Weight and Grade report (form COC-3).

Step 1. The first step in grading olives is to determine whether they are "natural condition olives" or "canned ripe olives of the tree-ripened type." The former are freshly harvested olives, generally in field bins, but they may be in water or a preserving solution. The latter are packaged, but not oxidized, olives of advanced maturity. If lots are combined before inspection, they must be accompanied by a

Lot Combining Authorization (form COC-23) to certify grower authorization. Generally, growers combine lots for a single inspection if they are of the same variety and are delivered within a 24-hour period. Individual lots from different growers are also combined if all the above requirements, including grower authorization, are met but no individual grower's contribution weighs more than 500 pounds (226.8 kg).

Step 2. The second step is to verify the olive variety and, therefore, the variety group. The division of the five commercial varieties into the two groups shown in table 21.1 is based on size. Group I olives are generally much larger than Group II olives and constitute a much smaller proportion of total production. The dates of color break are based on historical observation.

Table 21.1. Olive varieties and the break between early and late season.

	San Joaquin Valley	Sacramento Valley
Group I		
Ascolano	Oct. 15–25	—
Barouni	—	—
Sevillano	Oct. 22–27	Oct. 20–25
Group II		
Mission	Nov. 5–10	Oct. 5–10
Manzanillo	Oct. 16–21	Oct. 20–25

SOURCE: California Department of Agriculture and USDA, *California Fresh Olive Inspection Circular* (Federal Marketing Order 932), Washington, D.C., 1987.

Step 3. The third step, removing immature or overripe culls, is done before size grading. Growers should start picking Missions and Manzanillos (Group II) when they have no more than 20 percent immature fruit, and Sevillanos and Ascolanos (Group I) when they have no more than 15 percent immature fruit. They should cease picking when more than 10 percent of the fruit are overripe. An olive is considered immature if it does not produce the characteristic white exudate under moderate finger pressure (see color plate 20.1). An olive is considered overripe if its skin coloration—deep purple or black in the early season, red through black in the late season—penetrates the olive meat. Penetration of skin color into the fruit usually does not occur before October 1. There are other maturity characteristics specific to individual cultivars.

Within Group II, Missions and Manzanillos should have an even, pale green color with a minimum of whitish lenticels visible. For Manzanillos, pale green through to a straw color is acceptable (see color plates 20.2 through 20.6). During the first half of the season, a light red blush covering less than 50 percent of the surface is permissible; later than that it is undesirable. Mission olives are still considered optimal when dark red through the first half of the season, but not later. The break between the early and late season for Missions is October 5–10 in the Sacramento Valley and November 5–10 in the San Joaquin Valley. For Manzanillos the break is October 20–25 in the Sacramento Valley and October 16–21 in the San Joaquin Valley.

Within Group I, Ascolanos are optimal when they are evenly pale green, with a minimum of whitish spots, through a straw color. Sevillanos are optimal when straw colored. During the first half of the season, blush is permissible if it is limited to the shoulder of the stem end; no blush is permissible during the second half of the season. Ascolano olives should be picked starting when they are pale green and the lenticels have disappeared, on through their straw-colored phase.

Olives may be culled for other reasons. These include machine or hail damage, *Parlatoria* or other scale damage, mutilation, wrinkling, being dropped or "ground" fruit, deformation, contamination, and frost damage.

- Machine damage is caused by trucks, tractors, and spray equipment as it moves through the grove after fruit set. Where young fruit are bruised, dimples or brown scar tissue form, making them unacceptable for processing as whole or pitted fruit.

- Hail-damaged fruit resemble machine-damaged fruit but are present throughout larger parts of the tree and may constitute as much as 60 percent of the crop. Processors generally agree to separate and salvage as much fruit as possible; if separation is not possible, they generally pay a price based on petite fruit and use the olives for chopped or sliced fruit.

- Infestations of *Parlatoria* no longer appear to be a great problem; however, when scale is attached to the stem end, the fruit are culled.

- Fruit mutilated in picking, loading, or hauling are culled.

- Wrinkled fruit demonstrating evidence of sustained water stress will not recover and are culled. Fruit recovered from the ground are also in this category.

- Fruit deformed as a result of insect bites early in its development or as a result of boron deficiency, which causes "monkey face," are routinely culled.

- Fruit damaged by frost show surface blisters and spots on the stylar end 3 days after freezing, indicating freeze damage around the pit.

- Fruit on which illegal chemicals have been used are culled.

- When varieties are mixed within a single bin, the fruit present in the lesser percentage is judged cull. When the mixture is even, the entire bin is culled.

Step 4. The fourth step, size grading the olives, is the most important. Sampling procedures are designed to ensure representative samples from each lot. Procedures vary depending on how a lot is delivered, whether a sample grader is available, and what a grower wishes.

When sampling lots arrive in lug boxes, the number of lugs to be sampled is determined as detailed in table 21.2. For Missions and Manzanillos, a minimum of ½ pound (.23 kg) should be drawn from each lug for lots of over 100 lugs; fewer than 100 lugs requires a ¾-pound (.34-kg) sample from each lug. A minimum of 1 pound (.45 kg) is required for Ascolano, Sevillano, and other large varieties. Inspectors randomly sample lugs from all rows within each layer of a lot.

When the lot arrives in bins, the number of bins to be sampled is determined as in table 21.3. The inspector determines the specific sampling bins by first pulling the required number of numbered bin cards from a shuffled "bin selector" deck. Then starting at the left front top corner (driver's side) of a bin stack, the inspector counts counterclockwise in the top layer until complete, then the second layer when complete, and so on. A minimum of 40 pounds (18.1 kg) is drawn from each bin.

Table 21.2. Size and number of samples for olives delivered in lug boxes.

Variety	Lot size in lugs	Number of lugs in samples	Sample size (lb)	Sample size (oz)
Ascolano and Sevillano	50 or less	10	10.0	160
	51 to 100	15	15.0	240
	over 100	20	20.0	320
Mission and Manzanillo	50 or less	10	7.5	120
	51 to 100	15	7.5	120
	over 100	20	10.0	160

SOURCE: See table 21.1.

Table 21.3. Size and number of samples for olives delivered in bins.

Variety	Lot size in bins	Number of bins in sample	Minimum sample size (lb)	Minimum sample size (oz)
Ascolano	1	1	10.0	160
and	2–4	2	15.0	240
Sevillano	5–11	3	20.0	320
	12–22	4	20.0	320
	23–39	5	20.0	320
	40–50	6	20.0	320
Mission	1	1	7.5	120
and	2–4	2	7.5	120
Manzanillo	5–11	3	10.0	160
	12–22	4	10.0	160
	23–39	5	10.0	160
	40–50	6	10.0	160

SOURCE: See table 21.1.

Whether delivered in lugs or bins, the selected sample must usually be reduced with a splitter, which halves the sample until specified weights are reached. The objective is to ensure that olives from all the sources are in the final sample in the same proportions as they are in an unreduced sample. Sample sizes designated as workable are shown in table 21.4.

For fruit run over a sample grader, three methods of sampling are acceptable. A sample can be "sheared" off the belt, using a board as field containers are dumped, or a small amount of olives may be dropped from the bottom of the

Table 21.4. Example of reduction by splitting (in lb).

	Manzanillo	Sevillano
Number drawn	48	104
First split	24	52
Second split	12	26

SOURCE: See table 21.1.

hopper as field containers are dumped. In either case, the size of the sampling conduit cannot be changed during sampling. The third method, hand sampling field containers, cannot be used for undumped bins.

In all of these methods, care is taken to produce a reduced representative sample that reflects the entire lot. However, a processor may also size-grade, by bins, entire lots. In this case the entire lot's identity must be maintained until inspection is completed.

Once a sample has been selected, or the entire lot has been submitted, the olives are run over a sample grader and the numbers of olives per pound (.45 kg) in each size category are counted. In this procedure, therefore, both size and weight of individual olives matter. If the olives meet the ranges designated by U.S. Standards and Marketing Order sizes, the lot is passed. In the case of lug, bin, shear board, hopper, and hand samples, the graded sample is viewed as representative of the entire sample. However, when the entire lot is sampled by bin, individual bins—containing one size—may fail to achieve average count ranges per pound; in that case the specific bins, and adjacent bins, are resampled until they do. This means the entire lot does not have to be regraded. If average count per pound ranges are not achieved, the grower is notified that entire lots of the sample variety group with a similar deficiency will not be certified in the future.

Olives that do not meet standards are reported on the Obligation Credit form (form COC-5). This designates that the olives cannot be used for canning. Both growers and processors have the right to complain about the inspection service, inspectors, and specific inspection results. Complaints about the service or its employees should be addressed to the state inspection service or the California Olive Council. In the case of a specified COC-3 reported, the appeal for reinspection is made to the state inspection service. The appeal inspection should be done as soon as possible, on a sample twice as large as the original.

22

PROCESSING CALIFORNIA OLIVES

B. S. LUH AND LOUISE FERGUSON

Olives grown in California are processed into black-ripe (99 percent) or California-style green and Spanish-style green olives (less than 1 percent). The method used is pickling—the process of adding an edible acid, generally lactic or acetic acid in the form of vinegar—to a food. The acidification preserves the olive without fermentation. The history of pickling olives extends into antiquity, but the methods of preparing and pickling fruits and vegetables presumably originated in Asia as early as 300 B.C.

OLIVE COMPOSITION

Chemical composition

Ripe Mission olives contain 55.0 percent water, 13.1 percent water-soluble solids, 21.4 percent oil, 4.6 percent total sugars, 1.65 percent protein, 4.4 percent mannitol, and 0.47 percent alcohol-precipitable solids. The same olives after pickling contain 63.4 percent water, 7.2 percent water-soluble solids, 26.4 percent oil, 0.10 percent total sugars, 1.56 percent protein, 0.94 percent mannitol, and 0.43 percent alcohol-precipitable solids.

Ripe Mission olives contain 20 to 25 percent oil, Manzanillo olives 16 to 18 percent, and Sevillano and Ascolano cultivars less than 15 percent. The fatty acid content of olive oils varies somewhat with cultivar, maturity, and growing areas. Generally, they are as follows: stearic acid (18:0), 2.0 to 2.7 percent; oleic (18:1), 70.5 to 78.4 percent; linoleic (18:2), 7 to 12 percent; linolenic (18:3), 0.4 to 0.8 percent; palmitic (16:0), 9 to 12 percent; palmitoleic (16:1), 0.71 to 0.76 percent; arachidic (20:0), 0.42 to 0.55 percent; and ecosanoic (20:1), 0.24 to 0.46 percent.

Oleuropein

Unpickled olives are very bitter due to the presence of the glucoside compound oleuropein. The bitterness is destroyed by treatment with a dilute base (alkali) at room temperature. Removing the excess base does not cause a return of the bitterness. Commercial processing destroys oleuropein by treatment with a 1 to 2 percent lye solution at room temperature.

Pigments

Anthocyanins are the major pigments in olives. The most prevalent anthocyanins in ripe fruit of eight cultivars are cyanidin-3-glucoside and cyanidin-3-rutinoside. During olive development, anthocyanins increase rapidly to reach a maximum, then decrease as the fruit becomes overripe. Light greatly influences pigment formation, and fruit ripened in light normally develop 10 times more anthocyanins than fruit ripened in darkness.

OLIVE PROCESSING

During harvest, most processing plants do not have enough vats to process all the olives available. Therefore, much of the crop is stored until pickling vats become available. Almost all olive storage today is done in a relatively dilute acidulant solution rather than in the traditional salt brine.

Salt-free storage

Because it is difficult to dispose of waste brines without contaminating the soil or water, an alternative method has been perfected that uses an acidulant solution containing 0.67 percent lactic acid, 1.0 percent acetic acid, 0.3 percent sodium benzoate, and 0.3 percent potassium sorbate. Sorted, size-graded olives are placed in open-top redwood tanks 5 feet (1.5 m) high and 6 feet (1.8 m) across, of 2.5-ton capacity, with a slatted false head fixed in place. The olives and the false head are covered with the solution, and then polyethylene sheets (6 mil thick) are spread over the solution and secured with pliable slats nailed to the inside of the tank. A wax compound, Sealtite, forms an airtight seal between the plastic and the inside of the tank.

No fermentation occurs in this system, unlike in brine storage. The flavor of olives kept in salt-free storage is as good as or better than that of the same cultivars processed from salt storage. The flavor and texture of Sevillano olives are improved, lacking the characteristic strong flavor and woody texture of brine-stored Sevillanos. Shrivel, always a problem with Ascolano and Sevillano olives stored in salt brine, is virtually eliminated, and so therefore is the step of passing the olives over a needle board. More than 90 percent of California olives are now stored by the salt-free method.

Holding in brine

The traditional method of storage in sodium chloride brine uses paraffin- or plastic-coated concrete tanks or wooden tanks of a 20-ton capacity. The initial brine contains 5.0 to 7.5 percent salt, or about 20° to 30° Salometer. (A saturated solution of sodium chloride, 26.5 percent salt, reads 100° Salometer.) At intervals of one to several days, salt or saturated brine is added so that the brine is gradually strengthened to 30° to 36° Salometer (7.5 to 9 percent salt); the brine is kept at this concentration for the first 3 months of storage. Added salt or brine must be mixed thoroughly into the tank by means of a circulating pump. As the weather becomes warmer, the brine should be strengthened to 40° Salometer. Ascolano and Sevillano olives require an initial brine of 15° Salometer to avoid shriveling, and the final Salometer reading should be maintained at 30° to 32°.

Holding tanks are located outdoors, where sunlight prevents the growth of putrefactive microorganisms. A mild lactic acid fermentation takes place that helps preserve the fruit until processing. The lactic acid content in the brine may reach 0.40 to 0.45 percent in 4 to 6 weeks. It is important that olives be kept under the brine. The head must have openings that allow circulation by pump when salt or saturated brine is added.

If the salt concentration is too low or the acidity insufficient, bacterial softening in the olives is apt to occur due to the growth of bacteria of the *Escherichia coli* and *Enterobacter aerogenes* group. These bacteria cause gas blisters in the olives and are responsible for what is termed fisheye spoilage. At the first sign of spoilage, the brine should be fortified to an 8 percent concentration and acidified with 0.5 percent lactic or 0.25 percent acetic acid.

Delay in placing the olives in brine after harvest may cause nailhead, a condition in which small depressions form beneath the skin. These depressions persist in the pickled product and are thought to be caused by bacterial action, as colonies of bacteria are found in them. Nailhead is avoided by pickling olives promptly after harvest or storing them promptly in brine.

The pink yeasts associated with softening of olives—*Rhodotorula glutinis* var. *glutinis*, *R. minuta* var. *minuta*, and *R. rubra*—produce polygalacturonases that cause a slow softening of olive tissue. Commercial control of these yeasts is easy when anaerobic conditions are provided. Otherwise, processors must remove the yeast film from the brine surface manually, by skimming or by flagellation.

Other methods

Chemical salts other than sodium chloride are partially successful in holding olives for several months without spoilage. Ammonium nitrate brines can be used for periods up to 15 weeks; however, it is difficult to remove the salt completely during preparation for canning.

Dry storage of freshly harvested Manzanillo olives has been studied experimentally. Storage at temperatures below 41°F (5°C) produces internal browning radiating from the pit, followed by surface browning. However, at 41°, 45°, and 50°F (5°, 7.5°, and 10°C), Manzanillo olives can be stored for 8, 6, and 4 weeks respectively, before chilling injury or excessive ripening occurs. Olives stored in a modified atmosphere containing 2 percent oxygen at 41° or 45°F (5° or 7.5°C) at 90 to 95 percent relative humidity last 12 or 9 weeks, respectively, without significant quality loss. Green olives generally store better than tree-ripened olives.

CALIFORNIA-STYLE BLACK-RIPE OLIVES

The industrial-scale processing of California-style black-ripe olives is laid out in figure 22.1. California-style black-ripe olives can be made from either fresh or stored olives. Generally, the olives are size graded before being loaded into tanks for lye treatment.

Loading

Size-graded olives are placed in paraffin- or plastic-coated cement tanks of a 10- to 20-ton capacity. The tanks usually have dimensions of $10 \times 5 \times 2\frac{1}{2}$ feet ($3 \times 1.5 \times 0.75$ m) deep. Redwood tanks can also be used. The tanks are supplied with four overhead pipelines containing water, dilute lye, dilute brine, and compressed air. Air for aeration and stirring is distributed by perforated pipes at the bottom part of the tank. The tanks are equipped with outlets for discharging spent lye, brine, and wash water.

Lye treatment

In the pickling process, olives are subjected to three to five applications of 0.5 to 1.5 percent lye (sodium hydroxide) solution for a short time, depending on the cultivar, storage time in brine before pickling, and temperature 50° to 70°F (10° to 21°C).

A more dilute lye is applied when previous storage time in brine was long. The greater the number of lye applications and the shorter the duration of each treatment, the better the color will be. Lye treatments help natural phenolic com-

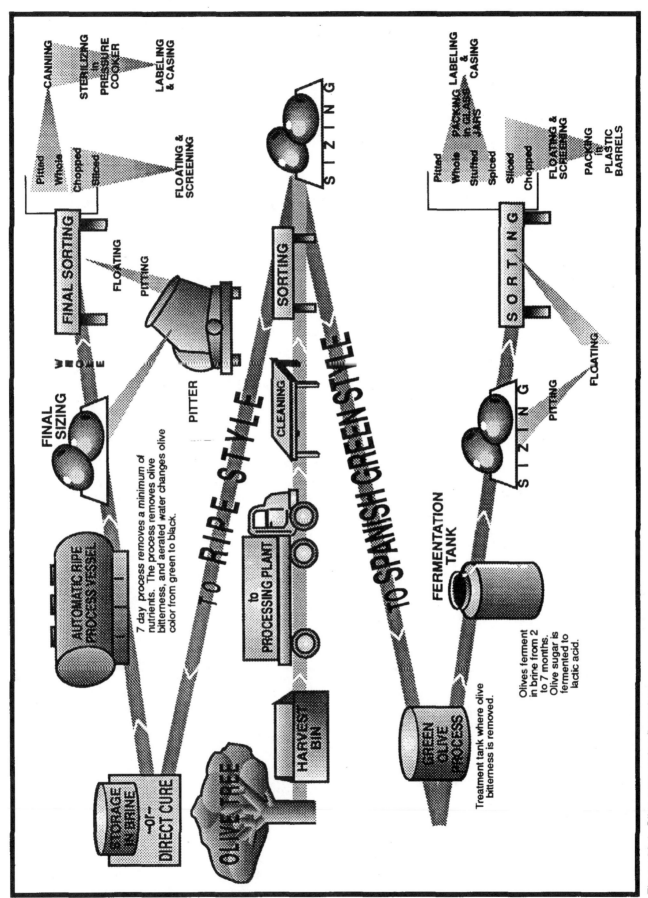

Figure 22.1. Olive-processing flow chart.

135

pounds in olives to oxidize and polymerize, forming a black pigment. Proper lye treatment and exposure of olives to air, or aerating olives in water between lye treatments, develops the black color.

In most processing plants, the first lye treatment is allowed to penetrate about one-fourth of the distance into the olive skins, determined by using a drop of phenolphthalein in 95 percent alcohol as an indicator on the cut surfaces of olives or by noting discoloration of skin and flesh. In other plants, the first three or four lye treatments last only long enough for the lye to barely penetrate the skins of all olives.

Color formation is most rapid at a pH of 8.0 to 9.5. Color retention is better in olives pickled in solutions made up with hard water, probably because calcium salts aid color fixation. Calcium chloride greatly improves color retention when added in low concentration (0.1 to 0.5 percent) to storage solutions before pickling, lye solutions, or the water bath between lye treatments.

The effects of harvest maturity on the pectin and texture of canned black olives have been studied. As the maturity of Sevillano olives advances from green straw color to bluish, purple-red, and then to dark black, firmness gradually decreases. Olives harvested at a green straw color have a firm texture after canning.

Lye removal

Lye is removed by changing the water in the pickling tanks at least twice daily and stirring it frequently by means of compressed air or paddles. If the wash water is stirred continuously, it is possible to remove the lye in 3 to 4 days. In several plants, the wash water is replaced with 10° to 12° Salometer brine after leaching in water for 2 to 3 days.

Curing in dilute brine

When all the lye is removed by washing, olives are stored in dilute brine for about 2 days, first in 3° Salometer brine, then in 6° brine, and finally in 10° brine (2.5 percent salt). Longer storage is undesirable because bacterial growth, texture breakdown, and other microbial troubles may arise.

Cured olives are sorted on a conveyor belt to remove those that show a mottled color at the blossom end. Broken and soft olives are sent to the oil mill. Olives to be pitted are put through an automatic pitter at this time. Pitted olives are canned in the same manner as unpitted ones.

Canning

The pH value of olives at the time of canning greatly affects color retention during canning and subsequent storage; a pH of 7.0 to 7.5 appears to be most favorable.

Well-pickled olives are packed by weight into cans with a protective C-enamel, which prevents bleaching of the olive color after canning. The most commonly used can sizes are No. 300 (300 × 407 mm), Buffer (211 × 304 mm), Picnic (211 × 400 mm), No. 1 Tall, and No. 10. For chopped or sliced olives, 4-ounce (113-g) cans are used.

After filling, a brine of 8° to 10° Salometer (2 to 2.5 percent salt) is added. The cans are exhausted at 199° to 205°F (93° to 96°C) for 5 minutes to reach 170°F (77°C) or higher; then they may be rebrined and sealed at 170°F in a double seamer. An alternative practice is to add hot brine at 205°F to the cans, followed by sealing at 170°F in the double seamer. If the olives are cold, it is advantageous to seal with steam injection at 0.35 kg/cm^2. Another variation of this procedure is to add a salt tablet and hot water at 205°F to each can, followed by double seaming with steam injection.

Olives in No. 300 cans are heat processed at 240°F (116°C) for 60 minutes in a nonagitating retort or at 250°F (121°C) for 50 minutes. For glass containers, the process is 70 minutes at 240°F. The California State Board of Health requires that a temperature-chart record of every retort load of canned olives be made available to the inspection service. Records of the double-seam inspection, fill weight, and temperature-time recording chart must be kept on each lot (coded with numbers) and be available to the inspection service.

Olives packed in water in glass jars must be sterilized in a retort with superimposed compressed air. Otherwise, the pressure that develops in the jar during processing forces off the lids.

Spoilage

Spoilage in California ripe olives during processing is characterized by the softening and ultimate sloughing of skin and tissue from the olive. Spoilage can be controlled by reducing the washing period from the customary 4 to a maximum of 3 days. Microorganisms associated with spoilage include some gram-negative pectinolytic bacteria (*Enterobacter aerogenes*, *Escherichia intermedia*, *Paracolobactrum aerogenoides*, *Aeromonas liquefaciens*, and *Achromobacter*).

CALIFORNIA-STYLE GREEN-RIPE OLIVES

For the manufacture of canned green-ripe olives, ripe Manzanillo, Mission, and Sevillano olives of pink or straw yellow color are subjected to successive treatments of a 1.25 to 2.0 percent lye solution at 61° to 70°F (16° to 21°C) until the lye reaches the pits. To avoid darkening between treatments, the olives are never exposed to air. The process may take 24 to 30 hours; the end point is indicated when a drop of phenolphthalein indicator (1 percent in 95 percent ethyl alcohol) turns red on the cut surface of an olive.

When lye penetration is complete, the lye solution is removed quickly and replaced with cold water to leach out excess lye. The leaching water is changed every 4 to 6 hours during a 24- to 30-hour period. Some packers add 0.25 percent hydrochloric acid to the washing water to neutralize the last trace of lye. Prolonged washing and undue exposure of fruit to air may result in an undesirable darkening. Olives are then stored in dilute brine for 2 to 3 days, first in 3°, then in 6°, and finally in 10° Salometer brine (2.5 percent salt) and then canned in 2.5 percent brine as described previously for black-ripe olives.

SPANISH-STYLE PICKLED GREEN OLIVES

Pickling of green olives is a minor industry in California, as the foreign product is more cost competitive. Sevillano and Manzanillo are popular cultivars for green pickling, although the Mission cultivar is also pickled green to some extent. Olives for pickling are allowed to reach full size but are picked before they have begun to darken. Fruit are graded for size and placed promptly in shallow paraffin- or plastic-coated concrete pickling vats

Lye treatment

Dilute lye solution (1.25 to 1.75 percent) is applied at 54° to 70°F (12° to 21°C). The alkali is allowed to penetrate three-fourths of the way to the pit in 8 to 12 hours. Round redwood vats, each holding 7 to 8 tons (6.4 to 7.3 metric t) of size-graded olives, also may be used for lye treatment.

Removing the lye solution before it penetrates to the pits leaves a small amount of untreated bitter flesh, which contributes to the flavor of the pickled olives. One drop of phenolphthalein indicator solution is applied to the cut surface of an olive to show the depth of lye penetration into the flesh.

After the lye treatment, olives are washed with cold water for 24 to 36 hours; the water is changed every 4 to 6 hours. After washing, the treated flesh of the olive should respond only faintly to the phenolphthalein color test.

Fermentation

Washed, lye-treated olives are transferred to 50-gallon (189-L) oak barrels or 180-gallon (681-L) chestnut barrels. To fill the containers, the heads are removed. After filling, the heads are replaced and the hoops driven into place with a mechanical hoop driver or a hand hoop iron. Brine of 11 percent salt (approximately 44° Salometer) is added through a side bung to fill the barrel. For Sevillano olives, due to the shrivel problem, it is customary to start with a 20° to 30° Salometer brine, and then add salt daily or every other day until the brine reads 30° Salometer.

The favorable temperature range for fermentation is 75° to 80°F (24° to 27°C). Some olive-processing plants in California now ferment green olives in closed redwood tanks, each holding several tons. Steam pipes beneath the tanks can maintain a favorable temperature, or tanks can be stored in a heated room. The total acid, expressed as the lactic acid content of the brine, should be 0.8 to 1.2 percent. In California, a small amount of glucose or sucrose is added to the barreled olives after fermentation has proceeded for several weeks. Total acidity, pH, and Salometer readings of the brine are monitored frequently.

The pH should be 3.8 or less when fermentation starts. Fermentation may be completed in 3 to 4 weeks or may take as long as a year, depending on the temperature, salt concentration, and number of lactic acid bacteria present. Control measures should be carefully integrated to maintain optimal brine temperature and concentration, to ensure the presence of lactic acid bacteria in the brine, and to add enough glucose or sucrose to the brine so that the right acidity is produced. Most processors do not use pure cultures of lactic acid bacteria as starters, but instead take 1 or 2 quarts (0.9 or 1.9 L) of brine per 50-gallon (189-L) barrel from a barrel of the current season in active fermentation.

Many processors perform all steps—lye treatment, washing, brining, and fermentation—in tanks of 10 to 20 tons capacity made from paraffin- or plastic-coated concrete, glass fiber, plastic, or stainless steel. The bulk fermentation process is more economical than barrel fermentation in terms of labor cost, but it requires supervision by trained personnel to avoid losses from acute microbial spoilage.

Under favorable conditions, lactic acid bacteria, some yeasts, and some gas-forming bacteria of the *Enterobacter aerogenes* group grow fairly well. Eventually, the lactic acid bacteria predominate.

Packing

Pickled olives are destemmed and size graded if they have not been earlier, then sorted on the belt to remove defective, blemished, and off-color olives. Defective olives may be made into minced olives or relish. Pickled olives should be free of fermentable sugar and have a total acidity above 0.75 percent (0.75 g lactic acid per 100 g). Other desirable qualities include a uniform yellow-green color, a crisp texture, and a pleasant flavor and aroma.

Sorted olives are packed carefully, often in glass jars in a definite pattern. Packed jars are then filled automatically with water or brine, then emptied to rinse off any adhering sediment. The jars are then filled with brine of 28° Salometer. Some packers may acidify the brine with 0.2 to 0.5 percent lactic acid if the olives are below the optimal acidity. Jars are then sealed in a capping machine.

Although it is not customary, it is advantageous to pasteurize bottled olives at 140°F (60°C) or to use hot brine at 175°

to 180°F (79° to 82°C). This will prevent sedimentation from bacterial growth.

Spoilage

Occasionally, barrels of olives develop an off-odor and off-flavor, termed Zapatera spoilage. This spoilage is characterized by a penetrating, unpleasant odor in fermenting olives. In the early stages, the odor is usually described as cheesy or sagey, but as deterioration progresses it becomes a foul, fecal stench.

Under California conditions Zapatera spoilage, unlike butyric fermentation, occurs when lactic acid fermentation is allowed to cease before the brine pH has dropped below 4.5. A continuous loss of acidity (or rise in pH) as the spoilage progresses begins only at pH values above 4.2. Hence, maintaining pH values below 4.2 is advisable.

Whereas normal brines contain acetic and lactic acids, suspect and spoiled samples contain additional acids. Propionic acid occurs most frequently, followed by butyric acid; succinic, formic, valeric, caproic, and caprylic acids have also been found. These latter volatile acids, together with butyric acid, are partly responsible for the odor of Zapatera spoilage. The lactic and acetic acids furnish energy for the bacteria—two species of the genus *Propionibacterium* and several species of *Clostridium*—that appear to cause Zapatera spoilage.

If the start of lactic fermentation in olives is delayed unduly, the continued high pH permits various butyric acid bacteria to grow, producing butyric odor and flavor and making the olives inedible. Either inoculation with lactic cultures or initial acidification will prevent butyric spoilage.

Yeasts and bacteria of the *Enterobacter* group may cause fisheye spoilage. Acidification of the brine with lactic acid and using a higher initial salt content (44° Salometer or higher) in the brine discourage this type of spoilage.

STUFFED OLIVES

To prepare stuffed olives, pickled and fermented green olives are pitted, either by hand or with high-speed automatic pitters. The pitted olives are stuffed with strips of red pimento previously preserved in heavy brine. Small onions and almond meats are also used. The stuffed olives are barrel fermented for several weeks in 30° Salometer brine before packing. Occasionally, stuffed Spanish-style green olives in bottles show gas formation and spoilage. To prevent this, the pimento must be properly treated in brine before stuffing to remove the sugars.

Stuffed olives are packed in the same manner as Spanish-style pickled green olives, described in the previous section.

GREEK-STYLE NATURALLY RIPE OLIVES

Greek-style olives are made from olives picked when they are purple or black. The fruit are put into wooden or concrete tanks of a 1- to 20-ton capacity that are coated with paraffin or plastic paint. These are covered with brine of about 40° Salometer (10 percent salt). Salt is added from time to time to maintain this brine concentration. Fermentation occurs through the action of lactic acid bacteria and yeasts. When fermentation is completed, the olives are graded for size and color and packed in fresh brine in tin containers or paraffin-coated barrels of about a 300-pound (136-kg) capacity. They may also be packed in vinegar brine to be used as an appetizer.

In an alternative method, olives are picked when overripe, placed in baskets, and washed with water. After 2 to 3 days, the olives are removed and placed in fresh baskets in alternate layers with solid salt. By this means, the natural wrinkles become more pronounced, and the partially dried product keeps well due to the high salt concentration.

The fermentation of Greek naturally ripe olives in brine is thought to be due to the activity of a mixed flora composed of coliform, yeast, and possibly *Lactobacillus* species. The total acidity of the brine is usually less than 0.5 percent. Sometimes a layer of molds, yeasts, and bacteria forms over the surface of the brine, causing removal of sugar and acids and thereby increasing the pH of the brine. This spoilage may also result from the growth of clostridia, propionic acid bacteria, and possibly sulfate-reducing organisms. Softening is another type of undesirable change.

As no lye treatment is used in the preparation of this product, bitterness and other fruit components are only partially and slowly leached into the brine. The degree of blackening depends on, and is favored by, high pH values. Under certain conditions, naturally ripe black olives undergo complete lactic fermentation, developing a total acidity as high as 0.8 to 1.0 percent. The product can be kept in brines of moderate salt content.

GRADES AND STANDARDS FOR PROCESSED OLIVES

Food standards are the body of rules directly governing foodstuffs, whether they are issued by official, semiofficial, or factory authority. The U.S. Department of Agriculture (USDA) grade standards for processed olives are voluntary, not required by federal law for olive processors or distributors. The standards are widely used, however, as an aid in wholesale trading because the quality of a product affects its price. The USDA grade is sometimes, but not always, shown on processed vegetables in retail stores. The justification for establishing food standards is threefold: (1) to prevent the transmission of disease, (2) to limit the sale of unsatisfactory products, and (3) to simplify the marketing of foods.

Canned table olives

Table olives are prepared from sound, clean, and sufficiently matured fruit classified according to trade type (in which both the fruits' stage of ripeness and the processes undergone are taken into account).

Trade types. Processed olives fall into five main trade types:

1. Green olives in brine: treated green olives (bitterness eliminated by treatment with lye), and untreated green olives

2. Olives turning color in brine: treated olives turning color, and untreated olives turning color

3. Black olives in brine: treated black olives, untreated black olives, and naturally shriveled black olives

4. Black olives in dry salt: treated black olives in dry salt, untreated black olives in dry salt, and pierced black olives in dry salt

5. Other trade types: bruised olives, treated split olives, untreated split olives, treated olives darkened by oxidation, and specialties

Styles. Whole olives may be offered in one of the following styles:

1. Whole: olives of natural shape from which the pit has not been removed, or with the stem intact

2. Whole stoned (pitted): olives of natural shape

3. Whole stuffed: whole stoned olives stuffed with suitable products, such as pimento, onion, almond, celery, or anchovy

4. Halved: whole stoned or stuffed olives that have been split into two approximately equal parts along or perpendicularly to the fruit's major axis

5. Quartered: stoned olives split into four approximately equal parts

6. Sliced: stoned or stuffed olives sliced into parallel segments of fairly uniform thickness

7. Chopped or minced: small pieces of random shapes and sizes

8. Broken: olives that have broken while being stoned or stuffed

Sizes. Table olives may or may not be size graded. Whole olives should be size graded according to the number of fruit

in one kilogram or hectogram. When the unit is a kilogram, the size range is expressed in steps of 10 units (olives) up to size 150/160, 20 units from this up to size 200/220, and 30 units up to size 370/400; above 400 per kilogram, the steps are 50 units. When the weight unit is the hectogram (not shown here), the range is expressed in steps of one unit up to size 15/16; two units from this up to size 20/22, and 3 units up to size 37/40; above 40 olives per hectogram, the steps are 5 units (table 22.1).

Table 22.1. Olive size counts.

| Count designations | | Count designations | |
Per kilo	Per pound	Per kilo	Per pound
400/450	181/223	140/150	64/68
370/400	167/181	130/140	59/64
340/370	154/167	120/130	54/59
310/340	141/154	110/120	50/54
280/310	127/141	100/110	45/50
250/280	114/127	90/100	41/45
220/250	100/114	80/90	36/41
200/220	91/100	70/80	32/36
180/200	82/91	60/70	27/32
160/180	73/82		
150/160	68/73		

SOURCE: FAO/WHO Codex Alimentarius Committee, "Proposed Draft Standard for Table Olives," Rome: FAO, 1971.

The suggested drained weights for different types of canned olives are presented in table 22.2.

Description of trade types of table olives

Green olives in brine. These are prepared from green olives harvested while still ripening (before full ripeness is attained but after fruit has reached its normal size). Green olives are firm, sound, resistant to slight finger pressure, and without marks other than the natural pigmentation. The color of the fruit may vary from clear green to straw yellow.

Green olives treated in brine are treated with lye and then stored in brine and preserved by natural lactic fermentation or partial natural fermentation. This is possibly followed by pasteurization, sterilization and pasteurization, the addition of preserving agents, or refrigeration.

Green olives untreated in brine are placed directly in brine and preserved by natural fermentation.

Olives turning color. Olives turning color are rose, wine rose, or brown in color. They are harvested before complete ripeness is attained and may or may not have been subjected to lye treatment.

Treated olives turning color are obtained from fruit treated with lye solution, preserved in brine, and heat sterilized.

Table 22.2. Suggested drained weight of olives as a percentage of fill weight.

	Content of containers			
Trade type, style, and size	250 g & less	251 to 500 g	501 to 2,000 g	2,001 to 10,000 g
Green olives*				
Whole and stuffed				
more than 300 fruit/kg	65	65	68	70
150 to 300 fruit/kg	60	62	66	68
less than 150 fruit/kg	55	60	64	65
Pitted				
more than 150 fruit/kg	50	55	60	60
less than 150 fruit/kg	45	50	55	55
Halved	45	50	50	50
Sliced	50	55	55	55
Broken	80	85	90	90
Chopped (minced)	90	95	95	95
Black olives in brine				
more than 300 fruit/kg	65	68	70	70
150 to 300 fruit/kg	55	60	65	65
less than 150 fruit/kg	50	58	60	60
Black olives in dry salt†	50	58	60	60
Whole and stuffed				
more than 300 fruit/kg	52	54	57	60
150 to 300 fruit/kg	50	52	57	60
less than 150 fruit/kg	48	50	55	58
Pitted				
more than 150 fruit/kg	40	44	45	45
less than 150 fruit/kg	38	42	44	44
Halved	45	50	55	55
Sliced	45	50	55	55
Broken	80	85	85	85
Chopped	90	90	90	90

* Olives that do not require heat sterilization for preservation.
† Olives that require heat sterilization for preservation.
SOURCE: See table 22.1.

Natural olives turning color are preserved in brine and are ready for consumption.

Black olives in brine. Black olives in brine are firm, smooth, and glossy skinned. Owing to their methods of preparation they may have slight depressions. The color varies according to production region and time of harvesting, from reddish black through violet-black, deep violet, yellowish black, to deep chestnut. Natural black olives retain a more pronounced fruity taste than treated black olives and may be slightly bitter.

Treated black olives are obtained from firm and practically ripe fruit treated with lye. After natural oxidation, they are preserved by one or a combination of the following: in brine, by sterilization or pasteurization, or by the addition of a preserving agent.

Natural black olives are prepared from firm fruit harvested when fully ripe or slightly before full ripeness is attained. They are placed directly in brine and preserved by means of one or a combination of the following processes: in brine, by sterilization or pasteurization, or by the addition of a preserving agent.

Naturally shriveled black olives are obtained from olives harvested when fully ripe, after they have become shriveled on the tree. They are placed directly in brine.

Black olives in dry salt. These have a shriveled or furrowed appearance, although the skin is intact. Natural black olives in dry salt retain a slightly bitter taste and a more pronounced fruity flavor than treated black olives in dry salt.

Treated black olives in dry salt are obtained from firm, practically ripe fruit. After a slight lye treatment, they are preserved in alternating layers of olives and dry salt or by sprinkling dry salt over the olives.

Natural black olives in dry salt are made by placing fully ripe olives immediately in alternating layers with dry salt or by sprinkling dry salt over the olives.

Naturally shriveled black olives in dry salt are obtained from fruit harvested when fully ripe, after they have become shriveled on the tree. They are preserved in alternating layers of olives and dry salt or by sprinkling dry salt over the olives.

Pierced black olives in dry salt are obtained from fruit harvested when fully ripe. After the skin has been pierced, they are preserved in alternating layers of olives and dry salt or by sprinkling dry salt over the olives.

Other trade types. These include bruised olives, split olives, and treated olives darkened by oxidation.

Bruised olives are obtained from whole fruit, fresh or previously treated in brine. They are subjected to a process whereby the flesh is bruised or crushed and the stone left whole and untouched within the fruit. They may be treated in weak lye to remove bitterness and are preserved in brine, sometimes spiced. There are three types of bruised olives: bruised fresh olives, bruised treated olives, and fermented green olives turning color.

Treated split olives are obtained from green olives, olives turning color, or black olives split lengthwise after treatment in a lye solution. They may be preserved in a vinegary brine, with or without the addition of olive oil and possibly aromatic substances.

Untreated split olives are obtained from green olives, olives turning color, or black olives split lengthwise. They may be preserved in a vinegary brine, with or without the addition of olive oil and possibly aromatic substances.

Treated olives darkened by oxidation are obtained from olives not yet fully mature. The bitterness has not been removed by lye treatment, but they have been darkened by oxidation. They are packed in brine and preserved by heat sterilization.

Qualitative classification of trade types

The following descriptions are adapted from the Standard of the International Olive Oil Council, applicable to table olives for delivery to international trade. More detailed tolerances are given in the Standard. Table olives ready for consumption are classified as first class, standard class, or market class. Stuffed olives may be prepared only from first- or standard-class (green) olives.

First-class olives. Olives classed as first class must be prepared using fruit of suitable ripeness, of one sole variety, and

having the organoleptic characteristics of this variety in the highest degree. First-class olives must be very uniform in color, taste, appearance, texture, and size. Provided that the general good appearance is not impaired, first-class olives may have very slight variations in color, shape, and firmness of flesh—if these slight variations do not upset the general uniformity—and very slight superficial damage, hardly visible to the naked eye, in the form of scratches or scalds, or that caused by insects or physical knocks. In the case of whole olives stuffed with pimento, very slight defects of color or very slight imperfections in the consistency or placing of the stuffing are permissible.

A tolerance of 10 percent not possessing the required first-class characteristics but having those required for classification as standard class is permissible, excluding such olives admitted into the standard class though in fact belonging to the market class.

Batches of table olives (including stuffed olives) meeting the requirements for the first class, but containing no fruit benefiting from tolerances of size or quality and packed in containers of less than 2.5 kg and of perfect appearance, may be offered on the international market under the description "extra."

Standard-class olives. Olives classed as standard class must be prepared using fruit of suitable ripeness, of one sole variety, and having the organoleptic characteristics of that variety. Standard-class olives ready for consumption must be very uniform in color, taste, appearance, texture, and size. Provided that their general appearance is not affected, standard-class olives may have slight variations in color, shape, and firmness of the flesh—if those slight variations do not upset the general uniformity—and slight superficial damage in the form of scratches or scalds or that caused by insects or physical knocks. In the case of whole olives stuffed with pimento, slight imperfections of color or slight imperfections in the consistency or placing of the stuffing are permissible.

A tolerance of 10 percent of olives lacking the required standard-class characteristics but having those required for classification as market class is permissible.

Market-class olives. Olives classed as market class must be prepared using fruit of suitable ripeness, of one sole variety, and having the organoleptic characteristics of that variety. They are prepared from fruit that cannot be included in the higher classes but that nonetheless meet the minimum quality requirements of goods recognized as sound, fair, and marketable according to international trade practices.

Provided that they do not in any way affect the nature of the product, olives with the following defects or blemishes are allowed: variations of color, shape, firmness of the flesh;

defects in the specific flavor of the fruit; damage in the form of scratches or scalds or that caused by insects or physical knocks; and olives not meeting the general specifications for ripeness.

....

REFERENCES

....

FAO/WHO Codex Alimentarius Committee. 1971. Proposed draft standard for table olives. Econ. Comm. for Europe Committee on Agricultural Problems. Rome: Food and Agriculture Organization.

Kader A. A., G. Nanos, and E. L. Kerbel. 1990. Storage potential of fresh Manzanillo olives. *Calif. Agric.* 44:23-24.

Luh, B. S., and J. G. Woodroof. 1988. *Commercial Vegetable Processing*, 2nd ed. New York: Van Nostrand Reinhold.

Woodroof, J. G., and B. S. Luh. 1986. *Commercial Fruit Processing*, 2nd ed. Westport, Conn.: Avi Publishing.

23

PROCESSING THE CROP

PRODUCING OLIVE OIL

G. S. SIBBETT, JOSEPH H. CONNELL, B. S. LUH, AND LOUISE FERGUSON

HISTORY

Olive oil is normally pressed from the fruit of the olive tree, but not from the kernel of the pit. The earliest records of Californians producing olive oil date to 1789. The first commercially produced olive oil in California came from the Camulos oil mill in Ventura, established in 1871. By 1885, California olive growers found they could produce a competitive quality oil, and production increased significantly, leading to sharply lower prices. However, by 1900 growers could no longer compete with imported oils, and production declined. Since 1945, California's olive industry has primarily produced pickled table olives. Production of olive oil has been a salvage operation utilizing unharvested, cull, or pickling cull fruit.

In addition to California's modest oil production, the Mediterranean and Arab countries, Australia, Brazil, Chile, Japan, Mexico, and South Africa also produce olive oil. Spain, Italy, and Greece (in that order) dominate world olive oil production, accounting for approximately 80 percent of the world's production and 75 percent of its consumption. The United States produces less than one-tenth of 1 percent of the world's olive oil but consumes 4 percent of it.

Since the decline in olive oil prices in the early 1900s, only a small number of California oil producers remain.

OLIVE OIL QUALITY

Quality is judged from both the oil's acidity (from oleic acid) and flavor. Acidity varies with harvest timing and olive cultivar. Oil flavor varies with the growing location, the cultivar and quality of the olives, and the method of harvest. Oil color is not an indicator of quality, because color does not influence flavor. Oil color depends on the olive cultivar, climatic growing region, fruit maturity, physical fruit condition at harvest, and processing and handling methods. However, good-quality oils are usually light yellow to greenish in color.

Olive oil is a world commodity, like wheat or sugar, and its production and quality are controlled by international legislation. In 1959, an International Olive Oil Agreement was developed for olive oil and administered by the International Olive Oil Council in Madrid, Spain. This agreement was amended in 1979 to include strict olive oil standards. It designates as "olive oil" that obtained solely from the olive and excludes any oil from olives extracted by solvents or re-esterification processes, and any mixtures with other oils. The designation "pure olive oil" cannot be applied to any olive residue oils. The following are oil definitions.

Virgin oil

Virgin olive oil is mechanically pressed from olive fruit without using heat; this "cold pressing" does not alter the oil. It is treated only by washing, decantation, and centrifugation and is thus termed a "natural product." Containers of virgin oil often display vintage years, as fine wines do. Three grades of virgin olive oil exist and must be designated on the label.

The descriptive terms *extra*, *fine*, and *ordinary* or *semi-fine* describe virgin olive oils. Extra-virgin olive oil is also called simply Extra, or Virgin Olive Oil Extra, *Extra Vergine* (Italian), or *Vierge Extra* (French). This is the pure, unadulterated oil from top-quality olives; it has perfect taste and odor, varying only with the year produced and the olive cultivar. Extra-virgin olive oils have strong flavors and a maximum oleic acid acidity of less than 1 percent by weight. Fine Virgin Olive Oil is also called Virgin Olive Oil Fine or Fino. It also has perfect taste and odor but is slightly more acidic than extra-virgin oil, containing at most 1.5 percent oleic acid content by weight. Semi-Fine or Ordinary Olive Oil, also called Virgin Olive Oil Semi Fine, Virgin Olive Oil Ordinary, *Corriente*, or *Semifino*, is virgin olive oil with good taste and odor and a maximum acidity of 3.3 percent by weight. Virgin olive oil not for human consumption is termed *Virgin Olive Oil Lampante* (lamp oil). It has an off-taste and greater than 3.3 percent acidity by weight. This oil is destined for refining or technical uses.

Refined oil

Refined Olive Oil is obtained from virgin olive oil by refining methods. It has certain organoleptic characteristics (odor and flavors) or other properties that must be corrected by refining. In the refining process, caustic soda (lye) is used to purify, decolorize, and deodorize the oil. Often refined oils are produced from damaged olives or culls from a pickling operation.

Blended oil

Olive Oil or Pure Olive Oil is a blend of refined and virgin olive oil. Many imported brands sold in the United States are pure olive oils, blended to obtain the uniformity of taste and color desired by the American consumer. Most California-produced oil is blended to make "pure" olive oil.

Residue oil

Olive-Residue Oil is obtained by treating the olive residue (pomace) from previous pressings with solvents. It excludes oils obtained by re-esterification processes and mixture with oils of other kinds. It is further classified as either refined olive-residue oil or refined olive-residue oil and olive oil. These classifications are suitable for human consumption.

Most California olive oil is pure olive oil, a blend of locally produced or imported refined olive oil and locally produced virgin olive oil. Several California producers sell limited amounts of virgin olive oil to specialized markets.

PRODUCING OLIVE OIL IN CALIFORNIA

Economic considerations

Most olive oils produced in California must be priced to compete with the cheap imported refined or pure olive oils. Consequently, most California olive oil sold is pure olive oil, produced as cheaply as possible. Producers commonly salvage low-cost cull olives from pickling operations or gather unharvested fruit from table fruit orchards owned by other people, avoiding growing costs themselves. Oil producers cannot afford to pay high production costs, so few cultivate olives exclusively for oil. California virgin olive oils are of high quality and are sold locally in specialty markets for premium prices. But olive production for pickling is more profitable than olive production for virgin oil. Consequently, specialty olive oil operations must use cheap olives for virgin oil production if the product is to be profitable.

There are two economic components to the olive oil business: growing the olives and producing the oil. One must decide if the operation will be exclusively an oil-processing business, which may or may not include a farm growing olives for oil or table use. Land, labor, and cultural costs are high and must be recovered from the production of olives and sale of the oil. A careful economic analysis of the olive farming enterprise, oil processing, and market potential for oil is recommended.

Cultural considerations

The following discussion is limited to considerations unique to growing olives exclusively for oil. When growing olives for oil, the objective is to produce an annual heavy tonnage suitable for high-quality oil. Site, cultivar, crop size, and harvest practices all influence oil yield quality.

Site. The highest oil percentages are recovered from crops of moderately vigorous trees. Tree vigor is influenced by soil type and water status. An ideal site for oil olive production has a clayey soil texture with a high water-holding capacity and good internal drainage. Deep, sandy loam soils should be avoided; the trees grow too vigorously to produce well and, due to the soil's lower water-holding capacity, require frequent irrigation to maintain optimal water status. Lower quality "watery oils" have been reported from olives grown on these soils.

The site should be free of hard winters and early fall freezing. It should have long hot and dry summers to produce fruit for maximum oil content. The olive is a subtropical plant, and small wood is injured by temperatures below 25°F (-4°C). Tree death can occur when temperatures fall below 15°F (-9°C). Except for the immature fruit used to

Table 23.1. Approximate range in oil content on a fresh-weight basis of selected olive cultivars.*

Cultivar	Percent oil
Small fruit	
Chemlali	26–28
Frantojo	25
Grappolo	15–34
Lucca	19–27
Moraioli	18–32
Redding Picholine	15
Medium-sized fruit	
Dolce del Marocco	26–26
Grosse Aberkan	23
Grossa di Spagna	26–27
Macrocarpa	14–16
Manzanillo	15–26
Maurini	13–25
Mission	19–24
Nevadillo	25–26
Obliza	20
Saint Catherine	21–28
Large fruit	
Barouni	13–18
Sevillano	12–17

*Fruit picked "black-ripe" in December through February.

produce special-use oils, oil olives are normally harvested at full maturity in November and December. Sites should be avoided where frost probability before maturity is high. Frost injures fruit, stopping oil accumulation, and renders them unsuitable for high-quality oil.

Cultivar. High-quality virgin olive oils are usually not made from cultivar blends. Oil quantity and quality (acidity and flavor) are highly dependent on the cultivar. The quality of pure olive oils (blends of refined and virgin oils) is adjusted in the blending process and is not so cultivar dependent.

Most olive cultivars range in oil content from 10 to 35 percent of their fresh weight at full maturity (table 23.1). Cultivars with an average oil yield of less than 20 percent— 53 gallons of oil per fresh ton of fruit (olive oil weighs 7.61 pounds per gallon)—are not usually profitable to use for oil. Of the major olive cultivars grown in California, Sevillano is the least desirable for oil due to its low oil content and occa-

sional poor flavor. Manzanillo, the most widely planted table olive, has a marginal oil content but produces a sweet oil. Mission averages 22 percent oil content by fresh weight and produces a high-quality oil.

Flavor is influenced by the cultivar used to make the oil. The unique flavors attributed to some selected oils derived from single cultivars are listed in table 23.2.

Crop size. Oil yields per fresh ton depend to some extent on crop size. For any given cultivar, large crops yield a lower percent oil per fresh ton than light crops. Yields of olive oil on a per-acre basis are moderated somewhat, because oil percentage on a fresh-ton basis varies inversely with crop size.

Olive trees are alternate bearing: heavy crops are usually followed by light ones the next year. Cultural practices, such as pruning, should be employed to moderate crops from year to year. The best overall oil yields are obtained from moderate crops produced on an annual basis.

Table 23.2. Characteristics of selected extra-virgin olive oils.

Nationality/brand	Acidity (%)	Color	Flavor
Italian			
Badia à Coltibuono	0.25	rich chartreuse	rich olive, peppery
Berio	0.46	light chartreuse	bland
Bertoli	0.46	light chartreuse	mild olive
Callisto Francesconi	0.64	light chartreuse	medium olive, thick
Colavita	0.69	light chartreuse	medium olive, thick
Colavita unfiltered	0.45	rich chartreuse, cloudy	rich olive
Dal Ralcolto	0.34	medium gold	medium olive, slightly peppery
Delverde	0.91	light chartreuse	acrid
Gaeta	0.82	rich chartreuse	rich olive
La Tavola di Lorenza d'Medici	0.29	light gold	medium olive, slightly peppery
Monini	0.71	light gold	bland, greasy
Olio Sasso	0.51	light chartreuse	mild olive, slightly peppery
Poggio ai Sole	0.43	rich chartreuse	rich olive
The Cellar (Macy's)	0.38	rich chartreuse	medium olive
Spanish			
Giraida	0.44	medium gold	bland
Gourmet Fesol	0.87	medium gold	acrid
Lenda	0.43	medium gold	mild, earthy
French			
James Plagniol	0.74	pale greenish	medium olive
Old Monk	0.77	light gold	musty
Greek			
Petrina	0.37	light chartreuse, cloudy	mild olive
Californian			
An American Delicacy	0.87	light gold	mild, slightly acrid
Unspecified orgin			
Pompeian	0.95	light gold	bland
Progresso	0.68	pale greenish	mild olive

SOURCE: *The New York Times*, June 7, 1989.

Harvest management. The oil percentage and acidity of olives increase as they mature to the black-ripe stage. The best-quality oil comes from olives matured to the red-ripe stage. However, uneven fruit maturity precludes a "once-over" harvest, so multiple harvests are necessary to harvest all the fruit at optimal maturity. This costly process is adaptable only to a small operation, in which pickers can be closely supervised. Fully mature black fruit yield a high-quality oil, but during harvest they are soft and easily damaged, resulting in a high-acid, poor-quality oil. Late January harvesting of black fruit also causes lighter cropping the following year. Immature olives that are green or straw colored are sometimes gathered because of the unique flavor that less mature fruit impart to oil.

Harvesting olives for high-quality virgin oils requires as much care as harvesting for table fruit. Oil olives should be hand picked to avoid fruit damage. Olive oil takes on odors and flavors readily, so contact with the ground or damage during harvest changes oil flavor. Oils from fruit harvested black or damaged during harvest are generally refined to eliminate off-flavors and -colors.

Postharvest handling also affects olive oil quality. For example, olives left in bins for long periods before pressing will ferment and mold; the resulting oil must be refined to remove the disagreeable flavor.

Generally, the cultural practices required for best oil olive production are also those used for table olives, especially pruning, fertilization, irrigation, and pest and disease control.

OLIVE OIL PRODUCTION METHODS

The oil in olives is found in the mesocarp, or flesh cells. The oil must be extracted in a way that allows it to separate from, rather than remain mixed with, the solid material. Almost all the procedures involved in olive oil production aim at increasing the efficiency of this separation.

Washing and leaf removal

The purpose of a preliminary washing is to remove any foreign material that could damage machinery or contaminate the oil. If olives are hand picked, or if the oil is to be separated from the must by pressing, this step is often eliminated. However, when centrifugation or percolation-centrifugation is used to separate the oil, washing and leaf removal are always done, as any foreign matter damages the machinery and decreases the oil quality.

Crushing

The objective of the first true step of olive oil production, crushing the olives, is to produce a paste with poorly emulsified, easily extracted oil droplets within the crushed pomace. Two types of machines are used to crush olives: stone mills and metal crushers. Each has advantages.

Stone mills. The older of the two methods, stone crushers consist of a stone base and upright millstones enclosed in a metal basin, often with scrapers to clean the millstones and paddles and blades to circulate and expel the paste. Using stone crushers ensures that the resulting oil is not contaminated with metal, that the emulsified paste produced is easy to extract, and that the paste is not overheated, a condition that produces poor oil. Due to the type of paste it produces, stone-crushed olive oil is often combined with pressing, although centrifugation is sometimes used. The major disadvantages of this method are the bulky machinery and its slowness, its high cost, and its inability to be continuously operated.

Metal crushers. These generally consist of a metal body that rotates at high speed, hurling the olives against a metal grating. The oil is generally extracted from the paste by continuous centrifugation. The major advantage of metal crushers is their speed and continuous operation, which translate into high output, compact size, and low cost. Their major disadvantage is the quality of the paste produced. The oil is in smaller droplets, more emulsified, and therefore harder to extract. Also, the speed of metal crushing can produce elevated temperatures and possible metal contamination. Both factors reduce oil quality.

Beating

Beating prepares the paste for separation of the oil from the pomace. This step is particularly important if the paste was produced by metal crushers.

Beating optimizes the amount of oil extracted through the formation of larger oil droplets and breaking up the oil-water emulsion. The speed, time, and temperature of beating can all produce the opposite effect—a stronger emulsion with less extractable oil—if combined improperly.

Extraction

The next step is extracting the oil must from the beaten paste. Oil must is a combination of edible oil and oil bound to water, often called vegetable water. The oil must can be extracted by pressing, centrifugation, or percolation, or by combining percolation with one of the first two methods. The method of crushing dictates the method of extraction, to some degree.

Various chemical and physical aids—primarily surfactants, electrolytes, absorbants, and enzymes—have been used to increase the efficiency of oil extraction. However, none has proved cost effective enough to become common production practice.

Pressing is the oldest and still the most-utilized method of oil extraction (fig. 23.1). The method involves applying pressure to stacked mats, smeared with paste, that alternate with metal disks; a central spike allows the expressed oil to exit. Pressing is seldom done more than twice on a single paste batch. Pressing has the advantages of needing little initial investment; using simple, reliable machinery, having a low energy requirement, and producing a pomace that is low in moisture, with little oil lost to the water component. The machinery, however, is cumbersome, the process requires more labor than other extraction methods, and the cycle is not continuous. Also, the filter mats can easily become contaminated.

In centrifugation, large, high-speed centrifuges extract the oil from the beaten paste through a finely perforated screen by centrifugal force (fig. 23.2). This method requires that olives be washed and all foreign matter removed. This method is fast, the machinery is compact and efficient, and little labor is needed. However, it requires a large initial investment and trained labor, and it has a high energy demand. The pomace has a high moisture content with more oil lost to the water component.

Percolation extraction of olive oil is not commonly used alone. It operates on the principle that a metal plate submerged in the beaten paste will become wetted only with oil, and not with oil mixed with water or vegetable water, when withdrawn. The adhering oil then drips off the plate, hence the name percolation, or dripping (fig. 23.3). Advantages of this process are its complete automation and its partial separation of oil from vegetable water. It is, however, an inefficient extraction method, leaving a wet pomace that still contains available olive oil. This disadvantage is overcome by combining percolation with other methods of oil extraction.

In percolation-pressing, the oil is first percolation extracted, then pressed. It yields more oil than a single pressing but has all the disadvantages of pressing listed previously.

In percolation-centrifugation, the greatest benefit is the continuous automatic operation with high output. It is as efficient as a single pressing, but the machines can be operated continuously (fig. 23.4). The major disadvantages are the high initial cost and energy requirements of the machin-

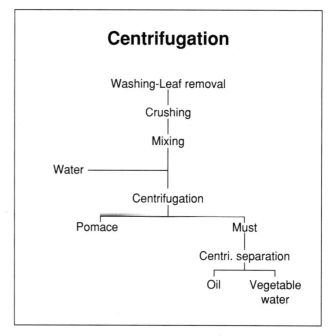

Figure 23.2. Sequence for centrifugation method of extraction.

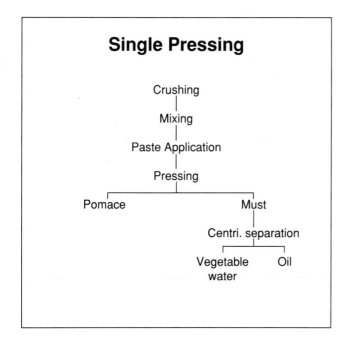

Figure 23.1. Sequence for single-pressing method of extraction.

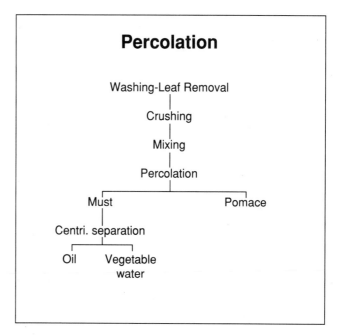

Figure 23.3. Sequence for percolation method of extraction.

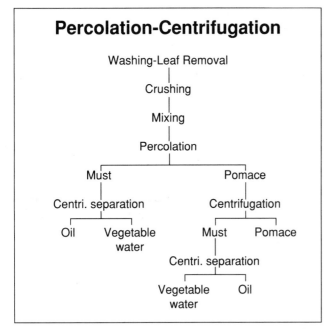

Percolation-Centrifugation

Washing-Leaf Removal

Crushing

Mixing

Percolation

Must — Pomace

Centri. separation — Centrifugation

Oil — Vegetable water

Must — Pomace

Centri. separation

Vegetable water — Oil

Figure 23.4. Sequence for percolation-centrifugation method of extraction.

ery, the production of a pomace with high moisture content, and the amount of oil still bound to water.

Oil separation

The oil must extracted from the solid phase consists of edible olive oil and vegetable water. The final step in olive oil production is the separation of the former from the latter.

The different densities of the two immiscible liquids facilitate separation by centrifugal decanting. Concentric spinning tanks called clarifiers draw off the oil, allowing the vegetable water to drain into lower tanks. The objective is efficient separation of the oil and vegetable water while minimizing contact between the oil and vegetable water, which produces an inferior oil.

REFERENCES

Campbell, R. 1979. Review of the olive industry. *Olive Oil Industry News.*

Dolamore, A. 1988. *The Essential Olive Oil Companion.* London: Macmillan.

Fabricant, F. 1989. Olive oil: Mediterranean gold rush. *New York Times* (June 7).

Hartmann, H. T., and P. Papaioannou. 1951. Olive varieties in California. *Univ. Calif. Agric. Exp. Stn. Bull.* 720.

Hartmann, H. T., et al. 1980. Olive production in California. *Univ. Calif. Div. Agric. and Nat. Resour. Publ.* 2472.

Klein, M. B. 1983. *The Feast of the Olive.* Berkeley, Calif.: Harris.

Olivae. Bimonthly publication of the International Olive Oil Council, Madrid, Spain.

Standards for Olive Oils and Olive-residue Oils. 1985. *Olivae* 8.

INDEX

149

153

154